Fenn's and Whixall Mc

Fenn's and Whixall Mosses

Edited by
André Q. Berry, Fiona Gale, Joan L. Daniels and Bill Allmark

Gwasanaeth
Archaeoleg Clwyd Archaeology
Service

Published with grant assistance from:

ENGLISH
NATURE

I

Designed and typeset by *Design* + **PRINT** Clwyd County Council

Published by Clwyd Archaeology Service, Clwyd County Council, Department of Development and Tourism, Shire Hall, Mold. Clwyd. CH7 6NB.

ISBN 1 85991 023 8

Front cover:

©Crown Copyright: Royal Commission on the Ancient and Historical Monuments of Wales. Ref. 94-CS-1738*.
04.10.1994

Frontispiece:
Curlew nesting amongst common cotton-sedge on dammed, recent commercial peat cuttings on Fenn's Moss.
©Woodfall Wild Images.

To the peatmen of Fenn's and Whixall Mosses

Contents:

Foreword:

by The Worshipful the Mayor of Wrexham, Councillor Mrs. Bronwen Greenaway

As Britain's third largest and southernmost lowland raised mire, with a documented history of peat extraction extending over at least four hundred years, the Fenn's and Whixall Mosses complex is a nationally important part of our ecological and cultural heritage.

Straddling the English/Welsh border at the eastern extremity of Wrexham County Borough, this extensive peat bog is generally little known amongst the public. It has a rich history, spanning finds of prehistoric bog bodies and military use during both World Wars. The cultural traditions of use of the peat by the local community and of its developing industrial use, together with the importance of the mire for some of Britain's most threatened wildlife, create a diverse and fascinating landscape which deserves wider recognition.

Since 1990 the mire has been under the joint stewardship of English Nature and the Countryside Council for Wales, whilst the former Clwyd County Council has been actively involved both in a planning context and, through Clwyd Archaeology Service, in understanding and management of the historic landscape and conservation of the former peat processing works, believed to be the last surviving example of their type in mainland Britain.

This volume brings together a range of experts involved in both research and management of the mire to provide, for the first time, a fascinating insight into its many facets. It is fitting that this volume should be published during the year in which the significance of the Mosses is recognised by their declaration as a National Nature Reserve.

Following Local Government Reorganisation in Wales, Wrexham County Borough Council has assumed the responsibilities of the former County Council and is fully committed to its role in assisting in the understanding, conservation and management of Fenn's and Whixall Mosses and their unique industrial heritage.

Councillor Mrs. Bronwen Greenaway
The Worshipful the Mayor of Wrexham

wrexham
COUNTY BOROUGH

BWRDEISTREF SIROL
wrecsam

Rhagair:

gan Anrhydeddus Faer Wrecsam,
Y Cynghorydd Mrs. Bronwen Greenaway

Mae gan Gorstiroedd Whixall - y gyforgors iseldirol drydedd fwyaf a'r fwyaf deheuol ym Mhrydain - hanes cloddio mawn yn ymestyn yn ôl dros bedwar can mlynedd o leiaf, ac mae'n genedlaethol bwysig o safbwynt ein hanes ecolegol a diwylliannol.

Ychydig a ŵyr y cyhoedd am y gors fawn hon sy'n pontio'r ffin rhwng Cymru a Lloegr ym mhen dwyreiniol Bwrdeistref Sirol Wrecsam. Mae hanes cyfoethog i'r lle: canfuwyd cyrff cynhanesyddol yn y mawn, ac fe'i defnyddiwyd at ddibenion milwrol yn ystod y ddwy Ryfel Byd. Rhwng traddodiadau diwylliannol y gymuned leol o ran defnyddio'r mawn, a'r datblygiadau diwydiannol yn yr ardal, ynghyd

â'r ffaith bod y gors yn hafan i rai o adar ac anifeiliaid prinaf Prydain, mae hyn gyda'i gilydd yn creu tirwedd amrywiol a hynod ddiddorol sy'n haeddu cydnabyddiaeth ehangach.

Ers 1990, mae'r gors wedi bod dan warchodaeth English Nature a Chyngor Cefn Gwlad Cymru, tra bo Cyngor Sir Clwyd wedi chwarae rhan mewn cyddestun cynllunio a, thrwy gyfrwng Gwasanaeth Archaeolegol Clwyd, bu'n ymwneud â deall a rheoli'r dirwedd hanesyddol, ac yn gwarchod yr hen weithfeydd mawn; yr enghraifft olaf o'u math, fe gredir, sydd ar ôl ar dir mawr Prydain.

Mae'r gyfrol hon yn dwyn ynghyd nifer o arbenigwyr sydd wedi ymgymryd â'r gwaith ymchwil a'r gwaith o reoli'r gors, ac mae'n cynnig, am y tro cyntaf, ddarlun cyfareddol o'r gwahanol agweddau. Mae'n briodol bod y gyfrol hon yn cael ei chyhoeddi yn ystod y flwyddyn pan ddatganwyd y Corstiroedd yn Warchodfa Natur Genedlaethol, mewn cydnabyddiaeth o'u harwyddocâd.

Yn dilyn Ad-drefnu Llywodraeth Leol yng Nghymru, mae Cyngor Bwrdeistref Sirol Wrecsam wedi mabwysiadu cyfrifoldebau'r hen Gyngor Sir, ac wedi llwyr ymrwymo'i hunan i'w rôl o gynorthwyo gyda deall, rheoli a gwarchod Corstiroedd Whixall, a'u hetifeddiaeth ddiwydiannol unigryw.

Y Cynghorydd Mrs. Bronwen Greenaway
Anrhydeddus Faer Wrecsam

VIII

List of Contributors:

Bill Allmark   10 Trentham Close, Wem, Shropshire. SY4 5AS.

André Q. Berry   32 Birkdale Avenue, Buckley, Flintshire. CH7 2NB.

Professor F. M. Chambers   Centre for Environmental Change and Quaternary Research, Department of Geography and Geology, Cheltenham and Gloucester College of Higher Education, Francis Close Hall, Swindon Road, Cheltenham. Gloucestershire. GL50 4AZ.

Dr. Joan L. Daniels   Site Manager, English Nature, Manor House, Moss Lane, Whixall. Shropshire. SY13 2PD.

Fiona Gale   The Old Vicarage, Rhosesmor, Flintshire. CH7 6PJ.

Dr. M. E. Grant   1 The Drive, Warwick Park, Tunbridge Wells, Kent. TN2 5ER.

Mike Grant   26 Windsor Drive, Caergwrle, Wrexham. LL12 9LU.

Dr. J. G. A. Lageard   Division of Environmental Science, Crewe and Alsager Faculty, Manchester Metropolitan University, Crewe Campus, Crewe Green Road, Crewe. Cheshire. CW1 1DU.

Derrick Pratt   The Grange, Welsh Frankton, Oswestry. Shropshire. SY11 4NX.

I. G. Richardson   Richardson's Moss Litter Company Limited, Tollund House, 8 Abbey Street, Carlisle. CA3 8TX.

Ms. L. J. Roberts   Centre for Environmental Change and Quaternary Research, Department of Geography and Geology, Cheltenham and Gloucester College of Higher Education, Francis Close Hall, Swindon Road, Cheltenham. Gloucestershire. GL50 4AZ.

Dr. P. A. Thomas   Department of Biologicial Sciences, Keele University, Keele. Staffordshire. ST5 5BG.

Rick Turner   Cadw: Welsh Historic Monuments, Brunel House, 2 Fitzalan Road, Cardiff. CF2 1UY.

Stephen Penney   Salt Museum, Cheshire Museums, Cheshire County Council, 162 London Road, Northwich. Cheshire. CW9 8AB.

Acknowledgements:

This book does not mark the culmination of research, but rather the first faltering step in understanding the evocative landscape that is Fenn's and Whixall Mosses. In taking that step the editors are grateful to the specialist contributing authors who have given generously of their time and expertise in preparation of their respective chapters and in support of research undertaken by the editors. Without their input, this volume would be significantly impoverished. Any errors, however, remain those of the editors.

The volume is born of the Fenn's and Whixall Historic Landscape Project, a part of Clwyd Archaeology Service's wide-ranging historic landscape research programme.

The editors thank the Royal Commission on the Ancient and Historical Monuments of Wales and particularly Chris Musson, Aerial Investigator, for the specially-commissioned aerial photography of Fenn's and Whixall Mosses, which has contributed significantly to research and does much to enhance this volume. Photographs form part of a partnership programme of historic landscape aerial photography funded jointly by the Royal Commission and Clwyd Archaeology Service and lodged in the National Monuments Record for Wales at Aberystwyth.

The editors gratefully acknowledge assistance given by the following during the course of the project: Mr W. Fancourt for providing Whixall manorial court rolls; Miss Eileen Simpson, Archivist, for sterling work in translation of Latin texts from the Whixall manorial records; Timothy Morgan for all drawings and figures; the staff of the County Record Offices at Hawarden, Flintshire and Shrewsbury, Shropshire; Dr. Paul Stamper; staff of the library H.Q. at Mold, the local studies library at Shrewsbury and libraries at Whitchurch and Oswestry; all at the British Library in the Industrial Property Dept. (Patents), Newspaper Library and Reproductions; the staff of the Public Record Office, Kew; staff of the Air Photographs Unit, Welsh Office; Flt. Sgt. D.J. Lee, formerly EOD (Ops) Flt., RAF Armament Support Unit, RAF Wittering, for identification of practice bombs (and removal of same from the one editor's kitchen window sill); Ms. Caroline McCreary, Ministry of Defence, for assistance in securing consent to publish details concerning practice bombs; V.J. Bradley for information relating to the industrial locomotives; Martin Limbert for comment on peat cutting and help in identification of the peat cutting machinery employed on Fenn's Moss; Ms. Denise Lynch, Graphic Designer with Design+Print, for design and layout of this volume and Laurence Sullivan, Print Manager for all his efforts in seeing it through to publication.

Thanks are due to The National Library of Wales for permission to reproduce images from the Geoff Charles Collection.

Especial thanks is due to the local community of Whixall who gave so freely and generously of their time, treasured documents, photographs and personal recollections during the course of research. This book is a record of their labours which have shaped the landscape of Fenn's and Whixall Mosses.

Participants in the Fenn's and Whixall Oral History Project:

Chris Allman	Richard Grice
Albert Allmark	Harry Hallmark
Bill Allmark	Alf Hamer
Herb Allmark	June Hankers
Abbie Austin	Joan Heath
Joan Austin	Les Heath
Alf Bailey	Raymond Heath
Cliff Bellingham	Sarah Heath
Mary Birch	Mary Hignett
Olive Birch	John Jefferies
Barbara Clorley	Jim Lindsay
Colin Clorley	Mrs Millwood
Mas Clorley	Iain Richardson
Stan Clorley	Bertha Saywell
Ted Clorley	Charlie Starkey
Lloyd Darlington	Jack Strange
Andrew Dekker	Jim Swire
Harold Dimelow	Mary Thomas
Phil Evanson	P. J. Warburton-Lee
	Edward Wardle

Using this Book:

This volume is intended to appeal to both the general public and an academic audience with an interest in the fascinating landscape of this important wetland site. In order to meet the sometimes conflicting needs of such a wide target audience, and to maintain the flow of the text, all references are given in order of chapter at the end of the volume and are cross-referenced to the relevant point in the text by chapter using superscript numerals. Similarly, only English names of species are given in the text (unless species referred to have no common name), the scientific name being listed at the end of the volume.

Colloquial or specialist terms relating to peat cutting are highlighted in **bold** where they first appear. A full definition of these terms is given in the chapter *Peat Speak*.

An endpaper pull-out plan provides your "navigator" in finding both local placenames on the bog and key features of historical interest referred to.

If, after reading this volume, you wish to visit Fenn's and Whixall Mosses you must first obtain an annual visitor's permit from:

The Site Manager, English Nature, Manor House, Moss Lane, Whixall. Shropshire. SY13 2PD.

Tel: 01948 880362

Iron precipitation, Lindow Moss.   Photograph: André Q. Berry

About Mires

Fenn's, Whixall, Bettisfield, Wem and Cadney Mosses are an extensive lowland raised mire on the English/Welsh border, 7km south west of Whitchurch (N.G.R. SJ 490 365). Together, the Mosses are the third largest and one of the most southerly lowland raised mires in Britain. They are home to many nationally rare plants and animals, and are of international importance for their wildlife, particularly the lower plants (mosses) and invertebrates.

English Nature and the Countryside Council for Wales jointly manage 553ha of the central area of the Mosses, rehabilitating them as a growing mire after almost 150 years of commercial peat cutting. This work is being undertaken to fulfill the UK's international obligations to protect this rare and threatened habitat. The irreplaceable record of past landscapes and evidence of past human activity which builds up so slowly in raised mires has been rapidly destroyed in many areas, and the carbon storage capacity of the mires has been greatly reduced. Common species of mire plants and animals have become nationally rare as their habitat has disappeared under farmland and forestry and into fires, composts and mulches.

•What are mires?

Mires are wetlands where the substratum is largely composed of peat, the accumulated remains of the plants which have grown on the site - essentially, pickled plants. The peat has accumulated because waterlogging and the accompanying anoxia (lack of oxygen) has retarded the decomposition of plant material.

Mires cover 400 to 500 million hectares, or 3% of the earth's land surface[1,2]. Of this, Europe holds 44%, North America 42% and Asia 11%[3]. In Britain, the area of peat extends to 1.6 million hectares[4], or 7% of the total land area, of which 1.4 million

hectares is bog peat. Mires can be divided into two types:

- ombrotrophic sites - "bogs", which receive their water directly from precipitation (rain, snow, fog, etc.), and are generally poor in nutrients;

- minerotrophic sites - "fens", which additionally receive mineral-rich ground water.

Bogs are very hostile places in which to grow. The greater availability of nutrients on minerotrophic sites results in a much greater decomposition of plant material, so much less peat forms than on ombrotrophic sites. Plants growing in fens often root through any peat and down into the mineral-rich substrate.

By contrast, in excess of 10m of peat can accumulate in ombrotrophic mires. The plants growing there are rooted in the peat and are totally dependent for their nutrient supply on precipitation and any nutrients released from dying plants as they break down to form peat.

Bogs need water to form. Ombrotrophic mires depend for their formation on an excess of precipitation over evaporation and evapotranspiration (loss of water through the plants on the site). Consequently they are geographically restricted to oceanic areas and are of particular importance in north-west Europe, especially Britain. This gives us a special responsibility for their conservation.

There are two main kinds of ombrotrophic mire - "blanket bogs" and "raised mires" or "raised bogs".

Raised mires are domes of peat, characteristic of relatively flat underlying topography or lying over basins in the substrate. They occur in the lowlands with c.800-1200mm rain per year[5], whereas blanket bogs occur in the uplands of north and west Britain where there is sufficient water availability (i.e. greater than 1200mm per year) for peat to form on slopes of up to 30 degrees. In blanket mires the peat clothes the landscape, following underlying contours.

Some bogs show a combination of blanket and raised bog features and are referred to as "intermediate mires". "Basin mires" and "valley mires" are fen/bog complexes.

•What are lowland raised mires?

Lowland raised mires occur as isolated peat deposits often set in a sea of agricultural, forestry or sometimes urban land. Their gently sloping domes, up to 10m in height are independent of underlying contours and are bounded by steeply sloping margins or "rands". Any mineral-rich water flowing towards the mire is deflected around the margin of the bog in a "lagg" stream or fen. The peat forms a dome because water flows off the mire more quickly through the marginal slopes than the stagnant, central area. This brings more nutrients to the marginal peat resulting in greater decay of plants and slower peat accumulation. On the stagnant centre of the dome, plant material accumulates into peat more rapidly so the dome grows upward in height relative to the margins[4]. The domes are thought to reflect the shape of the dome of water, or "ground water mound", which can be sustained by the local climate and this determines the height to which peat can grow[6]. The firmer, more decayed rand peat retains the more liquid central "quagmire" peat, the overall consistency of which can be likened to the amount of solids in milk (some 3%), with the mire vegetation forming a surface skin.

Lowland raised mires develop when a shallow, open water body fills with swamp and fen peat and then progresses on to ombrotrophic peat development. A wooded "carr" phase may intervene, and in some cases the bog can extend by progressively raising water tables in surrounding mineral ground.

Over the last 12,000 years raised mires have accumulated, layer upon layer, a record of the evolution of post-glacial vegetation and landscape, climatic change and human activity. This "story book" of our past dates back far beyond any written records. Peat cutting in itself has contributed to our industrial heritage.

Peatlands play an important role in being nett "fixers" of carbon. Globally they are estimated to store 500 billion tonnes of carbon[1] and the use of the peat resource therefore has implications for "global warming".

Raised bogs have an uncompacted aerobic living surface layer, the "acrotelm", through which excess rain water rapidly permeates (at c.1cm per second). This covers the compacted anoxic, more decayed peat, the "catotelm", which is much less permeable (water passes through between 1,000 and 10,000,000 times slower)[7]. The surface acrotelm (usually less than 50cm depth) comprises the living skin of plant cover, especially bogmoss (*Sphagnum*) species, passing downwards into recently dead plants and then into more decomposed peat. The level of the water table in the bog determines the rate at which peat accumulates at the top of the catotelm. If the climate becomes drier the bog water table falls and air can reach the dying plant remains for a longer period, causing greater decomposition before they become peat. If the climate becomes wetter less decomposed peat is added to the catotelm. Such changes reflect in bands of darker and lighter coloured peat respectively.

•The rarity of raised mires

Raised mires are one of the most threatened habitats on earth.

Lowland raised mires are a very uncommon type of bog. Of Britain's 1.4 million hectares of bog peat only 5% (69389 ha) is raised mire peat. Over half of this occurs in England[4].

As a reflection of the particular importance of lowland raised mires in Britain, many of them are not only designated nationally as *Sites of Special Scientific Interest* (SSSIs) but also have been, or are in the process of being, recognised as *Special Areas of Conservation* (SACs) under the European Habitats Directive and as *Wetlands of International Importance* under the RAMSAR Convention.

Almost every one of the lowland raised mires in Britain has been radically altered by human activity. Their typical bogmoss-rich vegetation has often been lost.

hydrology affects the remaining good parts of the mire. Only one bog in Britain, Glen Moss, a 6ha site in Scotland, is thought to be undamaged[8]. The situation is even worse in parts of Europe, with Denmark having less than 2%, and Germany and Poland less than 0.1% of their raised mires with natural vegetation[8].

In Britain, the major causes of loss of lowland raised mires vary between countries. In England, losses have mainly been to agriculture and commercial peat extraction for horticulture. In Scotland, to these losses may be added loss to forestry.

Table 1. The extent of raised mire with near-natural vegetation in Great Britain.

Location	Total extent of raised mire	Extent of near-natural vegetation	
	hectares	hectares	%
Britain[4]	69389	5375	7.7
England[4]	37413	8	0.02
Scotland[4]	27890	2673	9.6
Northern Ireland[8]	27800	2000	7
Ireland[10]	311000	20000	6.4
Wales[4]	4086	2694	65.9

In Britain less than 8% of our raised mires (5375 ha) support high quality bog vegetation[8,4]; in England this figure is less than 1% (Table 1). The Scottish raised bog survey[9] has shown that 8.7% of raised mire surfaces have near-natural peat-forming vegetation. Irish raised mires have 6%[10], and northern Irish raised mires 7%[8], but even these figures are very misleading. On each mire the area of good bog vegetation is only part of the mire surface, surrounded by extensive areas which have been drained and damaged. For example, between 25% and 84% of every Irish lowland raised mire has been damaged[8]. This damaged

In Ireland, as in many English and Scottish bogs in the past, the main loss has been for use as fuel. Losses have also occurred to mineral extraction, to waste tipping and through habitat deterioration as the effects of surrounding drainage take hold[4].

The Nature Conservancy Council's *Guidelines for the Selection of SSSIs* (1989) identifies a critical threshold for conservation of 10000ha of lowland raised mire. This significantly exceeds the area (c.7375ha) of near-natural raised mire in Great Britain. Consequently, the Nature Conservancy Council and two of its successor bodies, English Nature and the Countryside Council for Wales, have acquired several of the larger damaged raised mires as National Nature Reserves for rehabilitation, including Fenn's, Whixall and Bettisfield Mosses.

•The nature conservation value of lowland raised mires

The vegetation of ombrotrophic bogs is comparatively uniform and species-poor because of the limited amounts of nutrients available. Many of the species grow in other places but it is the combination of species or "communities" which occur on the raised mires which are unique. The National Vegetation Classification (NVC) community type M18, the *Erica tetralix-Sphagnum papillosum* (cross-leaved heath - bogmoss) community, is the core natural vegetation of most lowland raised mires[2]. There is a distinct progression of vegetation zonation from the wet, central pool and hummock areas of the bog dome to the drier conditions on the rand slopes.

The vegetation of an actively-growing mire is mainly comprised of bogmosses *(Sphagna)* and it is their remains which generally form the bulk of the peat. Like our own species,

Sphagna (Plate 1) have the ability to modify their environment to make it tolerable to relatively few other species - unlike ourselves, however, they can thrive in the hostile environment that they create!

Bogmosses are largely composed of complex sugars (polysaccharides) including galacturonic acid[2]. This chemical is very efficient at releasing hydrogen ions into the bog water, acidifying the environment, whilst effectively "mopping-up" available nutrient ions. The acidity enables toxic elements such as aluminium to be released into solution. Few other plant species can compete as effectively for nutrients or tolerate the effects of the acid conditions which bogmosses generate.

Bogmosses also waterlog their environment. Their cellular structure includes empty barrel-like or "hyaline" cells. These have pores which allow water to enter and be stored in them. Some of the branches of bogmosses lay downwards against their stems creating a fine network of spaces and these, together with the spaces between plants in the moss carpets, draw water upwards by capillary action adding to the waterlogging[12]. Few other plant species can tolerate such water levels. When bogmosses become desiccated, if the mire

Plate 1. *Sphagnum fimbriatum* bogmoss acts like a sponge to raise water.
Photograph: J.L. Daniels

dries out, they turn white reflecting sunlight away from the mire, thus helping to maintain cool temperatures and conserve water. Their cells are rich in fats (lipids) and in the phenolic Sphagnum acid. These chemicals result in very slow rates of decomposition of dead bogmoss, aiding peat accumulation[13].

Other plants which grow on active raised mires often show adaptations to the extreme conditions. They are generally other Bryophytes (mosses and liverworts) which need damp conditions, or are slow-growing perennials which are often evergreen. Many of the higher plants root above the average water table to avoid the waterlogging, often growing on raised hummocks. Leathery, waxy-coated, hairy or in-rolled leaves serve to slow the rate of water-loss when the water table falls in summer or when drying winds sweep across the Mosses. The plants also recycle nutrients very efficiently to prevent them washing away when their leaves die. Other plants have strategies for increasing their nutrient supply, for example by catching insects.

A few plant species of lowland raised mires are uncommon or rare including bog rosemary, great sundew, oblong-leaved sundew, white beak-sedge, the moss Dicranum undulatum, and bogmosses Sphagnum fuscum, Sphagnum imbricatum, Sphagnum magellanicum and Sphagnum pulchrum.

Raised mires support many notable and rare invertebrate species with flies, moths and dragonflies being particularly important groups. However, there are only a small number of bog specialist species totally restricted to lowland raised mires, because of the oxygen-poor, waterlogged, acidic, nutrient-poor environment. Without the conservation of their habitat these rare species would become extinct.

The hostile environment also limits the numbers of other animal species. Bird populations may be important. Those species of particular conservation value which do occur in significant populations include breeding teal, red grouse, black grouse, dunlin, curlew, redshank, nightjar and twite and wintering populations of pink-footed goose, Greenland white-fronted goose, greylag goose, hen harrier and merlin[2].

• Consequences of utilisation of raised mires

Most uses of raised mires involve their systematic drainage, which permits air to permeate deep into the mire profile, causing oxidation and decomposition of the peat. This releases the stored carbon to contribute to global warming and rots the stored irreplaceable macrofossil, pollen and artefactual record. Peat cutting also physically removes this record.

Three methods of peat cutting have been used in Britain - "sod-" or "block cutting", "surface milling" and "extrusion". All require the drainage of the mire to permit access and to allow the cut peat to dry, and also the removal of surface vegetation to permit access to the underlying peat.

Of the three techniques sod cutting by hand gives the best chance of survival for mire species. Two major differences exist between hand and machine sod cutting which greatly influence the chances for survival of mire species: firstly, the hand peat cutter throws the surface vegetation down into the wet base of the cuttings, where elements of it can survive, whereas it is scraped to one side and left high and dry on the worked surface by mechanised cutting. Secondly, large-scale commercial operations use excavators to keep the drains open, whereas the hand peat cutters would only maintain the minimum necessary drainage in the immediate vicinity of their workings. Unused areas would gradually block up and water-levels would rise.

Surface milling removes all vegetation from the worked surface, leaving none to aid recolonisation once abandoned. There are also no high peat baulks to help in damming up and raising of water-levels for mire rehabilitation.

With extrusion the surface is often first stripped of vegetation or, where the vegetation is left, the equivalent of mole-ploughing results in dry surface conditions and the elimination of mire species.

The hydrology of drained mires is completely disrupted. Usually the acrotelm is destroyed, the dome of peat collapses or is physically removed, with surface water rapidly conducted away along defined drainage ditches. The lack of waterlogging and consequent breakdown of the peat releases nutrients. The nutrients permit more competitive species which are tolerant of drier conditions to invade, such as bracken, birch, heather and pine. Mire species are generally low-growing and are adapted to receiving full sunlight. The taller, invading species rapidly shade out bog species. They generally root deeper than the mire species and can continue to draw water out of the mire as water tables fall in summer for much longer than the mire plants, thus accelerating water-loss. Fires become more frequent and may be used as a management tool. The ash from the fires enriches the sites even further, encouraging the invading species and the flames may consume less mobile animal species.

Animal communities also become invaded by more common species particularly those of damp woodland and specialist mire species are eradicated.

The Nature of the Place

• The Importance of the Fenn's, Whixall, Bettisfield, Wem and Cadney Mosses Complex

Fenn's, Whixall and Bettisfield Mosses were first notified as a *Site of Special Scientific Interest* (SSSI) in 1953, with Wem Moss notified separately in 1963, reflecting the national importance of the sites for nature conservation. In 1994, the two sites were combined and extended so that 966ha of the mire is now an SSSI. 275ha of the SSSI lie in north Shropshire, with 691ha in Wrexham County Borough.

The Cheshire and north Shropshire area, together with the adjoining parts of Wrexham and Staffordshire is recognised by English Nature as a distinct part of Britain, the *Meres and Mosses Natural Area*. Here wetland habitats illustrate the full range of succession from open water through swamp and carr to mire formation. The whole area is riddled with meres and mosses, which have developed since the last glaciation on sites of impeded drainage caused by the dumping of glacial spoil as the ice retreated some 12,000 years ago.

Many of the SSSIs in this area are in the process of being designated as the Midlands Meres and Mosses RAMSAR site, a *Wetland of International Importance*, including more than 60 meres between 1 and 70ha in size. Fenn's, Whixall, Bettisfield, Wem and Cadney Mosses (Plate 2) comprise the only large lowland raised mire within this complex and at 966ha is by far the largest individual site therein. Chartley Moss at 105ha and Aqualate Mere at 241ha are the only other large sites.

The Fenn's and Whixall Mosses complex is also proposed as a *Special Area of Conservation* (SAC) to reflect its importance in a European context.

As noted in the previous chapter, the Mosses complex is the third largest lowland raised mire in Britain, the largest two being Thorne Moors and Hatfield Moors in South Yorkshire. Its size has been an extremely important factor in enabling species to survive alongside peat cutting, where they may have become extinct from a smaller site following a disaster such as an extensive fire.

Fenn's and Whixall remains as one major block of peat, although affected by peat cutting. From the air, the Mosses appear as an island of wild vegetation, with marginal forestry and poor pasture in the surrounding sea of improved agriculture.

Plate 2. Cotton-sedge on Whixall Moss. Photograph: J.L. Daniels

Most of the peat remains hydrologically connected, with water able to flow through the peat below the base of the drains. This has helped to cushion the effects of drainage of the site.

Additional importance arises because it is one of the most southerly lowland raised mires in Britain lying at the limits of growth for raised mires. Further south there is insufficient rainfall for raised mires to develop. Its location facilitates the overlap of southern and northern species. Southern species of Ericaceae (Heathers) such as the bog rosemary meet northern species such as crowberry. From an invertebrate viewpoint southern species such as the bog bushcricket, and the parasitic fly of bumble bees, *Sicus ferruginus,* meet northern species such as the large heath butterfly and the Tachinid fly, *Tachina grossa,* which is a parasite of the oak eggar moth.

• Tenure

English Nature (EN) currently own 93ha of Whixall Moss and 12.4ha of Bettisfield Moss, whilst the Countryside Council for Wales (CCW) own 33ha of Bettisfield Moss and lease 407.2ha of Fenn's Moss.

English Nature have established a nature reserve base at the former peat factory at Manor House, Whixall (N.G.R. SJ 505 366) managing the entirety of the EN/CCW holdings on a joint funding basis.

The Shropshire Wildlife Trust have acquired the rights of Lord of the Manor of Wem Moss which is still common land, and in June 1994 the Moss was declared a National Nature Reserve.

Today, almost all of the wild or semi-natural mossland communities of Fenn's, Whixall, Bettisfield and Wem Mosses are under management as nature reserves. The remainder of the peat body is in private ownership.

• Climate, Geology, Geomorphology and Topography

The Mosses lie at 90m above sea level in a region with c.700mm rainfall per year, and form part of the watershed of the rivers Roden and Dee.

Fenn's and Whixall Mosses are only divided from each other by the English/Welsh Border Drain, a ditch now indistinguishable from many others on the Mosses. The disused Oswestry, Ellesmere and Whitchurch railway line runs across north west Fenn's Moss and Fenn's and Whixall Mosses are separated from Bettisfield Moss to the south west by the Shropshire Union Canal. Bettisfield Moss, which lies both in England and Wales, connects through a narrow neck of peat with Wem and Cadney Mosses to its south west. The latter two, again, are only divided from each other by the Border Drain.

The bedrock below the Mosses comprises impermeable Upper Keuper Marls (fine red silt or sand) beneath Whixall Moss and part of the English Bettisfield Moss; and Upper Keuper Saliniferous (salt) Beds beneath Fenn's Moss and the remainder of Bettisfield Moss. These formed during the Triassic period, approximately 200 million years ago. The ice-sheets of the last Devensian glaciation advanced from the Pennines and the Irish Sea and covered the area until approximately 12,000 years ago. When they melted, as the climate became warmer, they left behind them a highly irregular, hummocky drift landscape as they deposited sands, gravels and till (glacial clay) which they had scoured from the underlying bedrock during their advance. These surface "drift" deposits lie up to 50m thick in places[1].This glacial moraine system characterises the Ellesmere-Whitchurch landscape, with small rolling hills and intervening depressions; with shallow valleys which have filled with peat, forming Mosses; and, with many deeper depressions or "kettleholes" which have remained as open meres.

The nature of the drift deposits beneath the Mosses is important as sands and gravels allow water to leak away from the base of the peat when the ground water table lies at a deeper level. The western side of Wem Moss is underlain by clays, whilst the south eastern side of the Moss is underlain by sands and gravels[2]. Pringle[3] proposed that much of Whixall Moss, the former Fenn's Bank Brick and Tile Works and Fenn's Wood are underlain by clay, whilst a small area in the east of Whixall Moss and much of Fenn's Moss are underlain by outwash sands and gravels.

Peat depth probing carried out by English Nature has shown considerable variation in the type of substrate immediately below the peat, but is in general agreement with the O.S. drift maps. Clay was found near to the former Brick and Tile Works, under the English and Welsh parts of Bettisfield Moss, under Cadney Moss and under fields and woodland on peat near to Morris' Bridge on Whixall Moss. Sand occurs below Maelor Forest, fields in the east of Whixall Moss and a small field near the canal on Bettisfield Moss.

The base of Fenn's and Whixall Mosses is not a deep basin. The undulating base slopes gently from the north east to the south west[4]. When the glaciers melted, the area would have been covered by a complex of wetlands rather than one large lake. It is likely that peat formation began in the deeper hollows and then coalesced over intervening ridges to form more extensive deposits. The base of North East Fenn's Moss lies at a distinctly higher level and peat formation may have started later there when drainage to the south was impeded by the accumulation of peat in the centre of Fenn's Moss and in Whixall Moss.

The raised peat domes of the Mosses have collapsed because of drainage, and peat cutting has also removed layers from the surface. In general, the site is relatively level with heights only varying by a total of 9m, sloping from north to south. Heights vary from the North East Fenn's Moss at c.92 to 93m OD, through the centre of Fenn's, Whixall and Bettisfield Mosses at 88-90m OD, to the marginal fields on Whixall Moss at 87.7m OD north of the canal and 86.6m OD south of the canal. The link from Bettisfield Moss to Wem Moss lies at

85-86m OD. Wem Moss still shows two domes of peat at c.85m OD, whilst Cadney Moss lies between 83.5 and 84.9m OD.

Peat depths vary considerably across the Mosses. The two domes of Wem Moss have peat depths of between 3 and 10m[5], and Cadney Moss has greater than 7m depth[6]. Working northwards, the English cut-over area of Bettisfield Moss has peats up to 3.5m depth and the Welsh part has peats in excess of 8m. The deep peats continued beneath the canal into Fenn's Moss where peats of up to 8m depth are found on the uncut area of Oaf's Orchard. However, the cut-over area of Fenn's and Whixall Mosses has only an average of 3m of peat. In a few areas, the peat cutting has actually bared the underlying mineral ridges and peripheral areas have only c.1 to 2m of peat remaining.[4, 6]

The North East Fenn's Moss sits at a higher level than Fenn's and Whixall Mosses and has generally shallower peats grading out to heathland without peat in its north easterly corner, although 8m deep peat occurs in the uncut basin of peat on North East Fenn's Moss near the "Lake".

It is difficult today to estimate how many domes of peat were originally present in the mire complex due to human interference with the site. The peat cutting has left the surface of the Mosses without the domes characteristic of raised mires, except at Wem Moss and possibly on Bettisfield Moss. Oaf's Orchard and the Cranberry Beds, the remnant of the centre of the dome of Fenn's and Whixall Mosses, still stand up to 1.5m above the surrounding peat cutting fields with a 2 to 3m drop to the peripheral farmland, but the centre of Fenn's and Whixall Mosses has been cut away leaving a depression running between Oaf's Orchard and North East Fenn's Moss. This disrupted surface topography will have a significant effect on rehabilitation of the Mosses.

●Habitats on the Mosses

As noted earlier, the typical plant community of undisturbed raised mire is the NVC M18 *Erica tetralix -Sphagnum papillosum* community. The subcommunity occurring at Fenn's and Whixall Mosses is NVC M18a *Andromeda polifolia -Sphagnum magellanicum* (bog rosemary - bogmoss). If the Mosses had not been subjected to drainage they would be covered by an active, peat-forming community dominated by bogmosses and having an undulating surface of hummocks and hollows with an amplitude of around 0.5m. The variations in water conditions between the hummocks and hollows would provide a wide range of habitats for many specialist mire plants to occupy, each species finding its own specific narrow band of water table conditions.

The pools would contain the large, "furry" green bogmoss *Sphagnum cuspidatum* with green algae in deeper areas, the strap-leaved common cotton-sedge, trifoliate bogbean and floating yellow "pea"-flowered bladderworts. Pools would be bordered by bogmoss lawns dominated by the "chunky", bright green *Sphagnum papillosum* with smaller, beaded *Sphagnum tenellum*, golden *Sphagnum pulchrum,* tiny pink-flowered cranberry, golden-flowered bog asphodel, spiky-leaved hare's-tail cotton-sedge, the tiny pale, bead-flowered white beak-sedge and the glistening sundews. Hummocks would have "chunky", red *Sphagnum magellanicum,* "chunky", green-brown *Sphagnum imbricatum,* the delicate, rich-red *Sphagnum capillifolium* and fine-leaved brown *Sphagnum fuscum.* The grey-green cross-leaved heath and mid-green bog rosemary, both with their pretty bell-shaped pink flowers, would thrive on the lower hummocks and the grey-green and white lichens and dark-green heather would cover higher hummocks, the latter colouring the mire purple in August.

This intimate chequerboard of subtle reds, oranges, greens, greys and browns gives lowland raised mires a myriad of attractive hues all year round. The need to recycle all too scarce nutrients by drawing them back out from their dying leaves adds to the autumn colours when common cotton-sedge leaves turn wine-red, the scimitar-shaped leaves of the bog asphodel stain ginger-yellow and bright red berries spangle the ladder-leaved carpets of cranberry.

Pool bogmosses form little peat. The "chunky" bogmosses of the lawns and the hummocks are the main peat-formers. Heather and lichens on the hummock tops shade out the bogmosses and terminate growth at that spot until surrounding areas grow up and raise water levels there. One of the main peat-formers at Fenn's and Whixall Mosses, *Sphagnum imbricatum,* is no longer to be found, eliminated by the regular burning of the site for peat cutting.

The plant communities on the Fenn's and Whixall Mosses complex have been substantially altered by human use of the site in the past. Drainage has caused the loss of all mire species from many peripheral areas of the Mosses and often other species such as conifers or agricultural grasses have been deliberately introduced in converting the peat to different land uses. The extent to which mire species remain on the semi-natural areas relates directly to the efficiency of the local drainage, but birch, bracken, pine and purple moor-grass now dominate many areas.

Although there are thirteen species of bogmoss recorded on the Mosses, the damage to the site is reflected in the two most common bogmosses being *Sphagnum cuspidatum*, the species which colonises the bases of wetter peat cuttings and *Sphagnum fimbriatum,* a species typical of damp woodland.

The Mosses have been the subject of several ecological surveys[7, 8, 9, 10, 11, 12, 13]

The Mosses are surrounded by marginal agricultural land, with forestry plantations on Cadney Moss and northern Fenn's Moss, birch and pine woodlands on Bettisfield

Moss and mixed woodland, heathland, scrub, acid grassland and bog communities on Wem, Fenn's and Whixall Mosses. An alder carr, known locally as "The Quob", with willows and alder buckthorn runs along both sides of the canal between Bettisfield and Fenn's and Whixall Mosses, reflecting the high base status of the water leaching out of the clay which was used to line the canal. This is the nearest approximation to the lagg communities which may originally have bordered the Mosses and which now have disappeared under farmland. The canalside carr woodland harbours a wide range of swamp, fen and carr species.

Peripheral drainage ditches receiving minerotrophic waters have swamp and fen species such as marsh cinquefoil, bogbean, water violet, marsh violet and marsh pennywort. Deeper into the Mosses, fen and carr species including alder, willows, alder buckthorn, bulrush, bog pondweed, soft rush and *Juncus kochii* only occur where there are nutrient-rich conditions[14]. Enriched water (pH 6-7.5) occurs in the Fenn's Moss Main Drain which receives septic tank outfalls from the Moss Cottages and this has back-flooded into nearby cuttings giving poor-fen conditions (pH 4.6-6.9). One area of Fenn's Moss

Figure 1. The distribution of peat cutting types on Fenn's, Whixall and Bettisfield Mosses[14].

Recent cuts

Recent cuts intermittent

Old commercial cuts

Hand cuts

Uncut areas

0   1   2   3 km

N

receives enriched basal spring waters (pH 6.2). The central lagg of Wem Moss has been enriched by pig effluent from an adjacent farm. These enriched areas are strictly limited however, and the bulk of plant communities on the Mosses are ombrotrophic with waters of pH 3.2 to 4.5[14].

Most of the semi-natural ombrotrophic vegetation communities present reflect the type of peat cutting which occurred on each area. The distribution of different peat cutting types on Fenn's, Whixall and Bettisfield Mosses is shown in Figure 1[12]. They can be divided into four main categories:

- uncut areas;

- handcut areas. Cut by hand for domestic or commercial purposes by local people renting 1-3 acre turf banks;

- old commercial cuttings. Systematically cut by various peat firms, initially by hand then, from 1968, by machine;

- recent mechanised commercial cuttings. Cut by *Croxden Horticultural Products Ltd* in 1989 and 1990.

Plate 3. NVC 18a bogmoss lawn with cranberry. Photograph: André Q. Berry

Some areas have a mix of old and recent commercial cuttings.

Looking in detail at the communities present on the different peat cutting types:

•Uncut areas

There are several uncut areas each of which differ in their plant communities because of variations in the types and ages of surrounding peat cuttings. In descending order of size they are:

Welsh Bettisfield Moss (N.G.R. SJ 476 355). The central, wetter areas are dominated by a wide range of bogmosses including the nationally rare *Sphagnum pulchrum* and also *Sphagnum magellanicum*. Crowberry, cranberry, hare's-tail- and common cotton-sedge, *Sphagnum papillosum, Sphagnum compactum, Sphagnum subnitens* and *Sphagnum cuspidatum* are all abundant. All of the raised mire species present on Fenn's and Whixall Mosses occur on this area, including the nationally rare moss *Dicranum undulatum* and the Royal fern. However, Scots pine colonisation has dried-out and shaded-out much of the mire community. In the more marginal areas the ground vegetation has changed to heathland mosses such as *Hypnum cupressiforme* and *Pleurozium schweberi,* with patches of the woodland bogmoss *Sphagnum fimbriatum* and abundant crowberry. The driest areas now support bramble, ferns (including bracken and lady fern), rosebay willowherb and birch. Under the very dense, recent pine colonisation all of the ground flora has been lost.

In the early 1960s, the central area of Bettisfield Moss was kept clear of Scots pine by *L.S. Beckett* who cut the pine for Christmas trees. The practice was abandoned following a severe fire in c.1965 which encouraged a "rash" of pine colonisation. This proved to be too dense to cut and rendered the pine unsuitable for Christmas trees.

Cranberry Beds (N.G.R. SJ 483 355). This area has extensive bogmoss lawns dominated by *Sphagnum papillosum* with *Sphagnum magellanicum,* and has species such as white beak-sedge, round-leaved sundew, bog asphodel and *Dicranum undulatum*, and of course abundant cranberry (Plate 3). The effects of the surrounding peat cutting are manifest in the spread of birch, pine and the moss *Aulocomnium palustre* across the area. This area largely escaped cutting because its proximity to the canal made it too wet to drain, although a large block to the north was opened up during the 1940s (Plate 69, p.152).

North East Fenn's Lake (N.G.R. SJ 492 378). This is a deep basin dominated by cross-leaved heath, hare's-tail- and common cotton-sedge, with heather. It was not cut because it lay outside the main cutting areas.

Oaf's Orchard (N.G.R. SJ 486 360). A raised area covered by damp heath communities dominated by heather and cross-leaved heath, with scattered common- and hare's-tail cotton-sedge and bog rosemary. Where drains have been cut in the past there are small patches of *Sphagnum tenellum, Sphagnum papillosum* and cranberry. The effects of the surrounding peat cutting is reflected in the loss of bogmoss cover and in the invasion of extensive spreads of purple moor-grass and a general covering of birch which was regularly coppiced by burning. Oaf's Orchard escaped cutting because of the high incidence of remains of hare's-tail cotton-sedge tussocks, or **nog**, which made it difficult to cut (Plate 69, p.152).

Relict lumps occur along the canal and on the Fenn's/Whixall Mosses border and on North East Fenn's Moss, including the *Cowberry Patch* (N.G.R. SJ 493 368), which stands 1m above the surrounding cuttings and is covered by a large colony of cowberry.

Plate 4. A Whixall Bible peat cutting pit on North East Fenn's Moss.
Photograph: André Q. Berry

•Handcut areas

These divide into:

• **Whixall Bible** (Plate 4) cut areas such as Wem Moss, North East Fenn's Moss, areas north of the railway line, English Bettisfield Moss and southern Whixall Moss;

• Traditional linear hand cut "acres" such as central Whixall Moss, areas of Fenn's Moss behind Moss Cottages and the southern centre of North East Fenn's Moss;

• Modern, tractor-extracted hand cutting areas such as areas north of the railway line, the south eastern area of North East Fenn's Moss and an area of Whixall Moss near Moss Cottages.

Whixall Bible cut areas. Peat was cut from oblong pits often linked together by narrow drains. The bottoms of the pits have recolonised with a range of pool and lawn communities including bogmosses, cross-leaved heath and common cotton-sedge, sundews and cranberry. The vegetation of the mire surface depends on local hydrological conditions but is often damp

**Plate 5. An old, linear hand peat cutting on Whixall Moss
Photograph: J. Robinson**

**Plate 5. An old, linear hand peat cutting on Whixall Moss
Photograph: J. Robinson**

edge of the Moss with a band of bog myrtle within this.

The lagg between the southern and northern domes has expanded rapidly in the last twenty years because of the nutrient enrichment from pollution by pig effluent. Bog myrtle now forms dense stands along with Royal fern, alder buckthorn, birch and willow (Plate 66, p.146).

Linear old hand cuts. These form a jumbled pattern of "acres" across most of Whixall Moss (Plate 68, p.150). They were dug in different styles and orientations and to different depths and into different layers of the Moss. They occur in areas of the Moss laid out in the Dutch pattern, but at most are only 44 yards long. The use of different areas ceased at widely differing times over the past seventy years and hydrological conditions have varied greatly when and since they were abandoned.

The old hand cuts hold a full range of plant communities from open bog pools and bare peat to dry heath and scrub communities on the tracks and high peat baulks (Plate 5). The open water in the most recently cut ditches adjacent to the peat baulks is initially colonised by *Sphagnum cuspidatum* and then by *Sphagnum recurvum, Sphagnum fimbriatum* and cotton-sedge species. The only known locations of the lesser bladderwort are in the deep pools in linear hand cuts.

The hand peat cutter used to throw the surface vegetation, or **fay**, from the top of the peat down into the base of the cutting. Now the fay usually forms a raised mound between the peat baulks, higher in the centre with lower damper areas nearer to the most recent cuts or ditches. The damper areas next to the ditches support lawn communities with *Sphagnum papillosum,* cross-leaved heath, sundews, cotton-sedges, cranberry, bog rosemary, bog asphodel and white beak-sedge. The higher, central areas of fay are drier and are dominated by purple moor-grass and birch, together with some heather and pine.

heath communities of heather, cross-leaved heath and cotton-sedges, with invading birch in many areas and some pine. Purple moor-grass and bracken are dominant in other areas, whilst dense pine and birch dominates on Bettisfield Moss and parts of Fenn's Moss. The most important areas for conservation are Wem Moss (N.G.R. SJ 473 343) and southern Whixall Moss (Plate 67, p.148).

Much of the surface of Wem Moss has scattered deep pits left from Whixall Bible cutting and is mainly covered by damp heath rather than mire communities. These are dominated by cross-leaved heath, heather, bog rosemary and cotton-sedges, with heathland mosses and birch. The southern dome of peat has some areas with M18a bogmoss lawns and the pits also have bogmoss with all three British sundews present. The effect of surrounding drainage, the cutting of the Border Drain, and the deepening of the southern drain is reflected in the presence of purple moor-grass, birch and deep surface cracks across the mire, together with birch woodland around the

The intervening peat baulks tend to be drier than in Whixall Bible cut areas, with more bracken, lichens, birch and bare peat and much more heather than the uncompacted, lower fay areas.

Modern tractor-extracted areas. The cutting produces large open pools, eventually removing all peat from the area. Fay continues to be thrown down into the base of the cuts, but generally the pools have a high proportion of bare ground with common cotton-sedge and *Sphagnum cuspidatum* in wetter areas (Plate 70, p.154).

•Old commercially-cut areas.

This cutting type occurs in three major areas, on Fenn's Moss adjacent to the canal (last cut over 50 years ago), on Fenn's Moss near Maelor Forest (ditto) and at the Lundt's cuttings on North East Fenn's Moss (cut until 1988).

In general these areas are more uniform than the hand cut areas. They have dry, linear peat baulks with heather, bracken and birch, with relict adjacent ditches and central fay areas. In 1991 these areas had more cross-leaved heath, heather and birch than other cutting types and the birch was also taller[12].

•Recent mechanised commercial cuttings.

This area covers the central 140ha of Fenn's Moss. In 1991, these areas had 3m wide "88 yards" long bare strips of peat at a minimum of every "11 yards" (Plate 6). The augered-off vegetation was dumped in a heap at one side of each bare strip. These heaps lay adjacent to the 1-2m wide ditches where the peat had been cut out, and which were generally dry and free of vegetation. These ditches led into a 2-4m deep ditch which lay down one side of the cutting field.

On the other side of each bare strip was a 3-4m wide strip of damaged vegetation over which the tractors and excavators had rolled in transporting the peat from the Moss. This was dominated by purple moor-grass, with bracken, bramble and short birch. Bordering the next ditch was a 2-3m wide remnant strip of the bog community which had been present before the recent cutting took place, with mire species such as cotton-sedges, cross-leaved heath, bog rosemary, bogmosses and cranberry.

Overall, in 1991, the recent commercial cuttings had a much lower cover of raised mire species than any other cutting type and also less and shorter birch. By contrast, they had more bare earth and more purple moor-grass than any other cutting type[12].

Plate 6. Recent commercial peat cutting, showing a row of augered-off surface vegetation; the bare, dry ditch from which peat blocks have been cut by machine; and, the remnant mire surface.
Photograph: J. Robinson

Locations of noteworthy plant species:

F - Fenn's; **W** - Whixall; **B** - Bettisfield; **WM** - Wem; **C** - Cadney Mosses.
The number in brackets reflects the number of other Shropshire (**S**), and Clwyd (**C**) localities from which the species is recorded.
Clwyd is taken as comprising principally botanical vice-counties Flintshire (**F**) and Denbighshire (**D**); t - 10km^2, a tetrad.

Species which occur nowhere else in either county:

Oblong-leaved sundew (*Drosera intermedia*) WM (S 0, C 0, D 0, F 0).
Lesser bladderwort (*Utricularia minor*) W (S 0, C 0, D 0, F 0).
Sphagnum pulchrum W, B, WM (S 0, C 0, 3 Welsh vice-counties).

Species occurring at few other sites:

Royal fern (*Osmunda regalis*) WM, B, F?, W? (S 4, D 1, F 2 introductions).
Bog myrtle, (*Myrica gale*) WM, C (S 2, C 3t, D 0, F 0).
Great sundew (*Drosera anglica*) WM (S 2, C 0, D 0, F 0).
Bog rosemary (*Andromeda polifolia*) F, W, B, WM (S 1, C 1, D 1, F 0).
Cowberry (*Vaccinium vitis-idaea*) F, W (S 3, C 8t, D 3t, F 3t).
Meadow thistle (*Cirsium dissectum*) WM (S 1, C 0, D 0, F 0).
Slender sedge (*Carex lasiocarpa*) WM (S 3, C 0, D 0, F 0).
Many-stemmed spike-rush (*Eleocharis multicaulis*) WM (S 2, C 2, D 0, F 1).
White beak-sedge (*Rhyncospora alba*) W, B, WM (S 1, C 2, D 0, F 0).
Dicranum undulatum (*D. affine*) F, W, B (S 1, Wales 3 tetrads)

Upland species common in the upland parts of Denbighshire but uncommon in the lowlands in Shropshire and Flintshire:

Cranberry (*Vaccinium oxycoccos*) F, W, B, WM (S 15t, C 10t, D 15t, F 2t).
Crowberry (*Empetrum nigrum*) W, B (S 4, C 17t, D 12t, F 5t).
Deer-sedge (*Trichophorum cespitosum*) WM, F (S 5, C 7t, D 8t, F 0).
Hare's-tail cotton-sedge (*Eriophorum vaginatum*) F, W, B, WM, C (S 17t, C 15t, D 12t, F 6t).

Uncommon species in either county, tending to be lowland species:

Creeping willow (*Salix repens*) W (S 2, C 7t, D 2, F 8t).
Early marsh orchid (*Dactylorhiza incarnata*) WM (S 8 tetrads, C 6t, D 0, F 8t).
Lesser butterfly orchid (*Platanthera bifolia*) WM (S 9, C 11t, D 0, F 5t).

Table 2. Species found on the Mosses which occur at few, if any other sites in Shropshire or north east Wales.

● The Conservation Value of the Plants of Fenn's and Whixall Mosses

The Mosses are home to several species which are found at very few other sites in Shropshire and the lowlands of north east Wales[15, 16, 17]. (Table 2)

● Mosses

In total Fenn's, Whixall and Bettisfield Mosses have 70 species of moss and 22 species of liverwort recorded[18], whilst Wem Moss has 28 species and 13 species respectively. These include 13 species of bogmoss (*Sphagnum*) from Fenn's, Whixall and Bettisfield Mosses and 10 from Wem Moss. Oligotrophic bogmoss species present run from *Sphagnum cuspidatum* in the pools, with *Sphagnum recurvum* and *Sphagnum tenellum* on the pool margins, through lawns of *Sphagnum magellanicum* and *Sphagnum papillosum* into hummocks of *Sphagnum capillifolium*. The abundance of *Sphagnum fimbriatum* reflects the widespread cover of scrub and *Sphagnum palustre*, *Sphagnum subnitens* and *Sphagnum squarrosum* indicate enriched water. *Sphagnum pulchrum*, a nationally rare and localised species, was found in the wetter parts of bogmoss lawns on the Cranberry Beds and Bettisfield Moss and although recorded in the past from Wem Moss[7], it has not been found recently. This species is confined to a cluster of sites on the south coast of England, near Aberystwyth in Wales, in the very north of Scotland and a band along the Scottish border.

Sphagnum compactum was found at one location on a track, and although widespread in Britain it is absent from the Midlands and Welsh Marches. Its nearest records are Ruthin, Church Stretton and Knutsford.

Dicranum undulatum, a nationally scarce moss, also occurs on the site, forming patches in amongst bogmoss in the **top moss** lawns.

•Higher plants

The Mosses are one of the most southerly stations for bog rosemary, a nationally scarce species in Britain (Plate 7). This dwarf shrub has mid-green, neatly-veined evergreen leaves reminiscent of the larger leaves of the garden rosemary, but the leaves are unscented. Its pale-pink bell flowers can be found throughout the year, except in the extremes of winter, and it forms spreading patches in a wide range of moisture conditions. It is scattered all over the Mosses, but is particularly abundant on the uncut areas.

Whixall Moss is the only Shropshire site for the lesser bladderwort. Mary Hignett, daughter of the famous entomologist James Hignett, recalls this species as being

Plate 7. The flowers of bog rosemary can be found in June and July. Photograph: J. Mason

abundant when she came as a child to the Mosses in the 1930s with her father. Now, the slender trailing stems of this species only occur in a very limited number of deeper peat cuttings in the area of Whixall Moss near the polluted Main Drain. This is also the area where the peat sequence differs from the normal sequence of **Coal**, **Black Peat**, **Grey Peat** and **White Peat** from the base to the top of the Moss. Dark fen, or black peat occurs all the way to the surface in this area, which may also create enriched conditions in these cuttings. Bladderworts add to their nutrient supply in the hostile environment of the mire by catching "packets of fertiliser" in the form of water insects. They entrap their prey by means of underwater leaves which are modified to form tiny bag-like traps, the mouth of which is closed by a hinged door which has sensitive hairs to trigger the trap. Water is pumped out of the trap and when a passing water flea touches the hairs the door flies open and the creature is sucked inside. The creature continues to live in the trap for a period. On dying and decomposing, its nutrients are absorbed by the plant.[19]

Wem Moss is the only Shropshire site for the great sundew and oblong-leaved sundew, although the round-leaved sundew occurs all over the Mosses. The three species can be told apart when not in flower as the former has leaves shaped like a dessert spoon, the second like a spatula and the third like a soup spoon. The attractive sparkling rosettes of leaves glisten like dew in the sun, hence the name "sundew"; the droplets of liquid on the ends of fine hairs on their leaves entice insects to land. Unfortunately for the insect, this again is a ploy to catch extra nutrients, this time from the air, as the globules are sticky and contain enzymes which digest the unsuspecting insect, the nutrients from which are drawn down the hairs and into the plant.

Wem and Cadney Mosses are also the only locations in Shropshire and vice-county Denbighshire for the pungent, evergreen bog myrtle which has spread rapidly in the past ten years on Wem Moss as it has dried out. It now forms almost impenetrable shoulder height thickets along the central lagg, in which the stately Royal fern hides its distinct sporing and vegetative fronds.

Plate 8. Female adder.
Photograph: J. Robinson

The tiny spikes of white beak-sedge, and golden *Sphagnum pulchrum* are also of regional importance[18], as is the attractive alder buckthorn. The latter is a tall shrub of peaty ground, with fine grey twigs and small white flowers which give rise to bead-like red berries which gradually turn black; the two often occurring on the bush together. Scattered along the sheltered tracks leading into the Mosses, the alder buckthorn provides larval food for one of the prettiest butterflies of the Mosses, the sulphur-yellow brimstone, which enlightens early spring days and emerges again in August.

●The Fauna of the Mosses

The Mosses are a huge area of wilderness, most of which is not managed intensively for either agriculture or forestry. They have not been sprayed repeatedly with insecticides, so a wide range of invertebrates thrive, providing the base for a diverse food chain. Moths, butterflies, leaf beetles and many other insects live on the bog plants. Flies and spiders and hawker dragonflies hunt for these and other insects and in turn provide food for voles, shrews, frogs and toads. Birds of prey and adders hunt in turn for the small mammals and amphibians. Waders probe the damp peat for invertebrates and in turn provide food for birds of prey and foxes. Wildfowl and waders are taken in small numbers in winter by the shooting syndicate which has a long-standing lease on Fenn's Moss.

The Mosses are of international importance for invertebrates. A total of 1688 species have been recorded for the site, including 11 Red Data Book (RDB)[20] and 12 potential RDB species. Entomologists from all over Britain have visited Whixall and Wem Moss since the turn of the century.

Birds are also of local importance and include two RDB species - curlew and nightjar.

Mammal species present on the Mosses include common-, pygmy- and water shrew, bank- and short-tailed vole, brown hare, rabbit, fox, mink, polecat and badger. Only two systematic surveys for mammals have been carried out by English Nature.

The National Hare Survey in 1992 indicated that there was substantial use of the central, commercially-cut areas of Fenn's Moss, probably because of the open ground and young purple moor-grass shoots available there. A live-trapping survey for polecats for the Vincent Wildlife Trust in 1993 afforded only one catch, in the middle of the Moss, rather than as expected, in hedgerows of surrounding farmland. The density of polecats established was in keeping with the general density of 1 per km^2 on the Welsh borders where they are spreading out from Wales, recovering from their past persecution by gamekeepers.

Amphibians and reptiles similarly have not been systematically surveyed, but include common frog, common toad, great crested-, common- and palmate newt, slow-worm, common lizard, grass snake and adder. Adder are now so rare because of persecution and disturbance that they are afforded total protection under Schedule 5 of the *Wildlife and Countryside Act 1981* (Plate 8). They are occasionally encountered sunning themselves on the tracks and peat baulks in all areas of the Mosses. The males are small, grey and strongly patterned, whereas the females on the Moss are larger and darker, sometimes almost black. This colour did not endear them to the peat cutters who were handling the dark peat blocks which had been stacked to dry - ideal warm, dry adder basking locations!

•Invertebrate Conservation Value of Fenn's and Whixall Mosses

Raised mires support many notable and rare insect and spider species. Fenn's and Whixall

Mosses has long been known as an important site for invertebrates, particularly for its moths (535 species), butterflies (27 species) and Odonata (dragonflies, darters and damselflies - 26 species), which include rarities such as the northern footman moth and the white-faced darter dragonfly. The Mosses support the most southerly colony of the large heath butterfly and are one of only three British locations for the RDB1 caddis fly *Hagenella clathrata*.

The Mosses are an amazing place in spring and summer with one species emerging after another the whole season long; and in summer, as dusk falls, the Mosses are transformed as the air is filled with ghostly-pale fluttering moths.

Upon taking over the site in 1991, English Nature commissioned survey work to identify and record the species present.

•Butterflies, dragonflies and moths

In 1991 Jenny Joy was contracted to investigate the distribution of the large heath butterfly on the Mosses[21]. This led to the establishment of a Butterfly Monitoring Scheme transect in 1992 [22]. From 1993 to 1995 two further transects were added, with both butterflies and dragonflies being recorded by EN's sandwich students and Training for Work placements.

The transects were designed to monitor large heath butterfly and white-faced darter populations, and also the area of the lime-rich disused railway line. They also cover the rehabilitated recent and old commercial cuttings and rehabilitated hand cuttings to determine the effects of management.

The large heath butterfly is a northern mire species, found at Fenn's and Whixall at its most southerly English location. It is a regionally notable species in England and Wales, protected from sale under Schedule 5 of the *Wildlife and Countryside Act 1981*. The large heath occurs as subspecies *davus*, the southern race of the butterfly, which is found in Lancashire, Westmorland, Cheshire and South Yorkshire. It is best recognised as a flash of brown, white and grey in June and July continually flying from one plant to another and refusing to pose for photographs! The upper side is dull brown with well marked eye-spots, the underside forewings are chestnut coloured and hind-wings grey, both with broad white stripes and large conspicuous white-pupilled eye-spots (Plate 9). The eye-spots are thought to frighten birds off. A unique form of this butterfly "*cockaynei*" also occurs on the Mosses. In this form the basal area of the hind-wing underside is marbled with white.

It has been shown[22] that the large heath apparently does not feed, as previously reported, on the white beak-sedge, but feeds and overwinters as a caterpillar on hare's-tail cotton-sedge. The butterfly takes nectar from cross-leaved heath. The juxtaposition of these two species is particularly common on the old hand cut areas of Whixall Moss and North East

Plate 9. Large heath butterfly.
Photograph: R.S. Key.

Fenn's Moss where ditches have become obstructed. However, the continual drying out of these areas because of peat cutting has limited the extent of large tussocks of this cotton-sedge to deeper cuttings. English Nature's management work aims to greatly increase the extent of the larval

food plant for this mire butterfly by raising water tables and a research programme is being conducted into the effects of submersion on the larvae, relevant to such work.

In 1990 Wem Moss held over 1200 large heath butterflies, largely confined to a small area of 100 x 200m restricted by the distribution of sufficiently dense tussocks of hare's-tail cotton-sedge[23].

There have been problems with large heath butterfly collectors who repeatedly visit the site in July. They aim to collect specimens with particularly prominent eye-spots. They either kill them and pin them for sale or breed from them and sell the progeny or, even worse, return them to the Mosses. The latter alters the balance of genetics in the local populations, as these butterflies have not been exposed to natural selection unlike the rest of the specimens on the Moss. In 1994, 44 live large heaths taken from the Mosses were recovered from collectors and re-released.

•Other butterflies[24]

The distribution of other butterfly species on the Mosses largely reflects their food preferences. Most are not species of the open mire surface and are only found in marginal areas and lagg communities. Some are tall scrub species. The sulphur-yellow brimstone is limited to the damp marginal trackways where the alder buckthorn grows and the green hairstreak, speckled wood and green-veined white are restricted to the railway line and trackways which have taller trees. Green hairstreaks camouflage themselves very well as birch leaves and can be difficult to spot.

Other species abound on sunny, grassy tracks such as along the railway line, including gatekeeper, small skipper, meadow brown, small heath, wall brown, small- and large white and orange tip. Those whose larvae feed on nettles such as small tortoiseshell, red admiral and peacock also occur on the peripheral tracks. Very low numbers of ringlet, comma, holly blue, purple hairstreak, dark-green fritillary and small pearl-bordered fritillary have been recorded, generally on marginal tracks.

The dingy skipper and common blue are concentrated along the lime-rich railway line where bird's-foot trefoil grows. The common blue has two broods, reflecting the southerly location of the site.

The species, in addition to large heath, which are most commonly encountered in the centre of the Mosses are the strongly flying large white, the small copper and the large skipper which occur wherever there is purple moor-grass and sheltering scrub. The small copper abounds because of the sheep's sorrel which has spread across the site with peat cutting. Two clouded yellow were seen out on the mire in 1994.

To compensate for the loss of common species from the central areas of the Mosses because of scrub clearance works, marginal areas have been managed specifically for butterflies. Sunny trackways leading up to the Mosses which were becoming shaded out have been lightly opened up, and scrub along the railway line is mown back on an alternating biennial strip rotation to encourage herbaceous species. In 1993 dingy skipper records had increased in this area, reflecting the success of management works.

•Dragonflies[25]

The Mosses have long-since been visited for their 26 species of Odonata, in particular for the white-faced darter. The number of species far exceeds that at any other site in Shropshire[26].
Some Odonata such as the banded demoiselle, beautiful demoiselle, the migrant hawker and the nationally notable white-legged damselfly are not bog species and occur where the less acidic, slow-flowing waters of the Shropshire Union Canal cross Whixall Moss[25, 27]. Other

species, such as the four-spotted chaser and black darter occur everywhere across the Mosses where the damming or blocking of drains has created open water, the former species in greater numbers than anywhere else in Shropshire. The emerald damselfly is also widespread across the site, but depends on both open water for breeding and purple moor-grass for camouflage, whereas the large red damselfly, variable damselfly, azure damselfly and brown-, common- and southern hawkers are most often found around areas with tall scrub. The common darter, blue-tailed and common blue damselflies are found around larger water areas on the Mosses.

Insufficient records of the broad-bodied chaser, the nationally notable ruddy darter and 1980s records of black-tailed skimmers, downy emerald-, scarce blue-tailed- and red-eyed damselfly and golden-ringed dragonfly exist to establish a firm pattern of distribution[26].

The emperor dragonfly, which is spreading northward, and the yellow-winged darter, a migrant species, have appeared on the site in 1994 and 1995 respectively.

The white-faced darter is a true mire species, requiring shallow, peaty pools with a mix of bogmoss cover and open water. Its red and black males (Plate 10) and yellow

Plate 10. Male white-faced darter, which can be found in June and July.
Photograph: P. Wilson.

and black females have a noticeably hunch-back appearance and can be seen from late May to early July. It is a nationally notable species (Na), restricted to a handful of sites in Surrey, Cheshire, Cumbria and north west Scotland. On the Mosses it has been principally confined to one corner of the site, in an area of old hand peat cuttings.

The British Dragonfly Society have expressed concern at the removal of bogmoss for holly wreath making, fearing such moss may contain larvae of rare species such as white-faced darters. The moss is, however, left to dry before being sacked-up and this may allow time for any larvae dragged out with the moss to find their way back into the water. The collection of moss is now licensed on the reserve, allowing the needs of this cottage industry to be balanced with the survival of dragonfly species. Bogmoss gathering may, in fact, have maintained conditions necessary for white-faced darters by creating open water areas in the bogmoss lawns. At Chartley Moss National Nature Reserve in Cheshire, numbers of this species have been increased by digging open water scrapes in the bogmoss surface.

English Nature's programme of ditch blocking has greatly increased the areas of open water. Immediately that areas are blocked and water levels increase, dragonflies such as the black darter are seen to expand their territories to take advantage of the new habitat.

•Moths

The 535 species of moths recorded up to 1992 include 7 Red Data Book species, 36 nationally notable species and 119 local species. Seventy-four of the resident species have not been recorded elsewhere in Shropshire[29].

One of the rarest moths, the RDB3 northern footman, a small grey moth with orange margins to its in-rolled wings, feeds on lichens and is common on Whixall Moss.

It is reputed to have become extinct from all of its other known locations. The RDB1 *Borkhausenia minutella* has not been seen since the 1930s. The RDB2 small eggar and RDB3 micro-moth *Coleophora currucipennella* are both species of scrub and woods. The RDB3 dingy mocha feeds on willow on damp heathland. Nationally notable species include the Na purple-bordered gold, larvae of which feeds on marsh plants; the Manchester treble-bar which feeds on bilberry and cranberry; the plain clay, the waved black and *Hypenodes turfosalis.*

Moths can be seen flying on the Mosses during the day. In the late summer, the large orange northern eggar which feeds on heather, the small yellow forester, which feeds on sheep's sorrel, and the strikingly-patterned wood tiger, a moorland species, join the myriads of common heath, small pale waves and silver-Y moths which fly up in clouds from vegetation as visitors pass[22].

The amazing caterpillars of some of the larger moths are frequently encountered: the bright green emperor moth larva with its black and yellow spots and tufts of black hairs; the large ginger and black, hairy northern eggar larva, and on the bushes the small hairy red, black and white yellow-tailed moth larva.

•Other invertebrates

Of the 1688 species of invertebrate noted earlier, that were listed for the site by Liverpool Museum in 1992[28], 97 nationally notable species and 169 species of local interest were identified, in addition to the 23 nationally rare species[20]. Thirty of the nationally rare or notable species have not been recorded during the last ten years. Of these thirty, twenty have not been seen for the last twenty-five years and are assumed to have become extinct from the site because of habitat deterioration. However, much of the invertebrate interest of the site remains, probably because the levels of commercial peat cutting remained low until 1989.

The old hand cut areas are structurally more irregular than the uncut areas and had the highest number of species of invertebrate, almost 600, twice as many as the uncut areas. The old commercially-cut areas had one and a half times as many species as uncut areas. However, species numbers on the recent commercially-cut areas are only half the level even of those on uncut areas.

The more diverse old cutting areas also have a greater number of nationally rare and notable species than the uncut areas. This is probably because the uncut areas have been damaged by lowered water tables and, as a result, have lost their natural hummock and pool systems. The only areas with open water would have been the old re-wetted peat cutting areas.

Although commercial peat cutting is considered undesirable, a limited maintenance of traditional hand peat cutting may assist in the retention of certain rare invertebrates which have colonised the Mosses as a result of this activity.

The Liverpool Museum study[28] highlighted the rare species of invertebrate present on Fenn's, Whixall and Bettisfield Mosses:

•Aquatic invertebrates

Heteropteran bugs such as the common backswimmer comprise a mix of common acid and neutral water species.

Caddisflies ranged from Britain's most threatened species, *Hagenella clathrata* (Plate 11), through locally important *Limnephilus* species and *Potamophylax rotundipennis*, which are characteristic of acid bogs and upland moorland, to *Limnephilus luridus* Britain's commonest acid water species. *Hagenella clathrata* is not a true mire species but lives in between the base of purple moor-grass tussocks in marginal areas of Whixall Moss. The species requires that the hollows between the grass tussocks must be flooded in winter, although they must dry out in the summer months to

Plate 11. The caddis fly *Hagenella clathrata*, one of the rarest insects on the Mosses. Photograph: P. Wilson

allow the larvae to emerge. Management for this species must therefore avoid high summer water levels.

All aquatic beetles are characteristic bog species including the nationally notable classic cut-over bog species *Acilius canaliculatus* and seven other nationally notable species. The water spider *Argyroneta aquatica*, which traps air in the hairs on its abdomen when it dives, is frequent in the hand peat cuttings. Few snails occur because of the acid nature of the site, but the RDB2 *Limnaea glabra* was found in polluted water. The occurrence of water crustaceans also reflects the contamination of bog waters on parts of the site.

•Terrestrial invertebrates

Spiders comprise the largest number of invertebrate species on the Mosses. However, most are common species. Although difficult to identify, the sheer numbers of different species with their myriad of shapes and vivid colours can be appreciated just by shaking litter or vegetation onto a white paper or tray. The delicacy of many of the species rapidly banishes the bad name given to this group by the large black ones so fond of bathrooms!

Scattered birch scrub near peat cuttings was found to be an important habitat for many species of spider.

Probably one of the most famous spiders of the Mosses is the great raft spider, a wolf spider with pale yellow stripes along each side of its body. The spider graduates from an insignificant juvenile life on birch bushes into a large, neat mid-brown spider the size of the centre of the palm of a hand. It walks on the surface of the water feeling with its feet for the vibrations of insects crash-landing onto the water. It also eats aquatic insects and even small fish from just below the surface. The other four Pirata wolf spiders present were also confined to bogmoss-rich cuttings.

Centipedes, millipedes and woodlice are generally restricted to leaf litter, but very wet, disturbed peat produced many specimens of two common millipedes, the snake millipede, *Proteroiulus fuscus,* and the flat-back millipede, *Polydesmus angustus.*

The nationally notable bog bushcricket, with its green and brown legs, is frequently found in the old hand and commercial cuttings. Of the four nationally notable bugs which were recorded *Pachybrachius fracticollis*, a species which lives on cotton-sedge, was the only true bog species. Several, less rare bogmoss bugs were found. Bug species characteristic of small, damp peat patches also occur, including the nationally notable (Na) *Microcantha marginalis.* Other species typical of fen, marsh and wet heath occur, but the majority of bugs found are common species of damp scrub.

All lacewings recorded are scrub species.

Beetles comprise the second largest number of invertebrate species on the Mosses. 12 nationally notable Nb species of beetle were found during the survey, two of which, *Agonum ericeti* and *Mycetoporous clavicornis,* are classic mossland species. Most, however, are species of dead timber reflecting the length of time that the margins of the Moss have been drained and

colonised by trees and scrub. An unmistakeable species, the green tiger beetle, 1.5cm long, bright green with yellow spots and red legs, can often be seen crawling along the bare peat tracks.

The stubby, dull-green leaf beetle *Lochmaea suturalis;* the incredibly variable irridescent weevils *Phyllobius* spp. and *Polydrusus* spp.; the neat, shiny black flower beetle, *Luperus longicornis,* with its long, black antennae and the tiny shining leaf beetles (*Chalcoides* spp.) which jump away when disturbed, can be found by shaking any bush on the Mosses throughout the summer season. *Lochmaea* leaf beetles are probably the most common insect on the Mosses and the effects of their larvae can be seen in the overnight browning of birch and heather, after muggy conditions. Together with high water levels and the ravages of moth larvae, this leaf beetle damage is probably responsible for the very slow growth rate of birch on hand cut and old commercially-cut areas.

A study of the changes in ground beetles from the mossland leading onto the marginal peaty pastureland[30] demonstrated that although the number of species increased on the marginal fields, the species present were in fact common species of damp woodland with aggressive non-specialist species such as *Carabus granulatus* and *Harpalus latus.* The mossland sites with species such as *Pterostichus nigrita* or *Dyschirius globosus* are the sites of most merit.

Ground invertebrates have been sampled by English Nature and the Field Studies Council in each of the four peat cutting types from 1991 to 1994. 177 ground beetle species have been identified so far, including the nationally notable species *Agonum ericeti* which lives in bogmoss, and the rove beetles *Sepedophilus lusitanicus* and *Atheta strandiella.* Changes in the communities of ground invertebrates found will in the future reflect the success of English Nature's rehabilitation management.

Flies (Diptera) are the third largest group of invertebrate species recorded on the

Mosses, with 11 RDB, 19 nationally notable and 119 species of local interest. The two most noticeable flies are the horse fly, *Chrysops relictus,* which attracts attention by its irridescent green and red eyes and black and white chequerboard wings, and the wretched black sweat fly, the bane of workers on the Mosses in late summer. Mosquitoes and midges are a major deterrent to summer evening visits, but they provide abundant food for swifts and swallows which skim the Mosses so gracefully.

The bulk of the rarer fly species are peatland specialists, from areas of bare damp peat and water-filled and bogmoss-rich ditches, including the nationally rare mire specialist *Hercostomis angustifrons.* The 47 hoverfly species recorded also include mire specialists such as *Chrysogaster virescens* and there are a whole suite of mire specialists from the Empidoidea family. Many of the flies have parasitic life-cycles like the large, black *Tachina grossa* (Plate 12), which lays its eggs in the caterpillars of oak- and northern eggar moths, its larvae literally eating the caterpillar from the inside out!

There are many interesting Hymenopteran species (ants, bees, wasps, etc.) on the Mosses including the RDB1 sawfly, *Trichiosoma vitellinae,* which is not now recorded from any other location. However, most species are only of local importance, although the total number of species of ants, for example, is on a par with that of other peatlands which are nationally important for invertebrates. Many of the species found are non-residents scavenging for nectar or prey. The majority of those species which do breed on the site nest in plant stems, peat stacks and rotting wood, although some are ground nesters. The ant *Myrmica scabrinodis* is the only true wet peatland species.

● Birds of the Mosses

Breeding birds were recorded on the site in 1988[31]. A much more extensive series of eleven transects covering most of the CCW/EN landholding were intensively

Plate 12. *Tachina grossa* **lays its eggs on caterpillars of oak- and northern eggar moths. Photograph: R.S. Key**

surveyed for breeding birds in 1995 with assistance from the Chester RSPB group[32]. The peripheral areas of the site are dominated by scrub/woodland edge species such as tree pipit, wren, robin, whitethroat, garden warbler, blackcap, chiffchaff and particularly willow warbler, whose descending call is constantly heard. The species present in 1995 were similar to those in 1988 as management has not changed the peripheral areas.

Species associated with Bettisfield Moss are typical of scrub and mature woodland e.g. treecreeper, great spotted woodpecker and goldcrest. The numbers of breeding pairs were small, because of the density of the woodland.

Breeding bird populations have changed on the central area of the Mosses between 1988 and 1995. The number of curlew (Plate 13) and lapwing breeding has increased with damming operations and both species are now nesting over a wider area. Teal and Canada goose now breed. There is no evidence of breeding by snipe, although the species is present throughout the summer. Black-headed gull colonies follow the larger areas of open water in attempting to breed but succeess is rare, probably because falling water tables allow predation by foxes. Little ringed plover attempted to breed in 1994, but were unsuccesful. Wheatear, whinchat and stonechat breed.

Scrub clearance from the centre of the site has caused a decline in breeding species such as tree pipit, reed bunting and green woodpecker, but numbers of species such as skylark and meadow pipit have increased. In spring the site is now filled with the plaintive call of curlew and the song of skylark; and the haunting churring of nightjar can occasionally be heard at dusk on warm summer evenings.

Raptors which regularly hunt include sparrowhawk, buzzard, peregrine, hobby, short-eared owl and kestrel. Marsh harrier, hen harrier and merlin are sometimes seen.

However, it is in autumn and winter that the dramatic changes in bird-life are apparent, now that there are extensive areas of water covering the Mosses. The dammed areas support high numbers of snipe, curlew, mallard and teal by day, with large flocks of black-headed gull and curlew flying in to roost at night. Short-eared owl can be seen regularly on Whixall Moss and new species of wildfowl and wader are beginning to use the site on autumn passage, including greenshank, green sandpiper, golden plover, ruff, dunlin and spotted redshank.

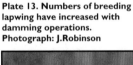

Plate 13. Numbers of breeding lapwing have increased with damming operations. Photograph: J.Robinson

The Palaeoenvironmental Record

Bogs are ideal for the study of environmental history. Their deposits accumulate sequentially and they remain incompletely decayed, so that over time the peat layers become a stratified repository of evidence for past environmental conditions. Depending upon their rate of growth and on how finely the peat is sampled for analysis, bogs can provide information about vegetational changes on timescales measured in decades and centuries. Some of their contained subfossils, undecayed tree stumps for example, may provide information on growing conditions for individual years, giving an immediate insight into past climatic and environmental conditions of the bog, thousands of years ago.

Most bogs in north-temperate regions are less than 10,000 years old. Many have formed either in areas glaciated during the last ice maximum, or in adjacent, former periglacial regions. If the pattern of environmental changes of the late Quaternary period is repeated, they can expect to be obliterated several thousand years from now, during the next cold stage. Bogs in north-temperate lands are therefore ephemeral features of the landscape, but they are nonetheless valuable archives of past environmental conditions[1, 2], providing an environmental record covering several millennia. Contained within, and often clearly visible in the peat stratigraphy are the major climatic and vegetational changes that occurred during their lifetime. This feature of bogs, that they act almost as "museums" of past conditions, allows reconstructions of the environmental history of not only the bog, but also the surrounding countryside.

•Palaeoecological studies

Palaeoecology is the scientific study concerned with the reconstruction of past environments. Palaeoecologists differ from ecologists in that they cannot observe their objects of study (the past environments) directly[3], but instead have to infer the past bog vegetation, the past environmental conditions and the past climate, from the available evidence. This evidence may take several forms. Both the macrofossils and microfossils (those visible to the naked eye or through a microscope, respectively) contained in peat are useful. Pollen trapped in the peat is indicative not only of what was growing on the bog but also of the regional vegetation, and hence the climate. Analysis of the abundant plant macrofossils in a vertical core of peat - particularly the remains of *Sphagnum* (bogmoss), Cyperaceae (sedge) and Ericaceae (heathers) - allows a reconstruction of the relative importance of these taxa on the surface of the bog during past centuries. When living, some of the *Sphagnum* and other bog species exhibit relatively narrow ecological tolerances, particularly with respect to mire surface wetness, and so become confined to particular microhabitats on a growing mire. Their position and relative abundance on the mire surface will be strongly influenced by the depth of the water table.

On a growing mire, there is often a microtopography of hummocks and pools, sometimes with extensive "lawns" of bogmoss. During times of wetter climate, the surface of the bog will tend to be wetter, the pools may expand and species preferring wetter conditions may be more abundant on the bog surface; whereas, during times of drier climate, the water table will be lower, the pools will contract, and so hummock-forming species may prevail. Detailed, quantitative analysis of the subfossil remains of these taxa in vertical cores of peat will provide clues as to the past surface wetness of the bog[2], and indirectly may provide evidence as to past climates.

In the case of raised mires such as Fenn's and Whixall Mosses, the plants on the growing surface are isolated from groundwater, and are therefore dependent upon rainfall for their sustenance. Such mires are said to be directly coupled to the atmosphere[2, 4], and it is believed that studies of their macrofossil record can provide a very good indication of past regional climate. The studies of plant macrofossils can be complemented by analysis of rhizopods. These are microscopic, mainly pool-dwelling animals, whose remains become stratified in the peat and whose presence as subfossils indicates wet conditions at the time of peat formation. Together, these techniques allow reconstruction of bog surface wetness through time, and so provide data on climates of the past.

•Relevance of the palaeoecological record

The study of palaeoclimates from peat stratigraphy is particularly relevant in the context of the current debate over "global warming", as reconstructions of past climate provide a baseline against which to test the alleged human-induced climatic changes of the present century. There is still doubt as to whether the recorded temperature changes of this century reflect a directional shift in climate or are within the range of natural variation. This is because the instrumental record is, in geological terms, very short. Meteorological records cover, at best, little more than 350 years, and so in order to understand the magnitude, rate and frequency of natural climatic changes on a millennial scale, "proxy" data on palaeoclimates are crucial. Bogs, particularly raised bogs, can provide such "proxy-climate" data, either through analysis of their contained subfossils, or by determining the degree of peat humification - a measurement of the degree of breakdown of the peat. The decay or humification of peat proceeds much faster in drier conditions, and so peat laid down in dry or warm conditions will be more highly decayed, and appear darker in colour, than peat laid down in cool, wet

conditions, when the vegetation will remain relatively undecayed, appearing "fresh", with leaves of pool-species of *Sphagnum* clearly visible. The data that can be obtained from detailed studies of peat stratigraphy can produce a sensitive, high-resolution record of climate change[4]. Whilst it is largely a record of past changes in bog surface wetness, rather than a temperature record, the magnitude and rate of past changes in bog surface wetness in Britain seem to indicate that climatic changes in prehistory at least matched and very likely exceeded the changes recorded for the present century.

•Studies at Fenn's and Whixall Mosses

The problem with the proxy-climate record from Britain's bogs is that, as most of them have been altered or destroyed in recent decades by human activities, so the past record of bog surface wetness cannot be related directly to a growing mire surface under the present-day climate. This is the case at Fenn's and Whixall Mosses, where large areas of the bog have been cut (either by hand or by machine) and drained. However, a bog with cut sections is, as we shall see, well suited for palaeoecological research.

In order to ascertain past rates of change, palaeoenvironmental studies on bogs depend upon methods of dating. In the late 1950s, radiocarbon dating became available to palaeoecologists, and one of the earliest studies in England and Wales that employed this technique was conducted at Fenn's Moss[5], in this case to date recurring phases of bog growth. Thirty to forty years later, more detailed, recent and current studies of palaeoclimatic "events" have been and are being conducted at Fenn's and Whixall Mosses[6, 7, 8]

At both sites there are clear indications of major peat-stratigraphic changes in mid-late prehistory. The relatively sharp stratigraphic change from a dark, sedge-rich peat at depth, to a fresh, light-coloured *Sphagnum* peat nearer the surface, was well-known to peat diggers on site, and featured in early palaeoecological research here. A "major humification change" at Whixall Moss was later the focus of part of a Ph.D. thesis conducted from Southampton University[6]. Other research into the prehistory of the mire, conducted initially from the then Environmental Research Unit at Keele University and latterly co-ordinated from the Centre for Environmental Change and Quaternary Research at Cheltenham, has concentrated on detailed studies of large macrofossils of Scots pine - bog timbers, stratified in the peat (Figure 2) - and on the environmental conditions that led to the establishment and decline of pine populations on parts of the mire in prehistoric times[7, 8].

● The History of Palaeoecological Research at Fenn's and Whixall Mosses

As has been intimated above, Fenn's and Whixall Mosses have earned themselves a hallowed place in the annals of the environmental history of the British Isles - indeed, they might be said to have two places, because there are separate entries for Fenn's Moss and for Whixall Moss in Godwin's famous *History of the British Flora*[9], although, curiously, both sites are listed by Godwin as being in Shropshire, even though

Figure 2. Plan of Fenn's and Whixall Mosses showing sample locations and areas known to have subfossil pine stratified within the peat.

Key: AA - Abbie Austin's;
CAN - "Canoe";
CON - Conery;
FF - Fenn's Forestry;
FW - Fenn's Wood;
M - Middle of the Mire;
RH - Ray Heath's;
S - The Sheds;
solid line - Nature Reserve boundary;
dot/dash line - England/Wales border;
shaded - location of subfossil pine stumps;
X - other WX discs.

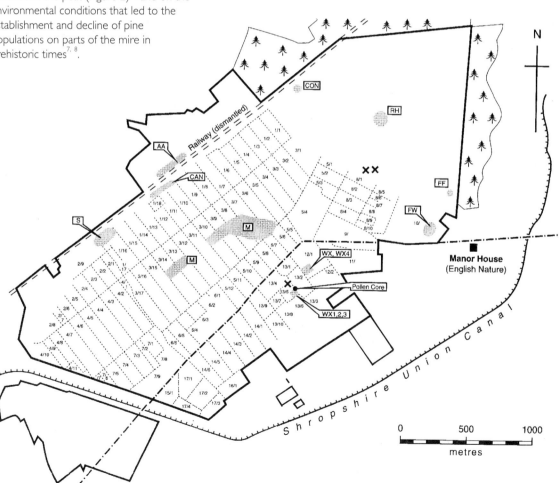

Fenn's Moss was clearly in Flintshire! Early work on vegetational history was conducted at Fenn's and Whixall Mosses before the Second World War[10], and this was followed by further research on both Mosses in the late 1950s and early 1960s[5, 11, 12]. There was then something of a gap in work on the environmental history of the Mosses, and it was not until the 1980s that further research was conducted, albeit largely unpublished[6,] followed by the recent phase of palaeoecological research, initiated in 1991.

●Early studies

The earliest detailed palaeoecological research at the site was conducted by Hardy[10], and was published in her account of the Shropshire and Flint Maelor Mosses in 1939. This early research involved the application of what was then a relatively new technique in studies of vegetational history - that of pollen analysis. This technique, which allows reconstruction of the vegetational changes of not merely the mire but of the surrounding region, had been pioneered in the 1920s in Scandinavia by von Post, and was later championed in England and Wales by Harry Godwin[13] based at Cambridge University. Hardy's paper was the fifth in a series that emanated from Cambridge concerned with the postglacial vegetational history of the British Isles; it preceded by a year the formal publication by Godwin[14] of a pollen zonation scheme for England and Wales.

The postglacial environmental history of the Shropshire region was compiled by Hardy from pollen and peat stratigraphic records from several mosses, and was summarised in her Table I[10]. In outline, the early postglacial forests were principally of birch, and these were succeeded by woodland containing much hazel, with some elm, and later, oak. Pine, although present in the early postglacial, may not have become abundant until somewhat later (Zone VI in Hardy's Table I and in Godwin's zonation scheme[10, 14, 9]). Alder representation then rose steeply as pine declined, after which

Quercetum mixtum (mixed oak forest of oak, elm and lime) dominated, together with alder. The upper part of Hardy's Table I contains information on peat-stratigraphic changes, including a particular episode when there are pine stumps in the peat.

Hardy described the condition of the Mosses as she saw them in the 1930s: drained, former raised bog, no longer actively peat-forming, and extensively cut. The peat stratigraphy in a number of borings was described, and attention was drawn to the division into "*an upper unhumified peat, and a lower dark compact humified peat*". Hardy drew parallels with raised bogs in continental north-west Europe, where the contact between the two peat types is known as the Grenz-horizont ("Recurrence surface" or "Rejuvenation surface"), supposedly caused by a climatic shift from an alleged "*dry Sub-Boreal to the cold and wet Sub-Atlantic*" (a boundary that was then conventionally placed at the start of the Iron Age), but Hardy[10] cautions us that after work by Granlund[15] in Sweden in 1932, there is "*some doubt as to whether any well-marked recurrence surface in a west European bog need necessarily be of this particular age*". As Haslam[6] found later, Hardy's caution was well-placed, and her comments proved prophetic.

One of the most interesting, and important, aspects of Hardy's paper was her reconsideration of the finding of a bronze looped palstave, which had been reported earlier by Chitty[16] (Figure 3). Hardy inter-viewed the finder, a Mr. George Saywell of Whixall, and obtained from him an account of the finding of the implement "*lying 'on top of the roots of the old pine, about 8 ft. from the surface'*". Hardy visited the exact location of the find in September 1937, and made a boring close to the find-spot. The pine layer was encountered at a depth of 130-160 cm (some 3-4 ft below the then surface), the difference in depth being attributed by Hardy to peat shrinkage after draining, with the pine rooted in a layer of cotton-sedge. Hardy claimed that pollen analysis of the peat showed a "*definite pine *maximum at the level equated with that of the stumps*", but noted that "*the pine* [pollen] *values are on the whole very low*".

Hardy used the find of the implement to date the pine phase to "*a time during the Middle Bronze Age or later*". This was a good example of the use of archaeological typology, that of the well-documented palstave, to date a peat section. Indeed, Hardy was able to go further than that, combining evidence of the palstave with changes in peat stratigraphy at Whixall, Bettisfield and Whattal Mosses, and the finding of a dug-out canoe at Whattal, to opine that "*the Middle Bronze Age was a dry period, while the period to which the canoe belonged* [probably Iron Age; possibly Roman] *was wet, or at least wetter*". This was a remarkable and precise feat of the use of inductive methods in palaeoecology - combining archaeological and peat stratigraphic techniques, but without the aid of radiocarbon dating - which our recent more detailed research has seemed to confirm.

Later, in the 1960s, a series of papers was published, each of which concentrated on particular aspects of vegetational history. Godwin and Willis[5] were interested in dating the so-called recurrence surfaces at a series of mosses in Wales, Cumbria, and the Welsh borders. Peat just above the upper recurrence surface of Fenn's Moss was reported as being consistent in age with that above a retardation layer (a darker band of slower growing peat) at Tregaron Bog in Wales. This implied regional climatic change. Whilst the details of the radiocarbon dates need not concern us here, the approximate age of this upper recurrence surface was 700 BP (i.e., 700 radiocarbon years before present, where "present" is AD 1950). Given their large standard errors (i.e., their imprecise nature), it is not really appropriate to attempt to calibrate the radiocarbon ages to calendar years. One curious feature of this dating programme was the reported age[5] of pine wood from Whixall Moss "*from* [the] *pine stump layer presumed to be that described*

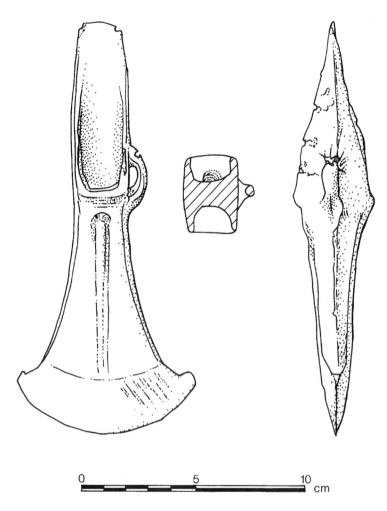

0   5   10 cm

Figure 3. Bronze Age looped palstave from Whixall Moss. Drawing: Timothy Morgan, after Chitty[16].

by Hardy (1939), and from which a Middle Bronze Age palstave was reported to have come. It forms the third recurrence surface from the top". The age of this sample was reported as 2307+110 BP (sample Q-383), which Godwin and Willis recognised as being "*too young for the Middle Bronze Age... Hardy's pollen zones might need reconsideration*"[5]. Recent work has shown that, far from Hardy's work needing reappraisal, it is the radiocarbon age of the pine stump, or its presumed stratigraphic position, that now needs to be reconsidered!

Perhaps the most well-known of the palaeoecological papers of the 1960s concerned with Whixall Moss was that conducted by Dr. Judy Turner, published in 1964[11]. The larger part of the paper was concerned with Tregaron Bog, in Wales, where the bulk of her research was then concentrated, but her research also involved pollen analysis and radiocarbon dating of the peat at Whixall Moss, through the highly humified peat described by Hardy and allegedly including Hardy's pine stump layer. Turner describes radiocarbon sample Q-383 as being from a "*pine stump from Hardy's pine stump layer*". This is a change in emphasis from Godwin and Willis's[5] more guarded description of the provenance of the sample. Discussion of rates of vegetational change and human influence at Whixall was based on the radiocarbon dating evidence, which in reality consisted of only two radiocarbon dates. One of these, that on the pine stump, might now be considered suspect. Either that, or one must allow that the pine stump, whose size is not reported, came from a much later horizon than the main (i.e., Hardy's[10] and Grant's[8]) pine stump layer.

Turner's research at Whixall was reported in two other papers[17,18], and was also referred to by Godwin[9]. The emphasis in the papers, and in Godwin's commentary, was on the "anthropogenic factor in vegetational history", and particularly on the possibility that human influence in the Bronze Age was responsible for an apparent regional decline in lime pollen. Turner's work had a major influence on other palaeoecologists. Her attempts to separate those pollen taxa indicative of pastoral and arable agriculture was then a significant advance, even if one might now quibble with some of the attributions made.

It is interesting to note that Turner's decline and disappearance of lime pollen, which is shown on her pollen diagram as apparently being well below the level of the pine stump, contrasts with the continuing pollen evidence for lime, up almost to a pine stump layer, in more recent work by Malcolm

Grant[8]. Moreover, Hardy's Table I[10] contains the observation: "Pinus [pine] *max., stumps.* Tilia [lime] *curve petering out.*" This might suggest that Turner's pine stump was genuinely younger than the main pine stump layer of Hardy[10] and Grant[8]. Final resolution of this issue - which might seem trivial but which has significant implications, both for the late-Holocene survival of Scots pine in the Welsh borders and for the climatic history of the region - must await not only the full publication of Malcolm Grant's research, but also the results of continuing research into subfossil pine on the site by several authors of this chapter.

Tallis and Birks[12] also touched upon the vegetational history and palaeohydrology of Fenn's and Whixall Mosses in their consideration of the past and present distribution of *Scheuchzeria palustris* in Europe. This plant, sometimes known as the Rannoch-rush in recognition of its abundance on Rannoch Moor in Scotland, is now rare in England and Wales. It had been reported earlier by Hardy[10] as having previously grown at Fenn's Moss and at Bettisfield in horizons that may be taken to be above (i.e., younger than) the main Whixall pine layer. Its palaeohydrological significance is that its former presence on raised mires is taken as indicating pool-edge vegetation, and so records of its distinctive rhizomes in the peat might be taken to indicate very wet episodes on the mire.

So, by the mid-1960s, a postglacial vegetational history of the region had been established, with increasing emphasis being placed on human impact on the regional forest. This impact was believed to be particularly significant from at least the Bronze Age. A picture was also beginning to emerge of the past mire environments of Fenn's and Whixall Mosses, with the past climate being characterised by alternating wet and dry episodes, superimposed upon a presumed long-term downward trend from a supposed postglacial climatic optimum.

•Recent research

Stimulus to the more recent phase of research was provided by Dr. Keith Barber at Southampton University, who had by then developed the technique of plant macrofossil analysis to generate proxy-climate data[19]. In 1983, the site was visited by a group of scientists, led by Dr. Barber, during an international conference on palaeohydrology being held at Attingham Park, near Shrewsbury. At the time, the site was being actively worked for peat, and the freshly exposed faces of the peat cuttings were ideal for observing the major changes in peat stratigraphy, including both the "MHC" (main humification change) and the discontinuous pine layer(s) on the site.

Keith Barber's new research student, Chris Haslam, principally employed the techniques of plant macrofossil analysis and radiocarbon dating to investigate the main humification change in raised mires on a transect, west-to-east, from Ireland to Poland[6]. He dated a shift to wetter conditions at the Moss to 2,180+50 BP (SRR-3074), and a major humification change was bracketed by radiocarbon dates of 1930+50 BP (SRR-3036, below) and 1750+60 BP (SRR-3035, above)[20]. The detailed results of his research remain largely unpublished and so it would be inappropriate to document them further here. Suffice it to note that Whixall Moss was one of Haslam's eighteen sites and selection of the site was in part a reflection of the ease of sampling.

•Current Palaeoecological Research

It is a little ironic, then, that the stratigraphy of working faces of a peat bog subject to cutting are easier to study[21] than by coring into an intact mire. They provide ideal opportunities for observing and sampling from laterally continuous, freshly exposed stratigraphic records; and this situation may be contrasted with the difficulties of observing and sampling from the degraded baulks and eventually re-wetted surface of a peat bog undergoing rehabilitation for conservation! In 1990, Rick Turner wrote to Dr. Frank Chambers (then at Keele University), alerting him to the diminishing prospects for stratigraphic research at the site if the planned conservation programme were to result in a swift raising of the water table. A linked programme of research was then instigated from Keele University, shortly after the acquisition of the site for nature conservation by English Nature, and funded initially by a small grant from the Countryside Council for Wales. The appointment of Dr. Joan Daniels as Site Manager undoubtedly contributed to the prominence and support given to the palaeoecological aspects, as her previous training in, and knowledge of, palaeoecology led to the formulation of a series of questions, which the new phase of research was designed to answer.

This new phase of research has involved a number of specialists. These include Malcolm Grant, as a postgraduate research student concentrating on fine-resolution pollen analysis and subfossil pine tree-ring analyses, supervised by Dr. (now Professor) Frank Chambers and Dr. Peter Thomas; Dr. Jonathan Lageard, engaged in parallel research on the dendrochronology of subfossil pines and of oaks, initially as a postdoctoral research assistant with the same supervisors; and Leri Roberts, about to commence postgraduate research on the environmental conditions leading to the establishment and decline of pine populations on the site. The programme is now co-ordinated by Professor Chambers from the Centre for Environmental Change and Quaternary Research at Cheltenham, and involves the team of researchers from their respective institutions.

•Focus of research

The current phase of palaeoecological research has largely concentrated on subfossil wood, both from the site, and from nearby. There are several reasons why tree remains have been the focus of the work. In part it is a reflection of the growing interest and expertise in the study of subfossil wood, both oak and pine, from bogs; in part also is the desire to understand when, why and for how long, raised mires might become part-colonised by trees. The pine layer at Fenn's and Whixall Mosses was also an enigma, in that its apparent dating by radiocarbon, as we have seen above, conflicted starkly with the archaeological evidence. All these aspects, combined with the aspirations and

expertise of the researchers, have resulted in an integrated approach to the problem, in which study of peat stratigraphy has been combined with dendrochronology to address a number of specific aims. One of these, which is being addressed in the first phase of current research, is to attempt to assess the palaeoclimatic and hydrological significance of the pine layer(s) at Fenn's and Whixall Mosses.

•Implications for conservation and management

The conventional British conservationists' view of raised mires is of a treeless environment: in their view, there is no place on a living, growing bog for trees. The tree remains stratified in some peats would seem to deny this view, although the reasons for and the significance of episodic tree colonisation of raised mires are incompletely understood. The pine layer at Fenn's and Whixall Mosses thus has implications for management. Under what conditions of climate, local hydrology, or degree of human influence (for example, of grazing or burning) can trees grow and survive on bogs? If, as at Fenn's and Whixall Mosses, the intention is, ultimately, to restore the conditions of a peat-forming ecosystem, what peat-forming plants would be expected, indeed encouraged, to grow there? Should any trees be permitted amongst them?

The prevailing bog-management view is that trees should not be encouraged, and particularly not pine trees, which with their ability to intercept rainfall and to transpire large quantities of water from the mire, might have the effect of drying the bog surface and of shading and drying out the peat-forming plants, particularly *Sphagna*, with implications for increasingly rare mire plants and animals. Pragmatically, this view has much to commend it: in attempting to re-establish the conditions of a growing bog, there is no point in making the task more difficult than it already is!

Plate 14. Stump of prehistoric Scots pine exposed in peat cutting.
Photograph: André Q. Berry

Yet, the evidence of subfossil wood from Fenn's and Whixall Mosses (Plate 14) implies that pines grew on some parts (though by no means all) of the site in the past, met their demise, and the bog survived: it had further episodes of peat growth. We do not yet know whether raised bogs in Britain naturally reach a stage at which short-lived tree colonisation is possible, and then pass beyond that stage, never to be re-colonised by trees; or whether raised bogs might naturally be susceptible to recurrent tree colonisation if the climatic or hydrological conditions are right. This is not an issue that can be resolved here, but the palaeoecological research being conducted at Fenn's and Whixall Mosses may help to provide answers to such questions. One can appreciate the need to understand both the preconditions for, and the legitimacy of pine growth on such mires if one considers the climate scenarios being offered by some climatologists for Britain early next century: the predictions are for warmer, drier summers, as a consequence of claimed "global warming". Will it be both feasible and "legitimate" to sustain a living, growing, treeless mire in such a climate, if in previous periods of warm, dry climate the bog became partly tree-covered?

•Aims

In outline, amongst the aims and objectives of the current phase of research are the following:

- •to test the synchroneity of past colonisation of the mire by pine woodland;

- •to build "floating" tree-ring chronologies by cross-matching the patterns of tree-rings from the pines, sampled at various locations on the mire;

- •to select suitable samples from each end of these chronologies for radiocarbon dating;

- •to conduct fine-resolution pollen analysis through the pine layer to isolate the peak(s) in pine pollen representation;

- •to date the apparent period(s) of pine colonisation by dating peat horizons that correspond with the high pine pollen values;

- •to ascertain the environmental conditions for bog-pine establishment and decline.

•Methods

In an early phase of this research, 150 discs were cut from stumps of subfossil pine from nine separate areas of the mire, using chainsaws or bow saws, and were transported from the site (Plate 15). Sample areas (refer Figure 2) could be divided into two categories:

Plate 15. English Nature transporting cut pine samples from the mire for analysis. Photograph: M.E. Grant.

- those where hand-cutting of the peat had revealed subfossil wood - for example, areas AA, RH and WX;

- areas where commercial peat operations had revealed subfossil wood - notably area M in the middle of the mire.

The sample discs were allowed to air dry, before preparation using a belt sander. Sanding creates a polished surface, allowing clear differentiation of tree-rings under a low-power stereo microscope (Plate 16). Tree-ring measuring equipment comprised a mechanical measuring stage, fitted with a linear transducer, linked to a computer via an electronic counter. Ring-widths were measured from the discs along 2-3 radii, working from the pith to the bark. These measurements were then combined to create a mean ring-width curve for each sample. The record for each disc can then be compared with those from other discs, using computer cross-matching routines, to establish the contemporaneity of samples. This initial phase of work has been followed by more detailed research on selected areas of the Moss involving fine-resolution pollen analysis from peat taken through the subfossil wood horizons, and by detailed examination of a new set of pine samples taken mainly from the English side of the border, from Whixall Moss. The detailed work has been conducted by Malcolm Grant[8], and required an application by his supervisors to the Natural Environment Research Council for high-precision radiocarbon dates on peat horizons and on pine wood from the site.

- Preliminary results

The palaeoecological and dendrochronological data are still being gathered and analysed. Preliminary radiocarbon dating of the peat suggests that the *main* phase of pine growth on the mire was c. 3200-2900 BP[8], and so was indeed earlier than the radiocarbon age of the pine reported by Turner, and is consistent with the archaeological dating evidence from the palstave. However, as yet, we

Plate 16. Examples of subfossil pines prepared for analysis. Note the different patterns of tree rings indicative of differing local growth conditions for these two trees. Photograph: M. E. Grant

do not know how many episodes of pine colonisation there were. What is clear is that the main period of pine colonisation at Fenn's and Whixall Mosses is different from those recorded in Cheshire at both White Moss[22, 23,] which culminated just after 4000 BP, and at Lindow Moss[24,] where the pine has not yet been dated but is apparently older than at Fenn's and Whixall. This may have palaeoclimatic implications, as the period of pine colonisation at Fenn's and Whixall Mosses may be a response to a later episode of "dry" climate. This hypothesis is being tested in the current phase of the research.

In discussions held in late-August 1995, with Professor Mike Baillie from the Palaeoecology Centre at Queen's University, Belfast, it seems there may be some interesting parallels with results of research conducted in Ireland. If these parallels are confirmed, then it is possible that the outcome of some of the palaeoecological work at Whixall Moss may be published in a research paper jointly with data from Ireland.

●Oak Timbers

Some oak timbers found at or near the Mosses were examined by Dr. Jonathan Lageard, independently of the pine studies. Methods were similar to those used for the subfossil pine, but it has also been possible to provide absolute dates for some of the oak timbers, by reference to master chronologies held at the Palaeoecology Centre, Queen's University, Belfast and at the Dendrochronology Laboratory, University of Sheffield.

●Dating of prehistoric bog-oak from Morris' Bridge

The ploughing of a field close to Morris' Bridge unearthed several large bog-oak trunks (Plate 17). By March 1992, these had been moved and had been left alongside

Plate 17. A large oak trunk unearthed by ploughing of a field near Morris' Bridge. Photograph: F. M. Chambers

37

other smaller timbers and stumps, at the edge of two fields and in a depression adjoining a neighbouring farm. The general location of these is shown in Figure 4. Nineteen disc samples were cut from the trunks by chainsaw (Plates 18 and 19). Dr. Jonathan Lageard prepared the sample discs and conducted measurements on the tree rings. The nineteen samples yielded four chronologies (Figure 5, Table 3); details of these have been published elsewhere[25]. The exciting aspect of this work was that it was possible to match three of the series with component chronologies of the English Bog Oak Chronology[26, 27,] with the result that the three ring-width series were combined to form a 293 year site

chronology. A sample of wood was taken for radiocarbon dating and gave a date of 5618+30 BP (Q-8655), which calibrates to 4498-4405 cal. BC (at one sigma) or 4524-4365 cal. BC (to two sigma). This calibrated radiocarbon age range is well within the absolute dates of 4596-4304 BC for the 293 year site chronology (refer Table 3), which validates the sampling, measuring and rigorous cross-matching techniques used. The data indicate oaks growing on the periphery of Whixall Moss in part of the late Mesolithic, some two to three millennia before the late-prehistoric pine layer(s) on the Mosses.

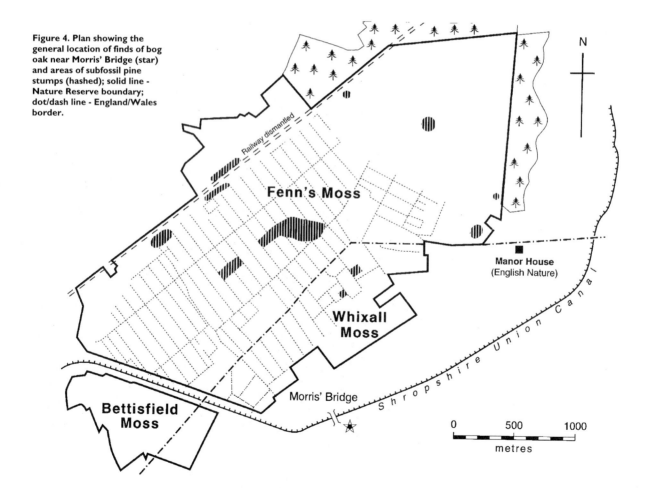

Figure 4. Plan showing the general location of finds of bog oak near Morris' Bridge (star) and areas of subfossil pine stumps (hashed); solid line - Nature Reserve boundary; dot/dash line - England/Wales border.

•Dating of medieval oak timbers

Two oak timbers found near Whixall Moss by Bill Allmark were also prepared for tree-ring measurement and one of these was found to match with three master English oak chronologies. Its rings spanned the period AD 1482 to AD 1583. The sample lacked sapwood, but allowance for the additional years suggested that the tree from which it came must have died or was felled soon after AD 1593. The timber resembled a weathered plank. The calendar dates for the timber suggest it may have come from a medieval building - perhaps even from the "Manor House" that once stood close to Whixall Moss at the Nature Reserve base[7].

•Future Research

The research at Whixall Moss conducted by Malcolm Grant will be succeeded by detailed work by Leri Roberts on the other plant macrofossils from the same location and on determining changes in peat humification through the period(s) of pine colonisation and demise. The data from Whixall will then need to be integrated with the work on subfossil pines from elsewhere on Fenn's and Whixall Mosses, and with survey data in unpublished reports[28, 29]. To assist in this, an application will be made for radiocarbon dates on wood samples that relate to the preliminary tree-ring chronologies gathered by Dr. Jonathan Lageard from various locations across the site. The direction of further research will be guided by results from the current studies.

Plate 18. Bill Allmark removes a disc from a bog oak for analysis. Photograph: M. E. Grant

Plate 19. Malcolm Grant shows one of the discs of bog oak cut by Bill Allmark. Photograph: F.M. Chambers.

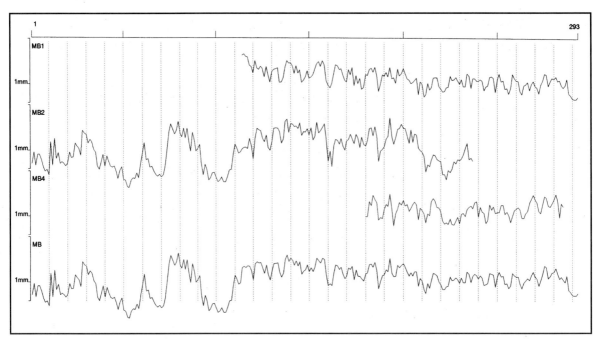

Figure 5. Ring-width plots from the bog oaks for the 293 years from 4596 to 4304BC: chronologies MB1, MB2, MB4, and the site "master" chronology MB (refer Table 3). Plots prepared by J.G.A. Lageard.

Site sub-master chronologies	Length (years)	Number of timbers	Absolute date (calendar years)*
MB1	180	8	4483-4304 BC
MB2	237	4	4596-4360 BC
MB3	220	2	Unmatched
MB4	106	2	4417-4312 BC
Site chronology (MB1+MB2+MB4)	293	14	4596-4304 BC

Table 3. Absolute dates for Morris' Bridge bog-oak chronology.
***Absolute dates courtesy of David Brown, Queen's University, Belfast.**

Bog Bodies

• The Discoveries at Whixall Moss

No more extraordinary discoveries have been found in the peat bogs of northern Europe than the remarkably well-preserved bog bodies such as Tollund- and Lindow Man. During the second half of the nineteenth century, three such discoveries were made in Whixall Moss. Three contemporary reports have been found of the last of these discoveries, one of which is quoted in full.

On 7th September 1889, the *Northwich and Winsford Chronicle* and the *Mid-Cheshire Advertiser* included the following report under the title "*A Grave in Whixall Moss, Mysterious Affair*":

"*Our reporter on Wednesday visited Whixall, where on the previous day two men, whilst engaged in cutting out a bed of moss, disentombed some human remains. The district known as Whixall Moss is an area of some five thousand acres of land and moss, mostly moss (or turf), in the cutting and sale of which some hundreds of people make a livelihood. In this respect it is a well-known tract of country, but what has made it more notorious, especially two years ago, is the well remembered fact that two tragedies were committed there, and still more recently it was to some extent devastated by a cyclone. It might, therefore, have been thought that the inhabitants had enough for the annals of their neighbours in respect of excitement and wonder. But this latest affair has aroused their feeling of dread and amazement afresh. It is a mystery which no one seems able to solve, and various theories are exercising their minds. To note the facts before the theories, the statement of the men who discovered the remains must be first mentioned. They, namely, Henry Slack and Thomas Parsons, turfmen, give the information that they were engaged in cutting through a plot of turf on their occupation, and had got to a depth about four feet six inches when they found human bones. In its natural formation the turf lies in three layers, which are made very distinct by three colours. The top layer or "lift" as the natives call it, is a brownish grey, the second is much darker (almost black), and the third perfectly black. It was between the second and the third layer where the remains were found. The body lay flat at full length with the face downwards. Some hair and small bits of flesh were still adhering to the skull and the ribs and legs were partly covered with flesh. It is supposed that these remains are those of a fully developed man, whose height was something like five feet eight inches. The bones were of a dark colour, and after some hours exposure to the air they turned almost black. The feet were not there and the cannon bone of the left leg was also missing. There was not the slightest trace of any clothing about the remains, and there is no doubt that the deceased went to his grave without a sheet or shroud. The skeleton was removed to the Waggoners Inn, a distance of over a mile from the grave. The police, including chiefly Superintendent Edwards and Sergeant Griffiths, with whom the discoverers promptly communicated, have been making investigations and taking information as far as they possibly can, and the district coroner, Major Warren, has the question to decide whether or not an inquest ought to he held. If he makes an effort to satisfy the curiosity of the inhabitants he will be attempting what now seems an impossibility. For everyone has a different question to put, and every question makes the mystery more difficult to solve. To one, almost the first query - Has there been a tragedy? - one of the answers offered by some of the inhabitants is that one might have been committed many years ago by gypsies who used to have short encampments and disputes with one another without holding any communication with the residents around them. It is also suggested that the deceased had by misadventure got into a hole, and since covered by moss which either rises or grows in course of time; but this theory is not satisfactory as regards the nudity of the deceased or the layers covering him, which did not appear to have undergone any change at any rate for a very great number of years. Moreover, the oldest of the inhabitants do not remember any disappearances that could not be accounted for. Two of them are octogenarians (one in his 85th year), and they are unable to throw any light on the mystery. One turfman did tell our reporter that his grandfather who lived near Whixall, remembered what he called a packman making almost daily calls, and suddenly disappearing. No one knew where he went, or how. If this is the skeleton of the packman where are his clothes or his wares? Some of the theories are obviously absurd. There is not one, indeed, which the police entertain, and they say they are quite unable to give any explanations. The occupier of a dwelling nearest the spot (a distance of about a quarter of a mile) says he cannot pretend to solve the mystery".*

On the same day, the *Whitchurch Herald* also included a report of this find and finally, on 11th September, a magazine describing unusual events entitled *Bye-gones relating to Wales and the Border Counties*[1], printed another version of these events. The basis of all three reports is similar but there are significant differences in detail and the range of information reported. The *Northwich Chronicle* gives the most evidence for the stratigraphic position of the body. It is unlikely that the two turf cutters were working down from the naturally-growing bog surface, as the cutting of peat for fuel had been carried out on the Moss since at least the sixteenth century. However, the *Bye-gones* report says the spot had never been touched by human hands. The description of what was preserved of the body is more complete in the *Whitchurch Herald*: "*Slack had cut through the bones beneath the knee. Otherwise the skeleton is perfect. There was flesh on the breast, chest, abdomen, and thighs, but the skull was denuded of flesh*". The *Bye-gones* report added that there were portions of a beard and that the feet and a bone of the lower leg was missing. It cannot be said if the man had worn shoes but the reports agree that otherwise the body appeared naked. Only the *Northwich Chronicle* describes the

posture, being face down and lying at full length. Whilst the *Northwich Chronicle* speculated about the cause of death, the *Whitchurch Herald* was confident that it had been there for a considerable time. In *Bye-gones*, the preservative qualities of peat were recognised and explained. Without a map showing which holdings the two turf cutters were working at that date, it is impossible to give an accurate location for this discovery. The only indication given is that it lay over a mile from the Waggoner's Inn, and about a quarter of a mile from the nearest dwelling. This gives an approximate position centred around N.G.R. SJ 494 363, close to the end of the modern trackway leading into the Moss from Moss Cottages, where there is only a very thin cover of peat and a stand of birch trees, and a little to the east of Oaf's Orchard, an island of uncut peat.

All the reports refer to two other bogs bodies having been found at Whixall Moss. Again, the *Northwich Chronicle* gives the most extensive report: "*Two very interesting facts are recorded, and the police have had them verified by persons under whose notice they directly came. One of them Henry Simpson, says that about 20 or 22 years ago he and a man named Thomas Woodward, whilst engaged in cutting turf at a depth of two of three feet, and a distance of 200 yards from the newly discovered spot, found the remains of a young man, in a sitting position, over a three-legged stool, and partly covered with a leather apron. No one could ever throw any light upon that discovery. Those remains were re-interred in Whitchurch churchyard. Some 12 or 14 years ago the remains of a woman were, according to the statement now made by George Heath, dug out of the turf at Whixall by him, and those remains were also removed to Whitchurch for re-interment. That was another mystery which no one could ever fathom. In neither of those two cases was an inquest held, and the coroner may follow precedent and allow this discovery to pass without troubling a jury*".

The *Whitchurch Herald* is briefer: "*It is a singular coincidence that some twelve or fourteen years ago a man named George Heath found portions of a skeleton, identified as a woman, at a similar depth below the surface, and about 300 yards from the place where the other remains have just been excavated. It was not deemed necessary to hold an inquest in this case, and the bones were interred in Whitchurch Churchyard. Supt. Edwards and Sergt. Griffiths in pursuing their investigations also ascertained from another turfman named Henry Simpson, that some 22 years ago he and a man named Thomas Woodward, whilst working on the moss, came across the remains of a youth in a sitting position embedded in a solid turf and lying near him a three-legged stool, on which he had apparently been sitting when engulfed in the bog. The stool remained in the possession of the Rev. J. Evans, Vicar of Whixall, until his death as a souvenir of an unsolved mystery. The moss in the neighbourhood of which the last skeleton was found is extremely treacherous and any stranger not knowing his way about might easily fall into one of the numerous holes which abound, and lose his life without anyone hereby made aware of it".* The mention in *Bye-gones* adds little to those given above.

The reports of the man found by Simpson and Woodward in c.1867 are essentially the same except for some divergence in describing the posture and the clothing. The *Northwich Chronicle* describes the man as sitting over the stool, and partly covered by a leather apron. The *Whitchurch Herald* agrees the youth was in a sitting position but with the stool lying nearby, and *Bye-gones* describes the body laying full length and face downwards with the stool alongside. Little information is recorded about the woman found by Heath in c.1875. Efforts to find contemporary descriptions of these two discoveries in local newspapers, parish registers and local and county histories have failed to provide any additional information.

All three bodies were subsequently re-interred. The find made in 1889 was buried in Whixall Churchyard and the other two at Whitchurch. This has been the fate of a number of other British bog bodies, and means that no detailed examination of the human remains will now be possible, as the organic tissue preserved in the peat will have decayed in the mineral soils of the churchyard. The stool was retained by Reverend J. Evans, vicar of Whixall, and there remains a distant possibility that this may survive for re-examination and dating.

Nevertheless, the descriptions of these bodies are perhaps the most complete of those reported in nineteenth century newspapers. Because they rely on eye-witness accounts, and in the case of the 1889 discovery, were made immediately following the discovery, it is possible to take the analysis of those discoveries further than in many other cases. However, it must be remembered that eye-witness accounts can be contradictory and there are differences in detail in the three reports that survive. For example, the following paragraph is appended to the report of the discovery of the looped palstave from the Moss in 1927:

" *Mr Saywell [the finder of the palstave] saw the complete skeleton of a man found seven feet deep in the moss; his whiskers and nailed boots were still preserved; it was clear that he had sunk when the ground was swampy and the peat had subsequently grown solid over the body ... The skeleton of a woman had previously been found*[2].

● The Date of the Whixall Moss Bog Bodies

Experience with the finds from Lindow Moss has shown that the dating of bog bodies is very problematic[3]. In the case of Lindow Man, the two radiocarbon laboratories who dated the human remains directly, produced mutually exclusive dates with Oxford suggesting a date centred on the Roman conquest, and Harwell a date at the beginning of the fifth century AD. These two dates were significantly later than the date of the stratigraphic position of the body for which middle Iron Age radiocarbon dates were obtained, a date which can be confirmed by pollen analysis.

To some extent the situation has re-occurred with Lindow III, the second male body found in Lindow Moss in 1987. Here Oxford and Harwell's radiocarbon dates for the body coincide, and give a date in the middle of the Roman period. Again the stratigraphic position is significantly earlier and estimated to be the middle-late Iron Age[4]. No datable artefacts were found in association with the Lindow bodies, to provide evidence independent of the radiocarbon method. Raised bogs are not like mineral soils and it is possible to imagine mechanisms whereby a solid object such as a body might move within, or be forced down into the peat stratigraphy so reconciling these different dates.

The only potential dating information available for the 1889 Whixall body is stratigraphic. Three broad layers were described in the bog, when it was in its "natural formation". The top layer was brownish grey, the second layer darker (almost black), and the third perfectly black. The *Northwich Chronicle* describes the body being "*between the second and third layer where the remains were found*". *Bye-gones* states that "*the body was placed below the second layer at a depth of about five feet*".

Whixall Moss has been the subject of pollen analysis on a number of occasions, as described in the previous chapter. Hardy made a number of borings in 1937, one of which was close to the findspot of the middle Bronze Age palstave[5]. The approximate location of this findspot (N.G.R. SJ 492 361) is close to the estimated position of the 1889 body. The palstave was recovered embedded in a pine stump, which in 1927 was eight feet below the surface. Hardy's stratigraphy can be equated to the three layers identified in the newspaper report. The first brownish-grey layer is equivalent to the fresh unhumified *Sphagnum* peat occurring to a depth of 55cm. The second much darker layer must

include the humified *Sphagnum* peat at 55-140cm, the cotton-sedge and pine stump layer at 140-150cm and perhaps the *Sphagnum* and *Phragmites* layers down to 190cm. The third layer of black peat is formed by the sedge peats running from 190cm-340cm, with the lake muds at the bottom of the sequence. Twigger and Haslam[6] obtained mean radiocarbon dates of AD 200 and AD 20, which bracketed the junction between the first and second layers. Turner[7], obtained a radiocarbon date of 2307 ± 110 BP (Q-383) from a stump from Hardy's pine layer which is significantly later than the date of the middle Bronze Age palstave from the same layer. A second date of 3238 ± 115 BP (Q-467) came from highly humified *Sphagnum* peats, near the base of the second layer. The peat might have shrunk between 1889 and 1937, but the depth of five feet (150cm) below the second layer is in Hardy's diagram close to the junction between the second and third layers. This is below the position of the middle Bronze Age palstave and close to Turner's earliest radiocarbon date. The conclusion must be that the stratigraphic position of the 1889 body suggests an early-middle Bronze Age date. However, the experience with the Lindow bodies might indicate he may have died several centuries later.

Dates for the other two bodies must be given with even more caution. The body found in c.1867 was found at a depth of two or three feet so is potentially younger than the 1889 body. If the cutting was from the surface then the depth indicated may have been close to the junction of the first and second peat layers. No depth is given for the body of c.1876.

• The Circumstances behind the Death of the Whixall Bog Bodies

Considerable controversy surrounds how bog bodies died and how they came to be buried within the bog. Theories range from those proposed by Glob[8] and other continental authors[9] that the vast majority of bog bodies are the victims of ritual sacrifice, to that proposed by Briggs[10], that there is no conclusive evidence that any bog bodies died in that way. None of the reports describe any ancient injuries or wounds on the Whixall bodies. There was only limited survival of tissue on the 1889 body so injuries associated with some of the best known bog bodies, such as cutting of the throat, or evidence of hanging and garrotting may not have been obvious.

The *Northwich Chronicle* reported that various theories concerning the death of the 1889 body were put forward by those gathered at the scene. One theory proposed was accidental death, with the man becoming trapped within a hole or deep pool within the bog and being drowned. This was rejected as the body was found naked. Another idea rehearsed was that the body was a murder victim. No specific incident could be remembered by two octogenarians, though there was some speculation about disputing gypsies and a packman who had disappeared from the area, a couple of generations earlier. The *Whitchurch Herald* and *Bye-gones* both favoured accidental death, particularly when considering the body of c.1867 found in an extremely treacherous area of the bog. The Chronicle concluded that: "*some of the theories were obviously absurd. There is not one, indeed, which the police entertain, and they say they are quite unable to give an explanation.*"

However thorough the descriptions of the discoveries of bog bodies have been in the past, there is often inconclusive evidence of the cause and circumstances of death. There was no suggestion that there was a ritual motive behind the death of the three Whixall bodies. This interpretation can only derive from considering the population of bog bodies as a whole, and by comparing these discoveries with other classes of finds from peat bogs. In seeking to support this interpretation it is also possible to draw upon the written classical sources, and the folk-tales and myths of the Celtic oral tradition.

• Comparisons with other British Bog Bodies

These reports of the finding of three bog bodies from Whixall Moss are an important addition to the growing list of the finds of all types of human remains from peat deposits in Britain[11]. There is now a total of over 106 such instances in England and Wales. These range in date from the Neolithic to the seventeenth century. Finds come from all types of peat deposit, from the inter-tidal zone to upland blanket bogs. The most interesting group, to which the Whixall bodies belong, are the twenty-seven which derive from the lowland raised mires of the northern half of England and extending into Wales. These discoveries are often the most spectacular, as a range of tissue and, more rarely, organic artefacts are preserved by the special qualities of the upper layers of these raised bogs. Whixall Moss has produced more bodies than are recorded for any other single mire - the finds made in Lindow Moss on four occasions are best explained as coming from two adult males. However, some early authors[12] imply that finds of this type were more widespread than the surviving records indicate.

Clothing is very rarely recorded from bodies found in British lowland raised mires, though woollen clothing and skin and leather garments would be expected to survive in these circumstances. The leather "apron" is therefore an important addition to this small group. The only comparison from England is from Scaleby Moss, Cumbria where the body was wrapped in a leather or deerskin cape[13]. A similar cape was found wrapped around the Castleblakeney Man, from Gallagh, Ireland[14] and both woollen and leather capes have been found, on the continent, for example, at Borre Fen, Denmark[8] and the middle Bronze Age body from Emmer-Erfschiedenveen, Holland[15].

The wooden object described as a "three-legged stool" found with the c.1867 body is without precedent. Sticks have been found alongside, over, beneath and even pinning down bodies. A simple peat spade was found near to Tollund Man[8] and tree-trunk wooden coffins have enclosed a number of bodies. Unless the stool can be found, or a drawing or photograph located, it would only be speculation to propose what form or function this object took.

In terms of date, the 1889 Whixall body may be significantly earlier than the main group of well-preserved bog bodies from Britain, Ireland and continental Europe. Where an extensive range of tissue and other organic finds are preserved, radiocarbon dating has suggested a late prehistoric or Roman date for finds in Britain, Ireland, Holland and Denmark[8]. In England, the body from Scaleby Moss was in a similar stratigraphic location and showed similar preservation. The only radiocarbon dated middle Bronze Age body where tissue and organic artefacts occur is from Emmer-Erfschiedenveen, Holland.

The dates for the other two Whixall bodies are not as easy to establish. The body of c.1867 seems to be higher in the stratigraphy, and perhaps closer to the junction between the first and second layers dated to the first or second century AD. If so, then he would belong to the much larger group of bodies from that period.

The recovery of hoards of objects or single objects often of great value from peat bogs is another feature of late prehistory in northern Europe. Beginning in the late Bronze Age with such finds as the Caergwrle Bowl, Wrexham[16], and those from alongside the Flag Fen Alignment[17] and ending with vast hoards from such sites as Llyn Cerrig Bach, Anglesey[18] and Illerup, Denmark[19]. Cauldrons, tools and weaponry form the dominant features of these depositions which are easily assigned to a ritual origin. The bog bodies of this period may have been ritual offerings as well, for to some communities a person of status or prize prisoner may have been the most valuable thing they had to offer. Bodies and hoards of objects rarely occur in the same bog. The only finds from Whixall Moss are the middle Bronze Age palstave, apparently lost while in use, and an unprovenanced gold coin[20].

The three bodies from Whixall Moss must have been extraordinary discoveries which clearly caused enormous local interest. The evidence contained within the descriptions which survive is quite extensive, but in the end is both tantalising and frustrating. Nothing certain can be said about their age, cause of death or how they came to be deposited in the Moss. Nevertheless, these finds reinforce the growing awareness, still under investigation at Whixall[21], that bog bodies are as much a feature of British prehistory as they are in the rest of northern Europe.

Framing the Landscape

● The Medieval Mire

The widespread heavy claylands of the region - prone to waterlogging in the winter, slow to warm in the spring and liable to set iron-hard in the droughts of summer - were undoubtedly a deterrent to extensive early settlement. The landscape of the area is characterised by few nucleated settlements and a preponderance of placenames indicative of woodland and its clearance, suggestive of relatively late intensive exploitation.

The impression gained of the Mosses during the medieval period from scattered documentary sources is of a little-utilised raised mire, fringed by extensive tracts of mixed species broadleaved woodland dominated by oak.

A writ of aid in favour of William le Botiler of Wemme dated 1282 refers to the clearance of trees from the pass of *La Rede Broc*[1], as part of concerted efforts by Edward I to secure his conquests of Wales. Such passes were to be a *bowshot in breadth*[2], some 250 metres, and thus the reference is indicative of the extensive nature of woodland to the immediate north east of Fenn's Moss. The nearby area, today the farmland known as Fenn's Wood (N.G.R. SJ 507 380), is first recorded as *Boscu' del Fennes* in 1284[3] when it undoubtedly formed a part of the widespread mixed oak woodland on the mineral ground around the mire.

13th and 14th century references to assart[4] record the process of piecemeal but increasing clearance of such woodland, but a process in which woodland continued to provide an important resource; the woods of Whixall affording common rights of housebote and haybote, together with pannage[5]. The recent identification of two moated sites[6] to the south of Whixall Moss is supportive of this process of woodland clearance, such sites having been suggested as indicative in the Maelor of pioneer agricultural settlement[7].

From 1407 the surviving Whixall manorial records[8] show a number of individuals presented before the Court Baron of the manor for felling of oaks in *le holynwood*[9], for cutting down and carrying away greenwood and underwood in the lord's wood of Whixall without licence[10] and the felling of oak saplings in the same[11]. Such references are suggestive of the continued value placed on woodland as a resource in the late medieval and early post-medieval period and a need to ensure its conservation.

Whilst records provide an indication of increasing utilisation of the natural resources around the fringes of the mire, reference to use of the Mosses themselves is not found until 1572[12]. The apparent absence of documentary evidence of medieval use of the Mosses is surprising, and almost certainly misleading. References to the right to cut turves or peat, known as "turbary", are found for the medieval period from across north Wales and Cheshire albeit not from raised mires. Whilst the researcher can hardly be said to be overwhelmed by the quantity of such references, they are an indication of the widespread recognition in the medieval period of the value of peatlands as a resource in providing fuel and, in some cases, pasture.

The Survey of the Honour of Denbigh undertaken in 1334 records the rights of turbary held by the tenants in a number of villes. In *Loydcoyd* the whole village held the lord's turbary, paying 2s a year at Pentecost and Michaelmas for the privilege[13], whilst at Gwytherin there was turbary in the common waste, for which the tenants gave 12d. for the licence to dig turves[14].

The Register of Edward the Black Prince also highlights the importance of turbary. In 1348 the bishop of St. Asaph "*prayed*" that the Prince grant him at farm *Gronandesmore* (Gronant), together with 2 acres of turbary there[15]. These coastal peats returned 20 marks yearly, although in 1357 they were farmed in hand by the Prince, his profit being derived from "*turbary and otherwise*"[16], the "otherwise" presumably being cattle ranching which was becoming an increasingly profitable enterprise in the forest of *La Mare* (Delamere). Order was also given to drain the moor "*by dykes, in such manner as shall seem most profitable for the prince*" and in 1359 it was further recommended that a great bund be constructed between the moor and the sea to prevent marine inundation and resultant loss of profit[17].

Turbary rights, granted to the burgesses of Frodsham, are also recorded from the extensive marsh between Frodsham, Elton, Hapsford and Helsby known as *Le Merssh*, which was protected by a sea-dyke[18] and formed part of the forest of *La Mare*[19]. Following the Black Death such rights were rendered free of charge "*until the times · improve*"[20].

On a number of occasions, the grant of a gift for life of turbary rights was made by the Prince in recognition of an individual's good service in the Prince's battles in Gascony[21] Such gifts are recorded from Rudheath[22] and, closer to Fenn's and Whixall Mosses, the mosses of *Pecforton* (Peckforton Moss; N.G.R. SJ 544 559) and *Bikkelegh* (Bickley Moss; N.G.R. SJ 545 490)[23].

In the majority of the grants recorded in the Register the rights of turbary are specifically restricted to the cutting of turves for the sole use of the individual or burgesses to whom the grant was made. In one exception we find an interesting reference[24] to possible early "commercial" use of peat, in which the King's yeoman Richard de Sutton is granted the right to:

"*dig turves anywhere on the moor pertaining to the said lands in the forest [La Mare] ..... and dig them, carry them away for his own use, sell them, or give them away, as he pleases, for as long as the land shall be in his hand or until further order .....*"

● Turves and Turbary

As noted earlier, such references show a general recognition of the value of peatlands in the medieval period and one must question whether the absence of documentary reference for Fenn's and Whixall Mosses from the period is really indicative of lack of use of this extensive resource or reflects the lack of need for burning peat in a well-wooded area. Evidence from the Whixall manorial records from 1572 until the time of the Inclosures shows a well-developed system of turbary on Whixall Moss and one which may have evolved during the earlier, medieval period.

The earliest reference to turbary, dated 31st October 1572[12], refers to the messuage or tenement know as "*The Hall Closes*" lying in Whixall "*with all the land, meadow, pastures, waters, fisheries, liberties and common and turbary whatsoever with their appurtenances appertaining to the same messuage*". This reference highlights a feature common to many of the turbary rights in Whixall up to the time of Inclosure, that is, the attachment of the right of turbary to property rather than the individual. This contrasts with the evidence described earlier from the Register of Edward the Black Prince in which such rights are clearly at the behest of the Prince and granted to the individual to be held for life or until further order.

Records also give an insight into the nature of the turbary:

The inhabitants of Welsh End and Stanley End, Whixall are recorded[25] as being "*in the habit of digging peats and turbary in the lord's heath called Fenns Heath between Thomas Bostock's pasture called Brockhurst and Fennes Wood*". From the feast of St. Andrew the Apostle and annually thereafter before the same feast, they were required to "*clean and scour the ditches next to the pits where they dig their turbary, sufficiently for the water to run down from there through the same ditches, for the betterment of the soil of the same turbary.*" A penalty of 3s.4d. was to be levied on any of them failing in this.

In 1608[26], William Higginson was granted the rights of peatrye and turbary "*in all the waste ground, common or heath ..... called Fennes Heath alias Whixall Heath ..... with free liberty to draw, wheele, reare, windrow, repayre, rucke and stack the same turves so digged and gotten so often as need shall require at all times and seasons of the year to be burnt, spent, used and occupied ..... at or in one messuage or cottage ..... in Tilley ..... in a pasture there called Overleassowe .....*"
A number of the terms used in describing the range of operations involved in winning the turves from the Moss in this reference are seen to be associated with the indigenous pattern of "Whixall Bible" peat cutting which persisted until the 1960s and strongly suggest that this pattern of cutting has a tradition extending back to at least the late 16th century (See Fact Panel Two p.105 and the chapter *Peat Speak*, this volume).

The grant of turbary was by licence from the Lord of the Manor. Records indicate that licence was granted for the use of the cut turves for fuel, to be burnt only within the curtilage of the property to which such rights were attached. The Court Baron, at which those individuals who transgressed were presented, was apparently essentially reactive, taking action against unlicensed activities when the liberties taken reached intolerable levels. The relative importance of turbary within the records suggest that activities on the Moss were closely monitored. However, the recurrence of named individuals in the records of the Court Baron year upon year suggest that the Court served as a means of deriving some income for the Lord of the Manor from all persons cutting turves on the Moss, rather than as a means of ensuring such rights were restricted to those granted formal licence. Fines for unlicensed peat cutting were variable ranging in 1590 from 3d. to 12d. (on average 6d.)[27], possibly related to the quantity of turves cut, although the records are somewhat inconclusive in this matter.

Whilst unlicensed peat cutting was clearly tolerated, the level of fines levied suggest that the sale of peat to persons living outside the bounds of the manor was to be discouraged. In 1599[28] Robert Higginson, William Curton, John Sherott, John Cocks and John Kettle senior were each forfeit a penalty of 6s.8d. "*because they gave turves to foreigners living outside the manor*". In 1630[29], eleven individuals were presented for the selling of fifty loads of peat and were fined proportionately at the rate of 1s. per load.

Fines were also levied for unlicensed use of the peat. In 1626[30], nineteen individuals were presented "*for burninge turves gotten on the Lordes wast uppon their severall fallowes*", for which they were each fined 2d. Thomas Benyon[31] was fined 2s.6d. "*for burning a load of turves to burne ground*" and John Challener, 6d.[32] for burning dug turves on his own ploughland. These references suggest the use of peat to clear ground of weeds or stubble and/or to provide potash and other nutrients prior to cultivation.

References to "*fleeinge the greene sward uppon the wast and burning it*"[30] are suggestive of the clearance of surface vegetation either in preparation for peat cutting or perhaps to encourage the regeneration of vegetation to afford more succulent grazing for livestock. Whereas, the digging of "*green turves*"[33] or "*flae turves*"[34] is clearly the cutting of turves from and including the surface vegetation, perhaps from areas in which the water table was high where cutting of the underlying peat was impeded by flooding.

From 1652[35] the increasing occurrence of fines for the sale of turves outside the Lordship, indicates an expanding and flourishing trade in peat. Again the recurrence of named individuals, together with the relatively low level of fine (2d. to 1s.), suggest that by the mid-17th century this trade in peat was tolerated, with emphasis being placed on securing appropriate remuneration for the lord's interest in the Moss. By 1702[36], however, we see the Lord of the Manor taking steps to more closely regulate the expanding trade in peat by levying a punitive fine on those persons who had not "*compounded*" with the bailiff of the manor before they cut and sold turves. The fine was set at 10s. over and above the value of the turves. Subsequently, a penalty of 30s.[37] was levied on anyone cutting turves or "*fleas*" in any of their neighbours accustomed turf pits or places of flaying.

•Inclosing the Waste

The increasing efforts at regulation of the peat cutting on Whixall Moss in the early years of the 18th century span the period of the first Inclosure from the mire and reflect the Lord of the Manor's efforts to both secure more direct control of his lands and better returns from them.

Powers to inclose the commonland of Whixall which included part of the Moss were sought under the Statute of Merton (20 Henry III) and Statute of Westminster (2 and 3 Edward I)[38] by Thomas Sandford, Lord of the Manor of Whixall, and John Lord Gower, who held diverse copyhold[39] lands within Whixall and claimed manorial rights in respect of their status as a separate manor[40]. Proposals were supported by some 50 freeholders and copyholders of the manor and, following protracted discussions spanning over twelve months, Articles of Agreement were drawn up and signed on 14th August 1704[41].

Under the terms of this agreement, 600 acres of the common within the manor were identified as "*dry and convertable to arable land, the residue being wet, moorish ground always used as a common of turbary*". Two-thirds of the land was to be allotted among the freeholders and copyholders, with three-quarters of the remainder allotted to Thomas Sandford, as Lord of the Manor, and one-quarter to John Lord Gower. Twenty acres were also assigned to the parson for the time being, in trust: "*there being little or no competence for the celebration of divine service at the Chappell of Whixall*". This allotment was later augmented by an annual endowment of £5, payable by Thomas Sandford as the issue from 30 acres of land which the tenants had agreed to transfer to Sandford out of their respective shares of the common[42].

Ancient rights of common were to remain unaffected, with the costs of inclosure to be divided amongst the parties on the basis of the Land Tax assessments[43].

As an incentive to copyholders Sandford agreed, over a three year period, to extinguish all heriots (death duties) and services and to enfranchise existing copyholds in exchange for three years' improved rent.

Six "*surveyors and mathematicians*" were engaged to lay out the Inclosure: Robert Hand and Arthur Ikin representing Thomas Sandford's interests; Robert Wood, gent. and John Carter for John Lord Gower; and Mr. Waterson and John Bostock of Marefen representing the free- and copy- holders[44].

A part of this land was apparently already inclosed, as Sandford "*caused to be thrown open all such ancient inclosures and improvements as his ancestors* [had] *made out of the common and permitted the same to be measured in hotchpotch together with the rest of the common*"[45].

Some 23 commoners opposed the inclosure as inconvenient and unprofitable and, it is said, "*pretended the allotment to be unequal and not enough for their rights of common*"[46]. This dispute was to prove acrimonious, the aggrieved commoners throwing down all existing inclosures upon the common and hindering the creation of new inclosures, whilst bringing a multiplicity of actions against those that supported the proposed allotment. The Statute of Merton, under which powers had been sought to progress inclosure, proved woefully inadequate to address such a dispute and it was not until after the 30th January 1710 that a decree was obtained in the High Court of Chancery enabling the inclosure to proceed[47].

The Deed of Admeasurement[48] suggests that only some 410 acres were finally inclosed and, unfortunately, no plan apparently survives to enable these lands to be accurately identified. However, later documents suggest that such lands were widely distributed across the manor and, at least in part, included areas of Whixall Moss.

For example, a dispute between Lord Gower and Thomas Sandford over a right of way dated 4th May 1714[49] refers to lands lately inclosed from that part of Whixall commons called the "*Horse stage*". This area may be clearly identified from the tithe maps[50], centred on N.G.R. SJ 490 334 some 2km to the south of Fenn's and Whixall Mosses, where a characteristically straight section of highway is also suggestive of inclosure[51]. Particulars of sale dating from 1829[52] and relating to the bankruptcy of the then Lords of the Manor record ten parcels of land, together with a house, outbuildings and fold as being subject to a perpetual payment of £5 yearly to the curate of Whixall. These lands, centred on N.G.R. SJ 5092 3651 (Yew Tree Farm), are no doubt part of the allotment granted under the inclosure of 1710 to enable celebration of divine service at Whixall chapel and lie on the now agriculturally-improved eastern margin of Whixall Moss.

The well-developed system of turbary and associated heriots and services on Whixall Moss co-existed with the changing landscape arising from the early 18th century inclosure and were not to be extinguished until the Parliamentary inclosure of Whixall in 1823. Manorial records continue to highlight the role of the bailiff or *Mossreeve* in regulating the cutting and use of turves, in the allocation of turf banks and the assignment of new banks when old ones had been cut out[53]. A number of leases dating from the first quarter of the 18th century[54] also record the service of carriage of one load of turf *per*

annum to Thomas Sandford associated with lands recently inclosed from the waste, presumably copyhold lands on which the agreed enfranchisement and extinguishment of heriots and services was progressively being introduced.

Court books also record fines levied "*for getting of black oake*"[55], undoubtedly referring to the digging out of preserved stumps and timbers of oaks which had once clothed the margins of the mire before becoming subsumed by the expanding peat body.

The inclosure of 1710 was an "inclosure by agreement", requiring all the interested parties' consent to the proposed allotment. It was a wholly different "animal", the "Parliamentary inclosure", that was to finally inclose the wastes of Fenn's and Whixall Mosses and extinguish all common rights. Parliamentary inclosure was achieved by Act of Parliament, the Bill having to pass through three readings in each house, together with detailed consideration in committee. By contrast with "inclosure by agreement", a Parliamentary inclosure required only the agreement of the owners of at least two-thirds of the land to enable its enactment[56]. Such inclosure was therefore frequently driven by the interests of the principal landowner, who saw the opportunity to free lands within his ownership from the shackles of common rights.

Inclosure of Fenn's Moss and Bettisfield Moss was enacted in 1775 as part of the parish of Hanmer, with the allotment of land, the "award", enrolled in 1777 and 1779[57]. Interestingly, there are only three earlier Parliamentary inclosures in Wales[58] and one imagines that the principal landowner, Sir Walden Hanmer, was familiar with the wave of inclosure sweeping England. The nature of the award for Hanmer, however, suggests that Sir Walden recognised more the opportunity to unlock the potential within the cultivable wastes of the parish than the potential within the peat of Fenn's Moss.

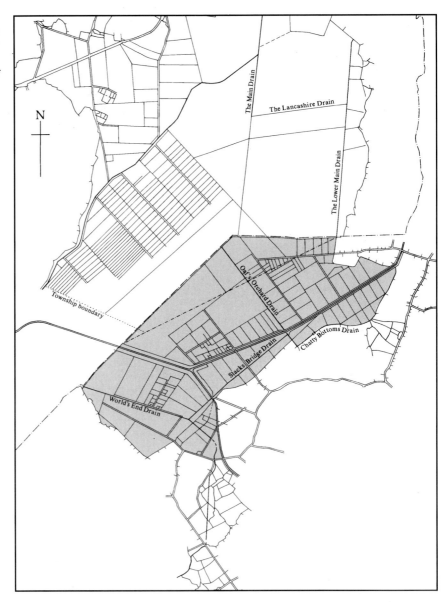

Figure 6. The pattern of Parliamentary inclosure of Fenn's Moss in 1777 and Whixall Moss in 1823 (shaded). Note the area of narrow turbary allotments on Fenn's Moss and the patchwork of small inclosures on southern Whixall Moss.
Drawing: Timothy Morgan.

Under the award, Sir Walden Hanmer was allotted almost 50% of the land, including the bulk of Fenn's Moss. The award created a complex of one hundred and eleven narrow turbary allotments (Figure 6), undoubtedly recognising and compensating traditional rights of turbary. Of these, fifty-six were allotted to Sir Walden Hanmer, with two to the poor of Bronington, one to the Trustees of the almshouse and school in Whitchurch and the remainder distributed

to thirty-one other individuals. With these allotments was assigned the rights to get sand for the repair of the designated roads leading from the Moss.

It is a common misconception that Parliamentary inclosure created new landscapes in their entirety. Rather, it is more often the case that inclosure, at least in part, formalised land divisions and other features created piecemeal in earlier times.

Such inclosures served to order and define the landscapes they treated, whether the elements within such landscapes were new or already established.

This characteristic is exemplified by both the inclosure of Fenn's Moss and that of Whixall and its Moss in 1823[59]. The award for Whixall defines occupation roads of breadths of 14ft, 21ft, 24ft and 30ft, two public footpaths of the breadth of 4ft, together with those responsible for their maintenance. The award also defines five principal public drains to carry water off Whixall Moss - *Hossage Drain, Slack's Bridge Drain, World's End Drain, Oaf's Orchard Drain* and *Chatty Bottoms Drain*, together with associated bridges, footbridges and culverts. Responsibility for the maintenance of these drains was assigned to the Lord of the Manor, who was empowered to levy a rate for the costs of this work upon the owners of allotments adjoining the drains. This arrangement, although eminently sensible at the time, was to lead to dispute in the later 19th century[60].

The fact that the drains to be defined were named suggests that they were already established prior to the inclosure. This is reinforced by the fact that the canal cuts across the line of the drains, under which they are carried through culverts, suggesting that the canal, constructed across the Moss in the period between 1801 and 1804, is a later feature. This is further emphasised by a clause in the inclosure Act[61] ordering that works of drainage were to be agreed with the proprietors of the canal and to be undertaken at a distance not to affect or be injurious to the canal. That substantial drainage works were undertaken as part of the inclosure is attested by the commissioners accounts[62], which record the payment of £3545 to William Morgan and £134.19s.3d. to William Jones "*for drainage of the moss*" and £379.14s.6d. to W. John Jebb "*for brick tile drainage and other things*". This is accompanied by compensation payments to Sir John Hill, the then Lord of the Manor of Whixall, and others "*for damage to his old inclosed lands in cutting drains*".

469a. 2r. 38p. of land was sold in sixty parcels to defray the expenses of the Act. Sir John Hill purchased 50a. 1r. 19p.[63] of this and, in addition, was allotted 25a. 1r. 0p. in lieu of his manorial rights and interests[64], and a further 159a. 3r. 11p. in respect of his old inclosed lands in Whixall[65], including a substantial block of Whixall Moss coterminous with the English/Welsh border and Fenn's Moss. This latter allotment accounted for some 54% of the lands allotted to the freeholders and copyholders. However, Sir John Hill's allocation was only to account for some 30% of the total lands subject to inclosure.

●The Legacy of the Past

As noted earlier, the Parliamentary inclosure of Fenn's and Whixall Mosses was to offer the principal landowners opportunity to free their lands from the constraints of common rights and enabled the subsequent commercial development of peat as a product on land over which they now held absolute control. The story of 150 years of the peat industry of Fenn's and Whixall Mosses is the subject of a later chapter, but it is useful here to review human action over the period 1572 until 1823. What is the legacy of this past in our present?

The two Parliamentary inclosures and the earlier inclosure by agreement, as comparatively recent episodes, have served to frame the landscape. They have defined the pattern of the fields which bound the mire to north and south and the expanding reclamation of the peatland to agriculture, particularly in Whixall. They have also defined the principal drainage network carrying water off the Mosses, which was later to aid the extraction of peat and now creates problems in rehabilitation of the mire. They also formalised the network of footpaths, tracks and roads which still serve the Mosses.

These inclosures were, however, influenced by earlier events. The probable existence of the principal drains prior to inclosure in 1823 has already been discussed, and the relationship of these features to the inclosure of 1710 is worthy of further study. It has been suggested[66], for example, that the Hossage Drain appears to cut across fields laid out as part of the inclosure of 1710, suggesting that the drain may post-date this episode of inclosure. Parliamentary inclosure frequently incorporated lands inclosed previously in a piecemeal fashion and served, perhaps, to legitimise such inclosure[67]. It must be a matter for speculation as to what extent such piecemeal inclosure has influenced the pattern of inclosure fields at Fenn's and Whixall, although the inclosure of 1710 clearly included lands formerly inclosed by the Lord of the Manor, as noted by contemporary documentary sources.

And what of the influence of the well-developed system of turbary on Whixall Moss? Discussion in this chapter has necessarily focused on such rights on Whixall Moss because of the wealth of surviving manorial records. This contrasts with the apparent paucity of such material for the Hanmer Estate relating to Fenn's Moss. Was a similar system in operation? Available evidence suggests not or at least, not on such a developed scale. This apparent dichotomy in early utilisation of the mire may define the later contrasting use on the English and Welsh side of the border. Inclosure of Hanmer parish in 1777 leaves the bulk of Fenn's Moss in the ownership of the Hanmer Estate and we see the progressive expansion of commercial peat extraction from 1851. By contrast, on Whixall Moss, the two episodes of inclosure create a patchwork of small inclosures across the southern margin of the Moss and a proportionately smaller area of the Moss in the ownership of the Lord of the Manor.

The numerous small inclosures were allotted amongst the freeholders and copyholders of the manor. Most of these have been converted to pasture or woodland, although a small number remain in use as turf banks, on which the owners have the right to cut peat only for their own use for fuel. These small inclosures and turf banks, assigned to individual properties in and around Whixall, are a characteristic feature of the area.

The central part of Whixall Moss adjoining the English/Welsh border and allotted to Sir John Hill as Lord of the Manor has been rented out on an "acre" by "acre" basis to local peat cutters since at least 1889. This extensive piecemeal renting of turf banks continued until 1956 when the area was acquired by Tom Allmark for the firm *L.S. Beckett*. It has created a unique patchwork of peat cuttings, with linear hand cut "acres" alongside Whixall Bible cuttings and "flaying", in which shallow layers of peat have been skimmed off the surface of the bog. It is in such areas that the traditional pattern of Whixall Bible cutting persisted until the 1960s, albeit on a limited scale practised by only one or two peatmen.

One must ask to what extent this pattern of use is reflective of the earlier, well-documented and apparently intensive utilisation of the marginal peats of Whixall Moss for turbary? Although all common rights to turbary were extinguished with the Parliamentary inclosure of Whixall in 1823, the ethos of small-scale use of the bog by the local community apparently persisted, defining the Lord of the Manor's development of areas of Whixall Moss in his ownership. This pattern of small-scale use contrasts markedly with the developing large-scale commercial utilisation of Fenn's Moss over the same period, and suggests that human use of the mire in the period up to 1823 is important in framing the landscape and defining the subsequent commercial exploitation of the peat.

Fact Panel One: Peat Houses

As a cheap, locally available sterile medium with good properties of absorption and insulation it is perhaps not too surprising that peat should have been utilised in the past as a building material. A peat house or "Turfcoate" is first recorded from the manor of Whixall in 1590[1] and peat was commonly used as a walling material in Whitchurch until the early years of the 20th century[2]. Reputed to be a healthier material than wattle and daub, peat was warmer and, in taking away the damp, was said to prevent rheumatism. It was also said to prevent infestation by bed bugs and cockroaches and so obviated the need for use of dangerous fumigants such as gas water.

Two peat houses survived on Whixall Moss until WW2 located at N.G.R. SJ 4890 3544 and SJ 4960 3597. The latter, known locally as "Cranberry Castle", was of single storey construction upon a brick foundation, with timber-framed and peat block walls and a galvanised sheet roof (Plate 20). Internally it was divided into two living rooms and a bedroom[3].

Life in a peat house on the Moss was hazardous, particularly during the dry summer months when the threat of fire must have been a constant cause for concern. In 1918, and no doubt on other occasions, Cranberry Castle came close to destruction when a fire raged across the Moss to within a few yards of the house, only being kept in check by the constant carrying of water from the Main Drain which ran nearby[4].

Plate 20. Mrs. Mary Jane Birch (née Allmark) with her grandmother Mrs. Mary Jane Allmark outside "Cranberry Castle" in c.1930. Photograph reproduced with the kind permission of Mrs. Mary Jane Birch.

Crossing the Moss

Fenn's and Whixall Mosses are crossed, respectively, by the former Oswestry, Ellesmere and Whitchurch Railway and the now Shropshire Union Canal, the latter effectively separating the Wem, Cadney and Bettisfield Mosses from Fenn's and Whixall. In viewing both the railway and canal today it is easy to overlook the engineering difficulties overcome in their construction.

An Act for Making and Maintaining a Navigable Canal from the River Severn at Shrewsbury in the County of Salop, to the River Mersey at or near Netherpool in the County of Chester; and also for Making and Maintaining certain Collateral Cuts from the said intended Canal was enacted in 1793[1], with works begun by the Ellesmere Canal Company on the Ellesmere to Whitchurch section in February 1797[2].

To the engineers, the crossing of Whixall Moss appears to have been "all in a day's work", there being a paucity of documentary references to the nature of the operations involved. By the 25th November 1801[3] the canal from Ellesmere was: *"navigable to Hampton-bank, and is now nearly completed to the west-side of Whixall-moss ..... Whixall-moss has been opened through its whole breadth (about two miles) for the purpose of draining off the water, in order to lower the surface, and consolidate the ground in the direction of the Canal; this operation promises to produce the desired effect."*

"Upon Wixhall [sic] Moss a perseverance of strict attention will be necessary for some time. Previous to this line being determined upon, the Engineers then employed by the Company were directed to examine the various ways by which it could be carried, and found that the present line, which is very direct, would permit the surface of the morass to be sunk (by draining) for five and six feet down to the top water of the canal; and if, at that depth, it was found necessary, a solid embankment might be formed of less height and length, than could be made by taking a more circuitous route, either to the S.W. or N.E. The drainage was therefore begun, and has been generally continued; which, by constant care, and carrying materials to the towing path and banks, has had the effect desired, and promises to be strong and durable" [4].

By 1804[5], Whixall Moss had been traversed and the canal reached Tilstock Park.

Today the canal is managed by British Waterways and modern problems hint at the engineering feat in construction, of which so little was made. Drainage and the resultant lowering of the groundwater table associated with commercial peat extraction have caused settlement of the ground surface as the peat has shrunk and with it the systematic subsidence of the canal[5]. Until the 1960s a *"Moss gang"* [6] was continuously employed in raising the canalside banks to maintain a sufficient "freeboard" (the distance between the water surface and the top of the bank protection) along the length of the canal over Whixall Moss. Members of the Moss gang recall finding the remains of birch trees in the middle of the canal, perhaps suggesting that engineers employed brushwood rafts as a foundation for the construction of the canal, a technique that was to be repeated in construction of the railway some sixty years later. In recent years[6] underpinning of the canal has been achieved through the use of steel-sheet piles driven through to the underlying mineral soils to effectively isolate the canal from the peat body.

No doubt the construction of the Oswestry, Ellesmere and Whitchurch Railway would have passed similarly unrecognised if it had not been for the opposition of some local landowners and the desire of the *Great Western Railway Company* to eliminate potential competition in any shape or form. Fortunately, the inevitable Parliamentary enquiry that resulted from such opposition was to generate great interest amongst the local media, enabling us to gain a greater insight into works involved in crossing the Moss.

Now redundant as a railway, its margins colonised by silver birch and willow, the trackbed crossing Fenn's Moss is a prominent landscape feature and still provides an important means of gaining access to, and across the Moss (Plate 21). Today, it is easy to overlook the impact of the railway - the divisions in the local community, the arguments before Parliament and the application of engineering expertise in traversing the raised mire.

Plate 21. The trackbed of the former Oswestry, Ellesmere and Whitchurch railway, as it appears today.
Photograph: André Q. Berry.

The line dates from 1861 as the Oswestry, Ellesmere and Whitchurch Railway (O,E&W) championed by George Hammond Whalley, MP for Peterborough[8]. As chairman of the Llanidloes and Newtown Railway and Milford and Cardigan Railways, Whalley had more than a passing interest in linking the expanding Welsh rail network with the English main lines. Appointed as chairman of the O,E&W Whalley was joined, as deputy chairman, by Captain Jasper Wilson Johns, Director of the Oswestry and Newtown, Mid-Wales and Milford and Cardigan Railways.

The first meeting of the embryonic *O,E&W Railway Company* was held at the Bridgewater Hotel, Ellesmere on 1st October 1860[9]. It was argued that Ellesmere had witnessed a reduction in trade, population and the value of its property as railway facilities had increased at surrounding towns; and that the new line would carry the produce of the country to the populous markets of the mining and manufacturing districts, bringing coal of a superior quality (and a greatly reduced price) from Lancashire in competition with the coal from Ruabon[10]. By 17th October 1860 the O,E&W had issued its preliminary prospectus and sought £150,000 in capital in 15,000 equal shares of £10 each[11]. The Company had established offices in Oswald Chambers, Oswestry appointing Messrs R. and B. Piercy of Welshpool as consulting engineers and George Owen of Oswestry as acting engineer.

Whalley was to be eminently successful in eliciting support for his proposed railway, having raised £14,100 from a preliminary subscription list of 78 names largely drawn from Ellesmere and the locality by the 9th October 1860[12]. However, the so-called "Independent Line"[13] was not to have things all its own way. The Great Western Company, allegedly acting more out of an interest in eliminating the competition rather than the desire to establish an effective rail link[14], put up two schemes (effectively connecting as one), in opposition to the O,E&W Railway.

This action was to force an enquiry before Parliament and divide the community. Prominent landowners including the Trustees for the earl Brownlow and Sir John Kynaston supported the Great Western line because of its reduced impact upon their estates. As too did many in Ellesmere who argued that the O,E&W did not afford good communication with Shrewsbury and beyond and promoted the interests of the London and North Western Railway

(LNWR) with whose main line it was to connect. Inhabitants also feared the creation of a monopoly, as the LNWR already controlled the Ellesmere canal[15].

At least one commentator bemoaned the unnecessary waste of time and money arising from the enforced enquiry, leading them to write: *"what a pity that so much good money should not be allowed to flow into the pockets of the navvies, rather than into the pockets of the lawyers, who 'cannot dig, and to beg are ashamed'"*[16].

The railway proposed by the "Independents" comprised a single line commencing at a junction with the Oswestry and Newtown Railway at Oswestry. From this junction the line ran to Whittington and from there to Ellesmere and Whitchurch where it was to connect with the London and North Western Railway Shrewsbury and Crewe line - a total distance of some 19 miles[17, 18].

The Great Western Company's first scheme comprised a double line, again commencing at Oswestry in a double station with the Oswestry and Newtown Railway. From here, however, the line was to run to Rednal station which lay on the Great Western main line, effectively placing Oswestry on the main line and materially shortening the distance between Shrewsbury and Oswestry. From Rednal the line was to run to Ellesmere. The second proposed scheme commenced at Ellesmere, taking a more or less direct line to Whitchurch where it was to connect with the Crewe line. The proposed Great Western railway was to be some four miles shorter than the "Independent" line and, more significantly, avoided Fenn's Moss - a fact not to be overlooked by the Great Western engineers during the heated deliberations over the two competing schemes that was to be played out before the Parliamentary Committee of the House of Commons.

The enquiry commenced on the 18th March 1861 and lasted for thirteen days. Aware that the Great Western Company

intended to make much of the engineering difficulties of crossing Fenn's Moss, the O,E&W felt it necessary to secure the services of Messrs Brun Lees, the eminent engineers of the Brazilian railways, to assist in arguing their case[19].

Benjamin Piercy, O,E&W's consulting engineer, had deliberately chosen a line across the Moss, considering any other to be a wilful waste of property[20]; this despite Sir John Hanmer having given his consent for the line to go around rather than across the mire. The line chosen by Piercy to cross the Moss had, in fact, been projected in 1845 for the Manchester and Birmingham Continuation Railway by the engineers Robert Stephenson and William Cubitt[21]. Stephenson had already constructed a railway across Chat Moss to the west of Manchester, using barrels strapped end-to-end to provide a drain and effectively "floating" the trackbed on a raft of hurdles[22].

The Great Western put forward a number of witnesses to support their claim that the O,E&W's proposal to cross Fenn's Moss was *"a grand engineering mistake"*. Mr. Wylie, surveyor for Great Western, alleged that the Moss comprised an *"upper crust of 3ft. pretty solid, but underneath it was liquid"*[23]. In sounding the Moss he claimed to have found depths of up to 36ft. of liquid peat along the proposed line. In support of his claim he produced a pickle jar of peaty liquid said to resemble *"sour coffee"*, leading Mr. Denison Q.C., advocate for the O,E&W, in later evidence, to make a memorable quip about *"sour coffee without 'grounds' "*[24].

Mr. Smith of Whitchurch, ironfounder and timber merchant, claimed the Moss to be *"a complete swamp"*[24] He alleged that it was with the greatest difficulty that he had been able to erect the lightest of machinery on the edge of the Moss, and that he had been unable to extract timber he had planted there because of the treacherous conditions.

Great Western further contended that the

O,E&W had greatly underestimated the costs of crossing the mire[26], one witness arguing that it would cost £23,000 more than the O,E&W had estimated.

G.W. Hemans, consulting engineer acting for the O,E&W, had experience in the construction of some forty miles of railway across the bogs in Ireland. He considered the sum of £3,000 more than adequate to meet the costs of crossing Fenn's Moss, having in Ireland constructed railway at a cost of no more than £800 per mile in some cases[27]. Mr. Hemans even produced a solid block of peat to counter Mr. Wylie's assertion that the Moss was mostly liquid.

At the close of the enquiry the Parliamentary Committee found in favour of the O,E&W Railway Company, but the decision was far from unanimous - two of the four members finding in favour of Great Western, a majority decision in support of the O,E&W only being gained on the casting vote of the chairman[28].

The "Independent's" Bill passed to the House of Lords with Great Western's assertion that it would fight it all the way. The Lord's Committee took evidence on 19th June 1861[29], but were not convinced of O,E&W's proposals for the line from Ellesmere to Oswestry. In enacting the "Independent" Bill, the Committee inserted a suspensionary clause, delaying consideration of the contentious Oswestry to Ellesmere section for twelve months, but freeing the O,E&W to commence construction of the line from Ellesmere to Whitchurch and across Fenn's Moss[30].

In celebration, the O,E&W drew up a *programme of rejoicings* in Ellesmere to mark the ceremony of cutting the first sod on Thursday 29th August 1861[31]:

"At 12 o' clock precisely, a public procession will be formed in the Market Place, preceded by Bands of Music, and headed by the Bailiffs of the Town, joined by the Directors and followed by the Committee and Friends, and proceed to the ground allotted for the ceremony, a field belonging to W.A. Provis, Esq.

near the Workhouse, where a raised Platform will be erected for the accommodation of the Subscribers, admitted by ticket. The sod will be cut at One p.m. by Sir John Hanmer, Baronet, M.P. assisted by John Stanton, Esq. (one of the Directors of the Company); immediately afterwards the procession will return in the same order."

"A public dejeuner will take place at 3p.m. in a tent at the Pleasure Grounds of Mr. Paddock, Bridgewater Hotel, adjoining the Mere, under the Presidency of G.H. Whalley, Esq. M.P., Chairman of the Company".

"On Friday the 30th there will be races in the Wharf Meadow, consisting of a Pony, Hurdle, Galloway, and Donkey race and a variety of rural sports and athletic amusements, under the superintendance of Mr. Allinson and Mr. Francis Povey.....to conclude with a dance at the above grounds adjoining the Mere. Tickets of admission, 1s. each, exclusive of refreshments.....An efficient Quadrille Band is engaged for the occasion. Dancing to commence at 4 o' clock."

"On Saturday, the inmates of the Ellesmere workhouse will be entertained with Roast Beef and Plum Pudding".

The day was heralded at 6a.m. by the pealing of the bells of the parish church and the firing of cannon in rapid succession[32].

By the middle of September 1861, the O,E&W had commenced the crossing of Fenn's Moss. A contemporary article in the *Oswestry Advertiser and Montgomeryshire Mercury*[33] graphically describes the process of construction and the engineering techniques employed:

"..... our ears are assailed with tidings of the maddest of all mad acts on the part of the maddest of madmen! Messrs. Savin and Ward, the contractors, who wont believe they are going to ruin although the Great Western Railway Times has over and over again proved the fact to the satisfaction of all reasonable men, have actually commenced crossing Whixall Moss!"

"Quietly and steadily has Mr. Ward been working at it, and in six weeks, with the help of 300 able-bodied navvies, he has fenced out some 4½ miles of the land, and formed the earth-works ready for the line of rails. From Cornhill to Fen's Bank a man may now walk where man never walked at this season of the year before, over a Morass, where Great Western engineers lost their rods of unheard of lengths, and found holes of unfathomable depths: where acres of soft bog floated on a sea of treacle, specimens of which in jars and bottles, astonished the committee when in Parliament, and demonstrated the fact beyond a doubt, that the man who could perform the Herculean feat of carrying a railway train over such a Slough of Despond, could be nothing short of a Croesus with a dash of the Magician! Without the powers of either, John Ward has gone far towards accomplishing the task. He has formed the road, and made it passable for man, and there is not the remotest probability of a doubt, that by the first of next May, an engine may be seen crossing the bog, at the very point, where, we are afraid to say how many hundreds of feet deep, Mr. Wylie found the soft mud he threw at Mr. Piercy!"

"But how has all this been done? By dint of hard work and patience. Mr. Ward first set his men to work in digging deep drains at some distance on each side of the line of proposed railway, then lesser drains each side, at a nearer point to the line, and again smaller ditches almost alongside the formation. At most points the permanent way will run on a bank varying from three to five feet in height and, as far as possible the bog has been thrown up out of these drains, so as to form a slope on each side of the railway, for the purpose of draining the water off into the ditches, and preventing its lodging on the surface. Where the permanent way is not raised, many hundreds of loads of bog have been cleared away so as to get deep drains to keep the foundation dry, and the consequence is, that every day, the peat becomes sounder, and it has been found that in a week after the new road has been formed, a man may walk comfortably over places where before his first step would have been his last."

"The bog varies at different parts. At some points it is barely three feet deep, and lies on a close hard sand, whereas at others it goes down to the depth of eighteen feet, and the work of filling up has been considerable. Nevertheless, at the very worst point, somewhere opposite Bronington, it has been found to dry more rapidly than at the shallower parts, and is fast becoming a hard and firm road."

"The work of forming the road is now done, and the 2½ miles of bog will have to lie at rest during the winter, a few workmen only occasionally going over the drains to keep them clear. In the early spring the next process will commence, which will be to make a firm ballast for the rails. This will be done by a simple and easy process, and nature has provided all the materials, close at hand. The Moss contains beds of sand thirty feet deep, and is skirted by a wood covering forty acres, from which any quantity of faggots may be cut. Nearly the whole surface of the bog is covered with **grig** [heather] - and here is all that will be wanted. A quantity of grig will first be strewed on the peat, on which will be placed bundles of faggots, on which again will be bedded a thick layer of sand. In the worst places stakes and poles will be laid across, and the rails will run on longitudinal baulk, instead of sleepers, in the same way as the broad-guage lines are done, but it is not anticipated that there will be a necessity for doing this over more than a few chains."

"That this process will be successful there can be no doubt, for at the very worst point in the Moss, there is now, and has been for a considerable period, a good sound cart road, formed by simply making ditches on each side, and the canal which runs not very far from the railway has a towing path as sound as any road need to be."

"The work was well calculated to frighten many contractors, for it looked in an 'awful mess' six weeks ago, and there are few men who would have accomplished in so short a time what Mr. Ward has done. Still the Great Western engineers must have known that they were stretching their consciences most severely *when they gave the evidence they did in the Commons, - that is if engineers have consciences at all; and another session will show a Parliamentary committee what a Shropshire farmer can do in the way of surmounting obstacles."*

"We trust our 'landed gentry' will learn a lesson too. Captain Cust in his evidence before the Commons, said that he could not support 'Whalley's line' because he did not believe it would ever be made, he could not see where the money was to come from. Sir J.R. Kynaston, was evidently of the same opinion, and others reiterated the belief. It was admitted on all hands that the Ellesmere and Whitchurch portion was not so likely to be remunerative as the Oswestry and Ellesmere, and yet, already, nearly five miles out of nine of this portion are fenced in. If this does not reach the 'landed gentry' that they have been grossly deceived by Great Western partizans, and cause them to alter their tone next session, the public will be assured of what they now more than suspect, that there is rather more in the opposition, than the fear of the funds of the Independent party not being forthcoming."

By the 27th February 1862 the line was laid and an engine and carriages was being run over the Moss to assist in the process of consolidation[34].

Goods services commenced on the line from 20th April 1863, with passenger trains from the 4th May[35]. Only the O,E&W's proposals were to emerge from the resumption of Parliamentary Committee battles arising from the earlier suspension of the intended section of line from Ellesmere to Oswestry, and these were never to come to fruition. In the end, a single line was continued to Oswestry which opened on 27th July 1864[36].

On the 25th July 1864, the Newtown and Machynlleth Railway, Llanidloes and Newtown Railway, Oswestry and Newtown Railway and the O,E&W combined to form the Cambrian Railways Company[36]. In 1922 the Cambrian amalgamated with the Great Western Railway[38] and GWR gained control of a line that sixty years previously it had fought so hard to prevent!

The Military Takes Over

Plate 22. Prees Heath Camp
during WW1.
Photograph: Private collection,
D. Pratt.

Large areas of Fenn's and Whixall Mosses were commandeered by the military authorities during both World Wars[1]. Lying within five minutes flying time of three (Service) Flying Training Schools [FTS/SFTS][2] and two fighter and bomber Operational Training Units [OTU] and their satellites[3], it was almost inevitable that a gunnery and bombing range and a decoy site should be located here during WW2. However, as regards military use a precedent had perhaps been set during, and prior to, WW1 with the building of large military camps within a few miles of the Moss at Bettisfield Park; Park Hall, Oswestry and Prees Heath (Plates 22 and 23). By 1st July 1916 a new camp had also been established at Fenn's Bank, for troops training on the North East Fenn's rifle ranges, with a capacity for 1,000 men under canvas[4,5].

Plate 22. Prees Heath Camp during WW1. Photograph: Private collection, D. Pratt.

Plate 23. The Officers' Mess,
Bettisfield Camp during WW1.
Photograph: Private collection,
D. Pratt.

It is difficult to unearth precise information, but ongoing research reveals at least eight Army ranges on Fenn's and Whixall Mosses. On the North East Fenn's the earliest pre-dated the Ordnance Survey 1909 re-survey of the area[6] (Figure 7a). Its capacity was rather limited and by September 1st 1915[7] it was replaced by a group of four larger ranges on a different alignment (Figure 7b). Three smaller ranges, on the western edge of the Moss (N.G.R. SJ 483 358), known locally as The Batters, were also used just for the period 1915-18.

More specifically "The Batters" refers to the three butt areas lying end-to-end, a high wall of railway sleepers against which peat, rather than the usual sand, was piled to absorb spent bullets. This was fronted by a similarly constructed rampart to protect the butt party. These were 300-yard ranges with access only from the towpath of the Shropshire Union Canal (Llangollen Branch) via a cinder track (Plate 65, p.144; Plate 69, p.152).

The Batters ranges were used by soldiers stationed at Bettisfield Park and Oswestry[8], and some credence must therefore be given, in the case of the former, to the strong oral tradition of troops arriving at the range by canal barge[9]. This makes better sense than picturing a large body of heavily equipped men, lumbered with ammunition boxes (if not carried by a mule!), negotiating a narrow, overgrown and occasionally deficient, canal towpath for nearly 1 1/2 miles.

If the 1,100-yard range on the Top North East Fenn's was in existence before 1909 it has its roots either in the South African war years or the expansion of local militia/territorial units. It was a standard ten-target 600-yard range with provision for a four-target 800, and single-target 900, 1,000 and 1,100-yard firing points. Up to 800 yards the firing points were made up of peat blocks held in place by timber revetments. Like The Batters, the target gallery had ramparts made up of timber and peat to the front and rear, with a range hut behind. The whole was kept relatively dry by two lateral drainage ditches 2,300ft (700m) and 2,500ft (760m) long, still discernible in patches. However, come the war a single range proved woefully inadequate for the Army units stationed in the neighbourhood. It was therefore abandoned and three new 600-yard ranges and one 300-yard range were laid out over and adjacent to it, spilling into the present-day Fenn's Wood which was then just scrub land through which firing lines were easily cleared.

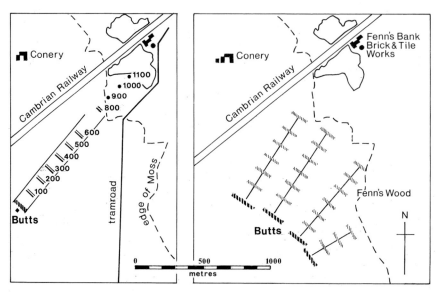

Figures 7a and b. Left - the pre-1909 rifle range as shown on the 1914 edition 25in Flintshire O.S. sheet XXVI.VII. This sheet was surveyed in 1872 and revised in 1909. Right - the four ranges which replaced it during WWI. Drawings: D. Pratt, re-drawn by Timothy Morgan.

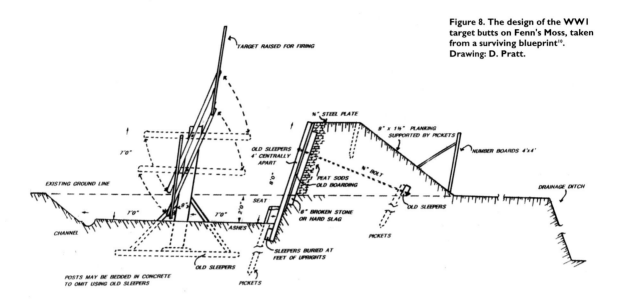

A fragile, possibly incomplete, blueprint for the *Proposed Rifle Range at Fenn's Moss* exists[10]. Each target gallery, separated by a target storage shed behind a protective wall of peat sods, now held thirty-two 6ft-square targets delicately balanced in pairs on a double pivot so that they could be either "at rest" i.e. not showing to marksmen above the 8ft front rampart, or with one target elevated for firing and its counterpart "grounded" for pasting-up and other repairs by the range party (Figure 8). This gave sixteen firing points to a range, each marked by a 4ft-square number board at the foot of the protective rampart.

The latter was 8ft high, the 2/3 slope stabilised on the firing side by $1\frac{1}{2}$ in boards held down by "pickets" (pointed wooden stakes or pegs). The flat crest of the rampart was further protected by $\frac{3}{4}$in steel plate. On the target side the gallery floor, some 14ft wide, comprised compacted ash on top of peat and had a slight fall to a rear drainage channel. The almost vertical inner face of the rampart was consolidated by tightly packed peat blocks fronted by six inches of broken stone or hard slag held in place by old boarding, and the whole buttressed by railway sleepers at 4ft

intervals, tied in by iron rods anchored to pickets set in the base of the rampart. Strangely, according to these plans, there was no provision for a rampart or stop-butt to the rear of the targets as is the norm with present-day rifle ranges. This has all sorts of implications for security and safety precautions!

The main use of the ranges was made by troops from the large WWI camp on Prees Heath and occasionally by soldiers from Park Hall, Oswestry. They would arrive by train, an extra long siding being provided off the passing loop at nearby Fenn's Bank station to accommodate them. With the closure and demolition of these camps after the war the ranges became redundant. Such fittings as were not salvaged by the Army were quickly stripped and recycled by local smallholders. Galleries and butts fell into decay, dissolving quietly into the surrounding peat to be obscured under a mat of heather, purple moor-grass, birch scrub and the odd Scots pine, or vanishing completely as peat cutters moved in to skin the area. Post-1963 tree planting in the Fenn's Wood area has further helped to reduce traces of the firing points (Plate 64, p.142).

Paradoxically, information on WW2 activities on Fenn's Moss is even more difficult to obtain. Neither bombing range nor decoy sites were independent units, but are rarely mentioned in parent station Operational Record Books[11]; possibly, in the case of the latter, on grounds of stringent secrecy. Many a spade of peat contained the fragmentary remains of the thousands of practice bombs that were dropped over a five-year period, and every Whixall schoolboy in his time carefully picked over the rifle and gunnery ranges for spent .303 and .50 ammunition to augment his pocket money. Yet there are scant physical remains apart from a brick picket hut, concrete plinths that once carried a control building, quadrant towers and "Starfish" bowls, sundry baulks of peat from which protrude iron rods that supported machine-gun targets (Plate 24), and a mysterious raised path across an area that has hitherto resisted peat cutters. Air Ministry Works Directorate drawings (AMWD) for the period February 1940-January 1945 that would show the evolution and expansion of the bombing range facilities no longer survive, at least in official repositories[12]. However, "earthworks" and other detail on a series of vertical and oblique aerial photographs covering the period 1946-94 enable some tentative reconstructions to be made[13].

From February 1940 the parent unit was 11 SFTS, Shawbury. They shared the bombing range with 10 SFTS, Tern Hill, which latter would have a monopoly of use from August-November 1940. From 7 November 1940 - 8 February 1942 the range was used by 306, 605, 403 and 131 Squadrons, operational units posted into Tern Hill for the defence of Merseyside and the West Midlands, and between April-October 1941 also by 'D' Flight, 57 OTU, refugees from RAF Hawarden where runway construction was under way. Rarer visitors were the 5-gun Masters which 5 SFTS had taken with them to Tern Hill. In October 1941 even the Wellingtons of 27 OTU, Lichfield, crowded off the Cannock ranges, pinched the odd day - and night - at Fenn's Moss for bombing and flare dropping practice[14].

From April-August 1942 Fenn's Moss was used by the Spitfires of 61 OTU at Rednal (N.G.R. SJ 375 275). The first aircraft had flown in from their temporary base at Heston (near Heathrow) on 13 April 1942. The first training accident was logged on 4 May when Pilot Officer Pensa and Sgt. P.R. Wright were killed in Miles Master W9003. But the first accident involving a Spitfire occurred over the Fenn's Moss range on 14 June 1942. According to eye-witnesses Spitfire II P7622, piloted by Sgt. G.G. Mager, was seen coming off the target area, flying very low. Over Cadney Bank it started a low, steep banking turn to port but then slowly flipped onto its back and dived into Cadney Moss (or Wem Moss according to which official record is consulted), the other side of the Shropshire Union Canal from the range area. Sgt. Mager was killed instantly. Like most of the Spitfires in 61 OTU, P7622 was a rather war weary machine having entered service with 616 ("South Yorkshire") Squadron at Kirton-in-Lindsey in February 1941 and passing through the hands of seven other operational squadrons before being put out to grass in the Shropshire countryside. It had come to 61 OTU in March 1942 from 154 Squadron at Coltishall, Norfolk, as the latter converted to Spitfire VAs and VBs. However, the resultant inquiry blamed inexperience and pilot error rather than poor maintenance[15].

Plate 24. Bill Allmark inspects one of the surviving iron rods from the air-to-ground machine-gun targets, set up during WW2 along the target butts of the WW1 rifle ranges on North East Fenn's Moss. Photograph: André Q. Berry.

In September 1942 Fenn's Moss was taken over solely as a bombing range by 81 OTU, 92 Group, Bomber Command, at Tilstock and (after April 1943) Sleap. 61 OTU had perforce to look further afield for its air-to-ground gunnery, namely the Talacre range. In January 1944 RAF Tilstock came under the control of 38 Group (Airborne forces) and home to the Stirlings of 1665 HCU (Heavy Conversion Unit) and a Whitley/Horsa combination glider training establishment. But it still retained the day-to-day running of the Fenn's Moss range now increasingly used by Wellingtons from OTUs at Peplow (Shropshire) (until squeezed out), Pershore, Honeybourne (Worcs.), and elsewhere on their cross-country navigational exercises, as well as the Spitfires and Mustangs from 41 and 58 OTUs at Hawarden and Poulton (N.G.R. SJ 400 600).

It was the demise of a Broughton-built Wellington III, BK430, whilst using the Fenn's Moss range that brought the horrors of war home to the tiny hamlet of Little Green, Bronington, on the northern edge of the range. Mrs. Marie Mottershead, now of *Oak Villa,* but then newly married with a young family, recalls her father coming into the house early morning his clothes blackened and singed by the heat, smelling of smoke and carrying the unmistakable stench of burning flesh, a smell that neither would experience again until the great foot-and-mouth epidemic of 1967-8. He issued the grim warning that women and children should best keep away from the crash site where police, Home Guard, range crew and farm-workers stood helplessly by, unable to approach the wreckage because of the heat and fear of exploding ammunition. The fire crews and crash tenders from Whitchurch and RAF Tilstock arrived within twenty minutes. All they could do was to dampen down.

23 OTU, based at Pershore (Worcs.), had the responsibility of training Canadian crews for the new Commonwealth squadrons. BK430 had taken off at 2200hrs on Friday, 6 August 1943 on a night navigational exercise

which included dropping practice bombs on the Fenn's Moss range. As it cleared Dawley and Wellington the crew reported engine trouble, but pressed on and actually communicated with the Fenn's Moss safety and control officer and took their place in the circuit over Whixall. But, as the post-crash investigation revealed, the supply of oil to the big-end bearing of the master con-rod of the port engine had failed. With the pilot unable to feather the engine the Wellington went into a steep dive from which it was just pulling out when it ploughed into the ground on the edge of the Moss and immediately burst into flames, trapping and killing all five crew members despite valiant efforts of the range crew and civilians living nearby.

As the sun rose next morning only the occasional wisp of smoke and a strange pungent odour mingling with the mists that hung over the Moss suggested that something untoward had recently happened in this remote part of Flintshire. At the crash site the Bronington police constable and two Home Guard sentries with fixed bayonets, their reliefs long overdue, prowled restlessly around the blackened geodetic skeleton of a Wellington that had survived bombing and minelaying missions with 196 Squadron (Leconfield) and 429 Squadron RCAF (East Moor, Yorks.) only to meet an inglorious end thus.

The Canadian crew of BK430 comprised Flight Sergeant J.P.R. Labbe (26, pilot); Warrant Officer F.C.J. Therien (25, wireless operator/air gunner) F/Sgt. J.P.G.M. de Bellefeuille (19, pupil bomb-aimer); Flying Officer N. Solomka (23, navigator), and F/Sgt. W. McKenzie Arril (25, air bomber). They all lie buried in the Commonwealth War Graves Cemetery, Blacon, Chester.

Whether the Wellington was loaded with 10lb Mk.III or 11½lb Mk.I (flash) practice bombs is uncertain, but the result would be the same. Practice bombs with flash filling (gunpowder and magnesium turnings) for night work would have had the cotter pin securing the striker removed as loaded into

Figure 9. Early wartime aerial activity on North East Fenn's Moss, 1939-40. Drawing: D. Pratt, re-drawn by Timothy Morgan.

the aircraft, leaving just the safety-pin that would spring-load out upon release. The impact of the crash would have shaken the bombs loose, triggering off an instantaneous conflagration which would have given the dazed and possibly injured crew no chance to escape.

The subsequent inquiry attributed the crash to "*failure to jettison practice bomb load. Pilot left it too late to order crew to bale out, which possibly led to confusion and the loss of control. Duration of flight was one hour*". To confuse the researcher RAF records claim *six* dead and attribute the site of the crash to a place called "*Badmington, Salop*" or "*Bodrington, near Shropshire*."

Continuing the story of Fenn's Moss range, from 1 April 1937 No.5 Armament Training Camp (later 9 Air Observer School/ 9 Bombing & Gunnery School) at Penrhos (N.G.R. SH 335 335) and Hell's Mouth (N.G.R. SH 207 285) in the Lleyn had provided the Advanced Training Flights from Tern Hill, Shawbury, Digby (Lincs.), Netheravon (Wilts.) and other FTSs with their final aerial gunnery and bombing practices, a month at a time, fitting them in

around the summer and week-end practice camps for regular, auxiliary and Royal Naval squadrons. But with the outbreak of war this happy arrangement was not to last.

Until the Miles Master and the North American Harvard came on stream in 1940 both 10 and 11 FTS used the Hawker Hart, Audax and Fury, the Avro Tutor, and the Gloster Gauntlet for single-engine training. Theoretically a FTS took in pilots who had already totted up 50 hours (including 30 hours dual) air experience at an Elementary & Reserve FTS (E&RFTS). But courses never reached the optimum nine months and by 1938, as the RAF geared itself for war, were already reduced to 22 weeks, divided into two equal terms. In the first term the aim was to produce pilots competent in the handling of service aircraft in addition to mastering the theory of flight and the rudiments of engines, rigging, elementary meteorology, RAF law and administration, etc. During the second term pilots of the Advanced Training Squadron [ATS] picked up on those skills which were a necessary pre-requisite to joining an operational unit i.e. formation flying, dog-fighting, air-to-air and air-to-ground gunnery, bombing from the air, etc.[16] But before proceeding to the Lleyn, to accelerate a pupil's skills in the handling of aircraft at low altitude and high speed and with live weaponry, a practice range was set up on Fenn's Moss. Such a facility was also essential for making up time and experience that might be lost at the Armament Practice Camp due to bad weather.

As seen from the accompanying plan (Figure 9), the Fenn's Moss range was initially nothing elaborate, a mere extension of the traditional "bombing circle", with machine-gun targets set up along the galleries of the former WW1 rifle ranges. Target circles could not be painted onto a moss, heather and moor grass surface. They were constructed out of timber and placed *in situ*. Each section was 3ft wide, painted white, and when assembled formed a hollow circle some 20-25ft in diameter. In the centre was a low, square "funnel" made out of galvanised metal sheeting. The latter could represent anything from a military truck to a gun emplacement.

It was not long before the first accident on the range emerges from 23 Group (Training Command) records. On 6 May 1940 Acting-Pilot Officer D.C. Leary, with 106 flying hours to his credit (49 on the Audax and 47 on other ATS types), was flying at Fenn's Moss in Hawker Audax K2011. This venerable bi-plane was delivered to the RAF in February 1932 and had seen service with 13 Squadron at Netheravon and (1937-8) with 211 Squadron at Grantham (Lincs). When the latter squadron moved to Egypt K2011 was taken over by 45 E&RFTS and in 1939 by 11 FTS Shawbury. At 1045hrs on the Monday morning A-P/O Leary had taken off from Shawbury to carry out low bombing and strafing attacks on the Fenn's Moss range. According to witnesses he had successfully dropped his practice bomb and was turning at low altitude on a north westerly heading over the railway when: "*he lost power, it seemed, and slipped sideways in the turn, ever so slowly and then plummeted into the peat workings. From where we were standing we could see people running over to the aircraft which looked just like a crumpled kite. There was no fire, and we learnt later that the pilot had survived his ordeal*". This crash is now part of Moss folklore, with details varying according to the narrator. It is often asserted that the Audax actually clipped a stack of drying peat as it turned, but official records make no mention of this.

As so often happens in isolated rural areas where there was no resident police constable, it was railway workers to the rescue. Station staff and permanent way workers took control of the situation and carefully freed the pilot from the crumpled wreckage. They were no strangers to aircraft crashes. Only a few months previously they had dealt effectively with a Miles Magister that crashed the other side of Bettisfield Station on 16 March 1939 whilst on a ferry flight from its Woodley factory to 10 FTS, Tern Hill, and came perilously close to blocking the single-line track.

At the subsequent inquiry the pilot of K2011 claimed that his attention was diverted for a vital second during the turn, with subsequent loss of control. The Chief Instructor put it more bluntly: "*it was just damn bad piloting!*" Thirty-five years later such remains of K2011 as had not been cleared at the time came to light during peat digging operations. Unfortunately no aviation archaeologist was contacted and the de-rated Rolls-Royce Kestrel X engine, of which so few now remain, promptly found its way to Furber's scrapyard just along the canal!

● The Art of Deception

Ten months into the war the military involvement of RAF Shawbury with Fenn's Moss suddenly became more complicated. Following the fall of France and the occupation of its airfields by the Germans, most of the United Kingdom now came within easy range of the bombers of *Luftflotten 2* and 3 (Second and Third German Air Forces). For the first time the *Luftwaffe* would turn its attention to the so-called "back areas" of the West Midlands, the Merseyside and Manchester conurbations, and industrial north-east Wales.

To its function as a gunnery and bombing range the North East Fenn's would add that of a "decoy" or fake target[17]. As its name indicates, the latter was a ruse to confound and confuse enemy bomber crews and to lure them away from the "real" target, in this first instance the rather vulnerable aerodrome at Shawbury.

Although born of momentary panic the establishment of a decoy on Fenn's Moss was nevertheless a clandestine, covert operation. Theoretically the nocturnal antics of a rather bemused body of troops were also shrouded in secrecy. The true purpose of the decoy was hidden from the mystified and apprehensive inhabitants of Bronington, Bettisfield and Whixall by some effective propaganda and disinformation. Not even the Local Defence Volunteers to whom fell the task of denying public access to this part of the Moss quite knew what they were supposed to be guarding. Fifty years on, garbled stories still proliferate and the researcher's task of establishing the exact chronology and shape of events on the Moss is made that much more difficult. However, some light begins to be shed on happenings at Shawbury and Fenn's Bank if consideration is also given to the first air-raid on RAF Sealand, Flintshire, and both are examined in the context of data-finding sorties flown by the *Luftwaffe* as a necessary first step in the drawing up of detailed plans for the invasion of this country. Such a move makes more sense than the comfortable, but ultimately unsatisfying, orthodoxy that the apparently random fall of German bombs in rural areas was occasioned solely by their being indiscriminately jettisoned by retreating enemy aircraft.

On the night of Wednesday, 26/27 June 1940, although "Red Alerts"[18] were in force at east coast ports, most of England was under a "Yellow" warning between 2300-0430hrs. In Flintshire, Areas 7 (Buckley/ Hawarden) and 8 (Shotton/ Sealand) went on "Yellow Alert" at 0135hrs, with status "White" (or "Cancel") being signalled at 0210hrs. There were no intervening "Purple" or "Red" alerts logged, and no sirens. This is hardly surprising, for all the night's action had occurred without warning ten minutes previously! At 0125hrs a HE (high explosive) bomb landed between the main gate and the Officers' Mess, RAF Sealand, leaving a crater and blowing in windows over a considerable radius as well as bringing down the telephone lines. A second bomb landed at Marsh Cottages beyond West Camp dispersal area and blisters, too close to Chester (otherwise Hawarden Bridge East) Junction on the old Great Central Wrexham-Chester line for comfort. The lone raider droned away at 13,000ft[19]. Aerodrome defences were quickly manned by the Army and the civilian workers' Local Defence Volunteers (Home Guard) platoon was stood to and issued with guns and ammunition from the armoury - a case of shutting the stable door after the horse had bolted!

Thirty minutes earlier RAF Shawbury had received the same treatment. Indeed, one suspects that the same German bomber may have been responsible for both incidents. The Shropshire airfield was lit up like a Christmas tree with night flying in full swing. At about 0100hrs a single raider dropped seven HE bombs, four inside and three outside the perimeter fence. All fell on grass areas so there were no casualties, but there was extensive blast damage to Station HQ, airmen's blocks, the Motor Transport section and parked vehicles[20]. There had been no advance on "Yellow Alert" status. Anti-aircraft defences were unmanned, indeed the Royal Engineers were still busy on their construction - not that much could have been done with Lewis guns against an unseen enemy at 10,000ft! Neither Shawbury nor Tern Hill would receive their complement of four Bofors guns until the following month. The whole raid took less than ten seconds. Ten minutes later Shrewsbury Police Division went on "Red Alert!"

On the face of it these were isolated incidents. Flintshire would receive no further attention from the *Luftwaffe* until the night of 28/29 July. Although enemy planes were tracked nightly over Shropshire, no more bombs fell on the county until 22/23 July when an exploratory stick of ten HE bombs straddled the A41 at Tern Hill. But, as already hinted, there is possibly a pattern to be discerned behind these chance hit-or-miss affairs. Twice daily, since he had been appointed Prime Minister on 10 May 1940, summaries and brief strategic appraisals of the previous night's *Luftwaffe* activities fell on Churchill's desk. Such reports[21] were compiled by the Ministry of Home Security, formed in September 1939 from the Air Raids Precautions Department of the Home Office. The effective conduct of civil defence operations was dependent on reliable intelligence channelled in to the Home Security War Room from the Regions, each of which in turn digested information from their own and RAF and Observer Corps Group and Control Centres.

In his appraisal of the events of 24/25 June 1940, Major R.R. MacBryan, War Room Operations Officer, drew attention to the *missing* of potential targets and suggested that the majority of these raids were either:

- large-scale training reconnaissance flights over open unobstructed wastelands and military and civil aerodromes (including landing strips listed by the Automobile Association in their *Register of Aircraft Landing Grounds),* or

- raids used to produce the exact timings necessary for the co-ordination of any invasion plan.

On 2 July 1940 Hitler ordered the necessary plans for *Operation Sealion* to be prepared. In a *Luftwaffe* directive Goering beat him by two days. A feature of the Danish and Norwegian campaigns had been the accuracy of timings in the assaults. Denmark fell in 12 hours. Norway, apart from the Narvik pocket, took a little longer - some eight days. The same meticulous planning saw Holland and Belgium fall in 18 days.

Major MacBryan went on to suggest that, since many of the current series of raids were designed *not* to cause extensive damage, close attention should be paid by various Intelligence Departments to the fall of bombs in relation to possible parachute landings at each place, with a view to capturing landing grounds for troop-carrying planes. Against such an appraisal the sporadic bombing by isolated German aircraft as outlined above suddenly falls neatly into place, especially if one also considers precautions, *ad hoc* or no, subsequently taken on the ground.

Reactions to the raids were predictable and the sense of desperate emergency is perhaps best summed up by former Pte. Eric Evans, King's Shropshire Light Infantry (KSLI), who in the summer of 1940 was part of the unit seconded from Shrewsbury to the ground defence of RAF Shawbury:

"Being Army we took great delight at seeing these toffee-nosed RAF types running round like chickens with the heads cut off! Jerry had put the fear of God into them. Everything now had to be done yesterday! [22]

This was a squaddy's succinct summing up of the new preventative measures introduced in great haste at Shawbury, ranging from replacing all lights in living and sleeping quarters with blue bulbs to the sinking of pre-fabricated Stanton-type air-raid shelters, 22 on the main technical site, which included 11FTS, and six for 27 MU, two each on sites "A", "B" and "C". Plans for the closure of the roads from Acton Lea and between Moreton Corbet and Shawbury village, drawn up in May 1940, were now suddenly implemented, with double sentries posted at road blocks and passes issued to civilians entitled to use the roads. The Acton Lea - Moreton Corbet road was never re-opened and after the war a permanent diversion was built. Airmen in great numbers, both "general duties" and "trades", were siphoned off for guard duties, especially patrolling the five-mile perimeter fence. However, within ten days 60 airmen arrived direct from "square bashing" or recruit training. They would form the nucleus of No. 6 Defence Squadron, formally embodied on 22 July with the arrival of a troop from No.161 Light Anti-Aircraft (LAA) Regiment, Royal Artillery, with their Bofors. They would hold the fort until February 1942 when elements of the RAF Regiment took over.

But more pertinent to our narrative, Pte. Evans found himself part of a detachment dispatched post-haste on 28 June to set up a decoy site on Shawbury's bombing range at Fenn's Moss. He recalls their being addressed by *"a big RAF type"*, i.e. the Station Commander, GP. Capt. H.P. Lalo, on the need for secrecy and the dangers of careless talk. Grins were wiped off faces when the CO snarled, *"one word out of place and I'll have you buggers shot!"* His words must have had some effect, for even today there is a marked reluctance to talk about things that went on at Fenn's Moss!

Decoys were nothing new even if the tentacles of "Colonel Turner's Department" had not yet reached out to embrace Shropshire and the Welsh border. The feasibility of setting up decoy dummy airfields had been established as early as September 1939. In the October Colonel John Turner, former Director of Works and Buildings at the Air Ministry (1931-39), brought out of retirement and charged with putting such counter-measures into effect, set up his Department's HQ at Shepperton film studios. The preliminary ground organisation that initially divided the country into four areas not unnaturally focussed on the east coast and S.E. England. It was not until July-August 1940 that official "professional" coverage was extended to the industrial north west, just in time for the Merseyside and Manchester *Blitze*.

The Shawbury decoy of June 1940 established on Fenn's Moss, not to be confused with the Q/QF site Colonel Turner would later set up at Withington on the flanks of Haughmond Hill, was a primitive in-house affair, doomed to failure from the start. Possibly more of a morale booster or conscience assuager than anything else - *something* was being done! The decoy squad did not enjoy the luxury of a portable generator and electric lights. Each night, after bombing and gunnery had finished for the day, "money flares" were set out and lit, double or single line. These were drums of paraffin with large wicks that gave off smokey flames 3-4ft high. For the moment little thought was given to realism. The flares were kept burning all night, almost daring German aircraft to drop their bombs. Even when enemy planes were tracked overhead no one thought of dowsing the flares as would happen on a real airfield if attacked. *Luftwaffe* pilots were not so easily fooled. The Army ground party was kept busy running up and down topping up drums and relighting wicks - a dangerous pursuit if the enemy had taken it into his head to drop his bombs! There was no splinter proof shelter or blockhouse for the decoy party, only a couple of tents and a sand-bagged observation post reinforced with blocks of peat.

As they warmed to their new role so the soldiers began to improvise and show touches of ingenuity - occasionally flashing the headlights of their 3-tonner or briefly unmasking Tilley lamps to give the impression of careless movement on the ground. Again, this was potentially dangerous, especially with Army property involved! With a little input from Royal Aircraft Establishment personnel they even managed to simulate a landing aircraft, as Pte. Evans put it: "*.... a bizarre method of two lights on a length of wood being towed along the peat cuttings*". Fifty years on he cannot recall who or what did the towing. "Bizarre" the idea may have seemed to him in 1940, but under prevailing conditions essentially practical. At that time the peat workings, and processing works were connected by a 2ft narrow gauge railway. A peat tramroad had once run to an exchange siding at Fenn's Moss brickworks. By coincidence its trackbed would be used as a base line to work out the geometry for siting the bombing target and quadrant towers of the later "Mark IV" bombing range. There were some four miles of track permanently laid on the Moss, the "main line", and about two miles of temporary track and points that could be taken up and relaid wherever it was needed. Some 300 yards of spare track was commandeered by the Army and the dummy "aeroplane" stuck onto the chassis of a peat wagon. The peat railway system's locomotive was a 20 h.p. petrol powered, chain driven locomotive built by the Motor Rail and Tram Company and bought new in October 1919. Since it was the only one, it is doubtful if it was used to pull-push the decoy. So must one envisage sweating, stumbling and cursing teams of soldiers pulling this contraption by hand up and down the short length of track in the hope that someone up there would drop bombs on them, or worse still, machine gun them intruder fashion? But not to worry. In the three months this decoy was operational it attracted neither German bomb nor British aircraft attempting an emergency landing, such was its overall ineffectiveness.

As the initial panic subsided and wiser and calmer counsel prevailed, an end was called to the Fenn's Moss nightly charade. Exact date is uncertain, but in August 1940 the KSLI detachment was returned to depot in Shrewsbury and 10 FTS, Tern Hill had almost exclusive use of the range. Round about this time RAF Shawbury, along with Tern Hill, Cranage, Sealand and Hawarden, got its "proper" Q-site at Withington, although the records of Colonel Turner's Department at the PRO are clearly incomplete and somewhat ambivalent in this matter [23].

● On the Bombing Range

In September 1941 Fenn's Moss was resurveyed, possibly marking the positioning of a "Strategic Starfish" site (described below) on the Top (No. 5) section of the peat cuttings (N.G.R. SJ 492 368 centre). In August 1943 the range was again resurveyed and enlarged. Thereafter there was very little alteration to lay-out, through a resurvey of June 1944 to the final disposition of January 1945 for which latter a diazo or dye-line drawing *does* exist[24] and which has served as the basis for Figure 10. Fortunately, too, the control and safety officer for the last 18 months of the bombing range's existence has been able to fill in on its day-to-day running[25].

In February 1942 the long-running dispute between Fenn's Moss peat cutters and the Air Ministry was abruptly determined. The smallholders were informed that under the provisions of the *Compensation (Defence) Act 1939* they were not entitled to receive one penny for the loss of profits consequent upon areas of the Moss being requisitioned. They were, however, allowed to claim the rents that peat cutters still had to pay their landlords. For many this amounted to £1 p.a. per holding. Since Fenn's Moss was officially requisitioned in October 1939, the grand sum of £2. 10s was now due! Magnanimously the Air Ministry agreed to a one-off lump sum payment of £5 and to pay the smallholders' legal fees. Additionally the Ministry agreed that any turf already cut

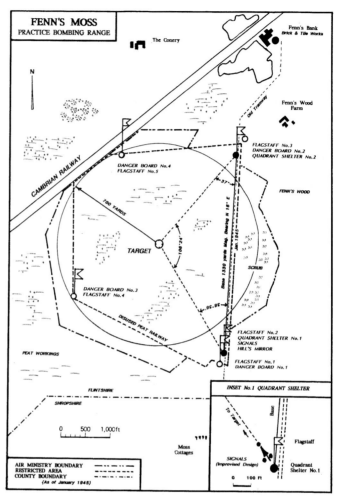

Figure 10. The North East Fenn's Moss WW2 bombing range as it appeared in January 1945, taken from a surviving Air Ministry drawing[24].
Drawing: D. Pratt.

could be removed immediately - too many stacks of peat standing proud were a potential hazard to low-flying aircraft using the gunnery range!

To rub salt into the wounds the Ministry pointed out to those who had lost a partial livelihood from the Moss, that they: "*should have been able to obtain work at Marchwiel* (the Royal Ordnance Factory), *Prees Heath* (RAF Tilstock) *and other places at a rate of wages in excess of nett profits from the turf cutting business, and therefore no loss should have been suffered* [26]. In a sense officialdom was quite correct in the stance adopted. Many farm labourers and smallholders from Bettisfield, Fenn's Bank and Whixall abandoned the land in favour of semi-skilled

Plate 25. The bombing range as it appeared on 17th May 1946. The white-painted double triangle of the target centre can be clearly seen in this RAF photograph[36], together with the white-painted navigational arrow to the south south east, which adjoined Quadrant Shelter No.1. To the north and east of target centre may be seen the target butts and shooting positions of the four WW1 rifle ranges; and a fifth target butt, disturbance around which may be indicative of its use for air-to-ground gunnery practice. © Crown Copyright. Ministry of Defence.

was permitted when bombing was not in progress.

The target was set upon baulks of peat on the highest point of the Moss. It was a 36 yard outer triangle on wooden supports, made up of $1\frac{1}{2}$ inch boards to a width of 9 feet and painted white overall (Plate 25). The centre was hollow apart from a smaller inverted triangle, also painted white, with its three points touching the larger triangle midway along each side of the latter. There were seven electric lights for night work, one in the centre and the others at the points of the two triangles. From the centre lamp the "bombing circle" was some 700 yards radius, deemed sufficient a safety margin where practice, as distinct from live, bombs were used. Not that many bombs went astray. One is recorded as going through the roof of Moss Cottages, fortunately a smoke bomb, not a flash, which could have had more serious consequences. Stray bombs had to be investigated by the range officer and damage to farm buildings and casualties to livestock assessed for compensation purposes. There were several near misses on the range's quadrant towers, and there was the rather smug Whitley crew from 81 OTU, Tilstock, the parent station, who in November 1943 succeeded in knocking out the central light of the target with a 10lb flash bomb. Congratulations on a fine piece of bomb-aiming were marred somewhat when it was realised back at base that the range had been temporarily closed to effect running repairs and that the range officer himself had been at the target! To reach the target at night a repair party simply followed the electric cables laid across the Moss, thanking their lucky stars that extensive peat digging had not yet spread into the North East Fenn's. Then there was the as yet unidentified Wellington crew from Pershore who, having introduced themselves to the range controller, suddenly lost their bearings whilst making their circuit and promptly proceeded to plaster the runways at RAF. Sleap with flash bombs, despite the fact that flarepaths were lit for night flying! Similar incidents were recorded with the bombing of Montford Bridge airfield and

and manual work on the myriad of defence projects in the region, ranging from the construction and maintenance of airfields, ordnance sub-depots, camps and military hospitals to running Motor Transport pools. Here they earned from £7 a week, three times the contemporary agricultural wage.

The target area of the bombing range, restricted to everybody, even peat cutters, took in the Nature Reserve sections called Fenn's North East Cutters', Lundt's, and Top North East Fenn's, with the marginal "Danger Areas" spilling over into the Smallholders' Triangle, Fenn's Wood Farm and Tom Jones' sections and the scrubland that was Fenn's Wood. Although the latter were necessary to absorb "overshoots" or stray practice bombs, limited peat cutting

Plates 26a and b. The remains of practice bombs are frequently encountered, including cast-iron nose cones from 10lb/11½lb bombs and bakelite fragments from 8½lb bombs, together with tail-fin sections. 26b - a surviving post from the WW2 bombing range target centre, with the cast-iron nose cones of 10lb/11½lb practice bombs to foreground. Photographs: André Q. Berry.

- the greatest indignity of the lot - RAF Tilstock itself! The perpetrators of such foul deeds could be easily identified from the call-signs, timings, their unexplained absence from over the range and the frenzied vituperative telephone calls from the bases under attack!

Less experienced bomb-aimers would start at the lower altitude of 5,000-6,000ft. Only when proficient would they drop their bombs from 10,000ft. No trouble at all was experienced from the North American Mustangs of 41 and 58 OTUs and 3 TEU (Tactical Exercise Unit) from RAF Poulton and RAF Hawarden. There the Advanced Training Squadron would drop some 16 bombs at Fenn's Moss as part of their ground support training. Air-to-ground and air-to-air firing would be carried out at the Talacre range, the units providing their own drogue-towing aircraft.

Generally practice bomb fragments are instantly recognisable[27] (Plates 25a and b). All bombs were painted white overall with two green bands around the centre of the tail. The 8lb Mk.I practice bomb was now rarely used since airfield ranges had virtually disappeared because of the inhibiting proximity of buildings and restrictions on ground and air movement when in use.

This light weight bomb, used for low level training purposes, contained no explosive and its construction was such as to leave no debris injurious to aircraft tyres. Basically it was an asbestos cement cylinder with a glass flask containing about ½ pint of titanium tetrachloride in the nose. The rest of the cylinder was hollow, acting as a tail unit. On impact casing and flask disintegrated, releasing the titanium tetrachloride as a smoke cloud.

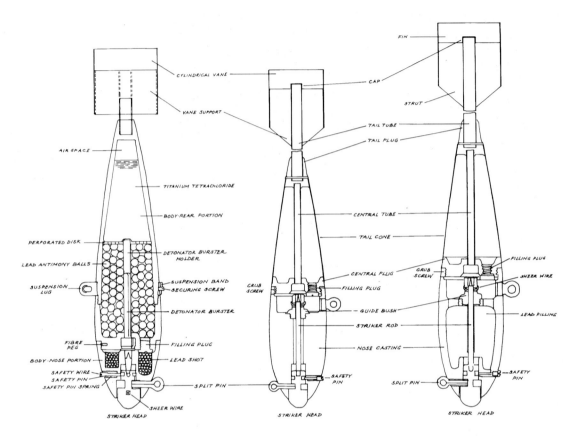

The labelled parts in the figure include:

CYLINDRICAL VANE
VANE SUPPORT
AIR SPACE
TITANIUM TETRACHLORIDE
BODY REAR PORTION
PERFORATED DISK
DETONATOR BURSTER HOLDER
LEAD ANTIMONY BALLS
SUSPENSION BAND
SECURING SCREW
SUSPENSION LUG
DETONATOR BURSTER
FIBRE PEG
FILLING PLUG
BODY NOSE PORTION
LEAD SHOT
SAFETY WIRE
SAFETY PIN
SAFETY PIN SPRING
SPLIT PIN
SHEER WIRE
STRIKER HEAD

FIN
CAP
STRUT
TAIL TUBE
TAIL PLUG
CENTRAL TUBE
TAIL CONE
CENTRAL PLUG
GRUB SCREW
FILLING PLUG
GUIDE BUSH
STRIKER ROD
NOSE CASTING
SAFETY PIN
SPLIT PIN
STRIKER HEAD

FILLING PLUG
SHEER WIRE
LEAD FILLING
SAFETY PIN
SPLIT PIN
STRIKER HEAD

Figure 11. Cross-sections of 8¹/₂lb (left), 10lb (centre) and 11¹/₂ lb (right) practice bombs, as used on the Fenn's Moss bombing range. Drawing: Timothy Morgan. Reproduced with the kind permission of the Ministry of Defence.

The 8¹/₂lb practice bomb (Figure 11), of which countless fragments still abound in the peat of Fenn's Moss, comprised a moulded bakelite plastic body made in three parts - a nose section housing the striker, a central section with detonator-burster, and a rear section which was hollow. The central portion was filled with lead-antimony balls, the interstices, along with most of the rear section being filled with titanium tetrachloride for white smoke emission at point of impact (Mk.I) or (Mk.III) a flash filling of gunpowder and magnesium turnings for night work. This bomb was used to break on impact without causing damage to the target!

The 10lb and 11¹/₂lb practice bombs (Figure 11), Mk.I "smoke", Mk.III "flash", were about 18 inches long, with a detonator-burster. These bombs, because of their cast-iron nose, could not be used against lightly armoured targets. Mk.Is carried a smoke

filling of 1lb of titanium chloride, and Mk.IIIs a similar weight of gunpowder and magnesium turnings to give that characteristic brilliant white flash on detonation. Occasionally, when the Moss surface vegetation was tinder dry, the flash filling would allegedly set parts of the Moss alight, "*allegedly*" because there was a running dispute between RAF Tilstock and the Great Western Railway Company, who operated services on the Oswestry-Whitchurch section of line across the Moss, as to whether it was actually a spark from the flash compound of bombs or from a passing railway engine that caused the damage. There was a considerable precedent for railway-initiated fires long before Shawbury's Audaxes ever appeared in Bronington skies, and fires would continue long after the range finally closed. Whitchurch and Wem AFS teams regularly attended the Moss fires, but because of "security" and too zealous an adherence to the *Official Secrets Act*, were never permitted to trespass on the range! Fires had to burn themselves out and for long periods a thick smoke-screen would hamper or prevent bombing runs.

Latterly the Fenn's Moss range was worked from 0800hrs to late in the evening, closure or opening being indicated by an illuminated ground disc near Quadrant No.1. The range was staffed by two shifts of a sergeant, corporal and four airmen, billeted locally, with their HQ at *The Waggoners* pub in Whixall. Operations were strictly controlled by the weather. It is strange to reflect that a second RAF party, a sergeant, corporal, and eight airmen who maintained the "Starfish" and decoy sites, were also billeted locally. Although they met socially at the pub and passed each other on the way to and from work, no one had the vaguest inkling, or for that matter evinced the slightest curiosity, about what each other was doing on the Moss. While good military discipline, it is very frustrating for today's researchers!

At each of the traditional access points to the Moss there were red warning flags indicating that the range was operational and, for the benefit of the unheeding local "peasantry", a notice board quoting the appropriate Defence Regulations bye-laws under which the range had been requisitioned and access restricted. There were only two quadrant towers or observation points, with large windows overlooking the target area. Being a *practice* bombing range they were of timber construction. Although they lasted some ten years or more after the war, only pieces of their concrete bases now remain. No.1 quadrant, at the south east corner of the range, was within easy walking distance of *The Waggoners* and billets. No.2 quadrant, although more remote, was the more popular venue with day-time duty crews. It was reached not via the old peat tramroad trackbed but by cycling up the Fenn's Bank road and thence up the track past Fenn's Cottage where it was often possible to buy eggs and scrounge some milk or, failing this, over the hedge and across the field to

Fenn's Wood Farm. The memory of summer days on the Moss waiting for the next Whitley or Wellington to trundle into view, of the smell of freshly brewed tea, and of eggs and bacon frying on a non-Government-issue primus, still lingers in the minds of former range staff fifty years later. Great care had to be taken not to offend the Tilstock and Prees ladies manning the WRVS mobile canteen that used to call regularly at the observation posts.

No.1 quadrant housed signals, both the improvised pointer indicating the target, and the radio transmitter for communicating with and controlling incoming aircraft. The transmitter worked off Canadian "Chore Horse" batteries and the equipment would be checked out early each morning by signals people from RAF Tilstock. The parent station also provided inspecting officers. There were frequent visits by "top brass", usually a Senior Air Staff Officer or Group Captain, but on at least two occasions by Air Vice-Marshal H.K. Thorold, Air Officer Commanding 92 Group, who never ceased to be amazed at the accuracy with which quadrant crews could estimate the height of aircraft as they made their run in!

Each observation post contained a bench on which was fixed a brass ring carrying compass markings and a telescope on a swivel. As soon as the smoke or flash bomb burst observers in both towers would take bearings to get an exact fix of the fall of bomb. This was telephoned to RAF Tilstock's operational centre for onward transmission to an aircraft's base if not from 81 OTU. Approaching aircraft would give *Big Spire,* otherwise the range control officer in the command quadrant, their identity and call-sign, and would be put into circuit to gain necessary height until called in on required bearing. The only surviving Air Ministry Works Directorate drawing, dated January 1945, makes provision for a large "improvised" arrow about 80ft long with three circles at the front and sides, and gives the impression that the approach to the target was generally made from the south east over quadrant No. 1. This would give a considerable safety margin of inert mossland in case of error. A vertical air photograph (refer Plate 25) taken a year after the range's closure, shows a white arrow and a single white circle, probably the range's "open/closed" indicator disc, still in place, although scaled measurement would seem to suggest the arrow's length being more like 50ft. Both were possibly of timber, the white colouring indicating a range for "smoke" or "flash" practice bombs only. If the pointers had been of concrete, one would have expected some trace still to be found on the Moss even as the concrete base to No.1 quadrant still survives relatively intact. (The base to No.2 quadrant has only recently been smashed to fill potholes in the old peat tramroad trackbed). Initially canvas covers were fitted over the arrow when the range was "closed", but as use of the range intensified - or range crews became rather lackadaisical about such things - the pointer was left permanently exposed.

It is interesting to note that as well as housing signals, No.1 quadrant boasted a "Hill's Mirror", a now long defunct piece of meteorological equipment (technically a "mirror nephoscope") used to estimate the velocity of winds in the upper air by using natural or artificial cloud. With natural cloud two horizontal mirrors were needed, apart from the disadvantage that cloud height could be only approximately estimated; with "artificial cloud" - a smoke cloud discharged from an aircraft at specified heights - only one mirror was needed, and the height was accurately known. Quickly replaced by weather balloons, the Hill's Mirror lingered on and performed a useful service in those places where aircraft were continuously making ascents for other purposes, i.e. bombing practice[28]. The release of a stannic chloride smoke cannister cost nothing, and the resultant observations could be quickly telephoned through to Tilstock meteorological office.

● Very Secret Decoys

The air war in north-east Wales and Shropshire border country had two sides - one furtive and clandestine and one highly visible. The location of decoys on Fenn's Moss, Ruabon Mountain and Burton Marsh, Puddington, and at Llandegla, Worthenbury/Shocklach, and Llanasa, was shrouded in such secrecy and subject to a smoke-screen of disinformation so dense that, half a century later, it is virtually impossible to discover anything concrete about them. Not even the Imperial War Museum can produce a representative photograph of these deception measures! So "hush-hush" were they that decoys were rarely, if at all, photographed, even for record purposes[29].

In his history of the Second World War Churchill reveals how, for the crucial period whilst scientists struggled to overcome technical problems in countering the new German navigational beam known as the "X-System" (X-Verfahren), this country's night defences relied heavily on decoy fires, "often with remarkable results." [30] Even while counter-measures had yet to be refined, from the settings of the beams and the time at which they were deployed, RAF Intelligence could reasonably forecast target, time, route and height of attack. But as Churchill ruefully admits: "Our night fighters had, alas, at this date neither the numbers nor the equipment to make much use of this information". The war was now entering its "high technology" phase. But the realisation that, eighteen months into hostilities, ground defences were relying on something straight out of a Spanish Armada scenario, comes as something of a shock to local historians.

As attrition set in, as the tempo of Luftwaffe attacks increased, as losses of pilots and aircraft piled up, as airfields were put out of commission, as fliers neared exhaustion point, something had to be done to relieve the pressure, to dilute the enemy offensive, however marginally. Hence the use of decoys, especially at night when radar, the

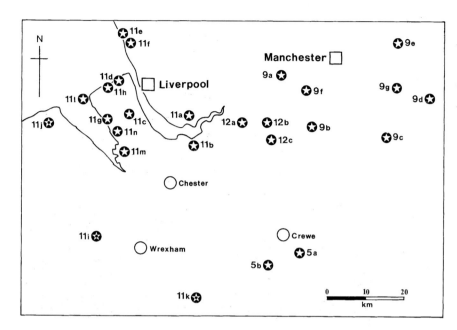

Figure 12. The distribution of "starfish" decoy sites in the north west, protecting Manchester, Merseyside and Crewe. Fenn's Moss (11k), Llandegla (11i) and Llanasa (11j) were designated as "strategic starfish". Drawing: D.Pratt, re-drawn by Timothy Morgan.

(Royal) Observer Corps and other defensive measures were least effective. To give Col. Turner as free a hand as possible, and to preserve secrecy, his "Department" was detached from the normal chain of command. Churchill, a firm believer in deception and subterfuge, personally monitored the spread of decoys throughout the land.

The early decoys were largely military, spawned of the Battle of Britain, protecting Fighter Command airfields in southern and eastern England. "Key Point" decoys evolved to cover factories, public utilities and establishments of national importance. In passing, it should be noted that the *Decoy Farm* in Marlston-cum-Lache (N.G.R. SJ 381 628) just over the Clwyd border is not called after the Vickers Armstrong and RAF Hawarden decoys set up a mile or so to the west. The farm name has a respectable pedigree going back to at least 1633![31] But following the bombing of Coventry on 14 November 1940 - the same night that RAF Hawarden was raided for the first, and only time - the decision was taken to provide decoy fires about those cities strategic to the nation's war effort. By December a total of eighteen "Starfish" protected Crewe,

Derby, Sheffield, Birmingham, Coventry and Bristol, each straddling approach routes initially favoured by enemy aircraft. The small numbers provided indicate the pressure that was being put on Col. Turner's limited resources. Following the mauling of Liverpool and Manchester over the Christmas period 1940 [32], the first decoys were provided for the industrial towns of the north west, especially those along the axis of the Manchester Ship Canal. They would be continually added to until May 1943, by which time Liverpool had 28 decoys on 14 sites, Manchester 10, and Warrington, Crewe and Northwich three each (Figure 12). Included in Liverpool's total were the "Starfish" decoys at Llanasa, Llandegla and Fenn's Moss.

Focusing on the latter, the researcher is immediately confronted with problems of chronology, with evidence for at least two, possibly three decoys on the Moss, but with little to suggest which came first or, indeed, whether they functioned together or separately. Because of the incompleteness of official records the researcher starts with the fact that some sort of decoy was in place by 15 September 1941, but from other evidence immediately has to

Plate 27. A surviving concrete plinth which, during WW2, supported a decoy. Photograph: André Q. Berry.

acknowledge that they were probably *in situ* some twelve months earlier.

The first series of "special fires" were simple affairs, possibly associated with Col. Turner's early "experimental" phase and at his suggestion installed to "upgrade" and lend much needed credence to RAF Shawbury's shambolic and short-lived decoy. Had the latter been attacked the provision of "fire damage" would have improved the deception and have given the German pilot the satisfaction of seeing splendid fires raging in the wake of his attack.

In the centre of the Fenn's Moss (N.G.R. SJ 493 368) at what used to be known as the Fenn's Wicket portable fire baskets were set up on 4in thick concrete slabs, 4ft square. Two blocks yet survive, devoid of any superstructure (Plate 27). Others existed but have been removed to facilitate peat digging or to fill potholes. These braziers were filled with scrap timber, weathered blocks of peat, old tyres, felting, brushwood and creosote, etc. scrounged from neighbouring farms and garages. The fires were ignited by electrical incendiary devices. Hopefully flames escaping into the darkness over Bronington would have been

impressive enough to convince an enemy aircrew that they had hit a fuel tank, hangar or dispersal on the makeshift airfield that was for the moment Shawbury's decoy.

Whether these particular "basket fires" continued in use after the abandonment of Shawbury's decoy in August 1940 is not known. Since they were supplementary to the "Q"-lights, probably not. However, since the more complex "Strategic Starfish" units were erected barely 100 yards away, the "baskets" may have been incorporated into that set-up.

Out of the Fenn's and Whixall Mosses Oral History Project[33] has emerged information relating to a possible second "basket-type" decoy somewhere to the rear (west) of Moss Cottages, Whixall (N.G.R. SJ 504 365). Although at first sight rather too close to habitation and enclosed crofts on the edge of the Moss, there is sufficient detail to give credence to the oral evidence.

This second set of fires comprised "*crates*" set upon a concrete base and holding a bed of peat, combustible and slow burning in itself. On this was piled, *inter alia,* metal shavings and filings. Above this, on tubular steel scaffolding was a drum of diesel or "*some other fuel*". Such is the detail absorbed and filed away by a peat cutter on temporary release from the Army [34]. He had served with the King's Shropshire Light Infantry and the 2nd Battalion, Herefordshire Regiment at Camberley, Horsham, Cromer and Bognor Regis during the Battle of Britain and the initial invasion threat. In other words a military head on rustic shoulders, quite capable of appreciating the strategic significance of these contraptions on the Moss.

Local tradition links this second set of fires with "*Marchwiel ammunition factory*", otherwise the Royal Ordnance Factory east of Wrexham in Isycoed parish, which came on stream early in December 1940 [35]. "Basket fires" would burn for about an hour and their ignition would be staggered to cater for successive waves of enemy aircraft whose presence over target could last for anything up to four or five hours. The adding of metal filings to the combustibles would affect the colour of the flames according to the deception intended. Thus iron shavings would burn with a bluish tinge, simulating poorly blacked out foundries or furnaces. The raised fuel tanks on scaffolding might also suggest the presence of troughing for water flushes, which when mixed with the burning oil would cause explosive bursts of flames, simulating the dropping of an oil-filled *Flammenbombe,* at 250kg and 500kg the largest German incendiary bombs.

In March 1942 both of the above mentioned decoys would be superseded by the establishment of a "Strategic Starfish" on the Moss (N.G.R. SJ 494 368), not far from the original "basket fires" and just beyond the southern boundary of the bombing range. It is the only decoy site for which some documentary and cartographic evidence exists to support testimony on the ground. Apart from a couple of marginal drainage ditches dug in connection with commercial peat cutting, this particular corner of Top section has for some hitherto unexplained reason not been commercially

cut for peat and vegetation-wise stands out as a distinctive patch of purple moor grass only slowly being colonised by heather and bracken. Making allowances for the natural accretions of 50 years it is still possible to discern a raised access "path" opening out onto a "square" where presumably materials were assembled for the maintenance and restocking of the decoys (Plate 68, p.150).

A vertical aerial photograph taken in 1946 [36] still shows, radiating out from the "square", the bases or remnants of at least eleven multi-unit combustion sites. These have been plotted in Figure 13. Their disposition clearly suggests streets of terraced housing

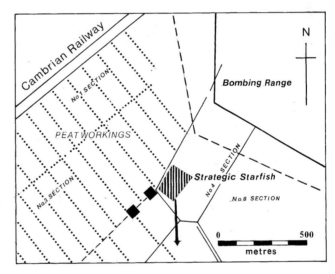

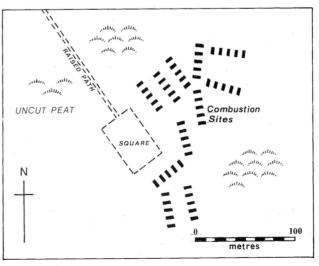

Figures 13a and b. The "strategic starfish" site on Fenn's Moss, 1942, which superseded earlier basket fire decoys. Enlargement shows layout of combustion sites. Drawing: D.Pratt, re-drawn by Timothy Morgan.

Plate 28. The surviving hut which, during WW2, housed the batteries to enable ignition of the "strategic starfish" site on Fenn's Moss. Photograph: André Q. Berry.

"general duties" men had special training in simple camouflage techniques and the use of decoys at Col. Turner's secret school at Hook, near Goole. Sergeant Vaughan reported directly to the decoy "area" Flight Lieutenant at Tern Hill Sector HQ, but for routine administration, supplies and inspections, etc. the unit's parent station was RAF Tilstock. In practice theirs was a monotonous but essential task, with daylight hours spent in checking generators, wiring, detonators, igniters, etc. and then at night sitting back waiting for something to happen.

The "Strategic Starfish" was controlled from the duty crew-room, otherwise a half-Nissen hut not exactly shrapnel proof, 1,000yds away beyond the last habitation in Moss Lane, on the Whixall/Shropshire side of the border (N.G.R. SJ 499 364). Its concrete base, used occasionally for the stacking of peat, is still visible, but its walls, some six courses high, and roof have been knocked down for infill and fencing. However, the battery storage hut (it looks more like a forlorn latrine!) still stands, albeit minus its door and corrugated asbestos roof (Plate 28).

From this command "bunker" electric wires ran out to the Starfish. Fires would be detonated to order by dialling the appropriate number and pressing a switch. Each evening a priority call was put through to the Air Ministry giving details of cloud amount and height, wind speed, visibility, and other information that might have had a bearing on the effectiveness, or otherwise, of a decoy fire. Someone would then await the instruction via Tern Hill (later Atcham) Sector Control (9 Group, Fighter Command), to light up selected fires. Before a land line was run to the command bunker this posed something of a problem, with a corporal having to ride into Whixall (Welsh End) to use the phone at *The Waggoners*. This was also used by the bombing range "HQ staff" and some conflict of interests arose. Time was of the essence and the messenger had about two minutes to get back to the control room with the order to

in a city suburb rather than some industrial complex. Nothing is shown on later photographs taken between 1983 and 1994. Each base carried two-tier shelving some 4ft wide, and over 6ft long, carrying a double row of sacks stuffed with saw-dust and wood shavings soaked in creosote. Each was screened from prying eyes by a light framework of scaffolding and sackcloth that blended well with the purples and browns of the Moss. Strangely, recalling the tight security that prevailed elsewhere, construction was largely undertaken by peat cutters from the Moss. Possibly this was because they were more familiar with the peaty terrain and the working of the peat railway used to get materials to the decoy site. They were, however, denied the use of the MR&T locomotive and trucks had to be manhandled along the track[37]. The whole lay-out was arranged and wired so that units could be fired individually or together or holding some in reserve so that the decoy could be fired on successive nights should the need arise.

The original "basket fire" sites required only two trained men to throw switches to create instant "fire damage". The more elaborate "Strategic Starfish" was operated by a squad of nine under a sergeant, the latter billeted in Fenn's Bank. All these

light up. Matters were eased somewhat when the RAF commandeered Manor House telephone and set up a continuously manned "signals centre" in the sitting room. Mr. Herbert Beckett, a successful market gardener, was allowed just two minutes to make private or business calls.

Strangely, for something some 41 miles as the *Heinkel* flies from the port, the Fenn's Moss "Starfish" was a Liverpool decoy (No.11k), deliberately placed so that enemy aircraft had to fly over it on their way to attack the port. Fires were lit only when bombs fell on or about the target, theoretically at the same time as the first of the real fires were tackled and extinguished. By reproducing the effect of a target being bombed it was hoped that follow-up waves would see the "Starfish" before the real target and be encouraged to waste bombs on the Moss.

However, such conditions were rarely met with in practice. Liverpool's hard-pressed fire fighters never won the race to extinguish early pathfinder fires. Indeed, when Liverpool burnt, as in the May 1941 *Blitz*, incoming bombers at high altitude could see the red glow that was a burning city from as far off as London. Under such conditions even the most sophisticated decoy would be useless.

What intrigues the researcher, however, is the differentiation of the Fenn's "Starfish" site as "strategic", one of only three of the twenty-eight "Starfishes" that protected Crewe, Northwich, Manchester and Liverpool, to carry that soubriquet. The other two were also in Clwyd, on Llandegla Moor, Denbighshire, and at Llanasa, Flintshire. The three are near enough in a straight line and may have something to do with the ability of British scientists to "bend" the German navigational beams. Thus, as a raider would be expecting to pick up flares or fires illuminating, say, Crewe, Bromborough and Birkenhead, its crew would see fires at the three "Strategic Starfish", two along the Dee estuary which was often confused with that of the Mersey.

Unfortunately, with pertinent documents in the PRO missing, one may never know the exact contribution made by this remote corner of Fenn's Moss to eventual victory in the night skies over north-east Wales and north-west England.

It should be remembered that in the early part of 1941, when decoys were reaching their maximum extent, night attacks on Britain were expected to continue at an infinite crescendo - one has only to recall the 7-day *Blitz* on Merseyside in May 1941 that almost brought the port to a standstill and how, thankfully but inexplicably, the merciless pounding ceased on the eighth night. Only after Hitler invaded Russia on 22 June 1941 would air raids gradually die away and stop. But this is with hindsight.

Until the penny dropped, scientists continued to strive to improve the measures and devices by which the nation had hitherto survived, and to develop new ones, notably radar in all its applications. Labour, material and manpower continued to be made available for decoys, spurred on by costly raids on ports and cities. But even as the network of decoys reached saturation point, the threat from the sky they were designed to meet suddenly came to an end. Yet such would be the uncertainty that for another 18 months, as the incidence of air raids over the north west and North Wales dwindled (the last bombs fell in Flintshire on 11 January and the last "All Clear" sounded over Merseyside on 9 August 1942) the Fenn's Moss "Starfish" continued to be manned. It was finally abandoned on 30 September 1943, but that on Llandegla Moors not until 30 December.

Inevitably there will be those who will underrate the military value of these decoys. Their true worth could only have been proved by major trial. Sergeant Vaughan and his men in their control "bunker" down the Moss Lane were ready and willing. Fifty years later, perhaps, one can only be thankful that events did not come to this pass.

Even before the "Starfish" fires were dismantled their part of the Moss was put to other uses by the RAF as an *ad hoc* specialist gunnery range. About 700 yards down the peat "road" or railway trackbed towards Oaf's Orchard (N.G.R. SJ 486 363) Sgt. Vaughan's squad erected a static mock-up of a railway train. The full-scale model was made up of galvanised sheeting attached to a tubular frame and painted on both sides to simulate a locomotive and carriages. It could therefore be approached from any direction.

This target provoked and disturbed local inhabitants, especially smallholders with livestock, more than any other military installation on the Moss: "*.... these blasted fighter planes, they'd drive you mad coming over with them practising shooting trains and railway engines up in France, see ...*" [38] A typical comment (minus expletives) - and this despite camera or cine-guns being used. When developed the film would reveal accuracy, opening and closing ranges, length of burst, etc. Such details would be compared with the pilot's oral or written version of his "shoot", which often entered the realms of near fiction! Day in, day out, weather permitting, as the build-up to D-Day gathered momentum, planes came screaming in, hedge-hopping across the Moss, usually from the direction of Morris' Bridge (N.G.R. SJ 494 354). Major culprits were the Allison-engined North American Mustangs of 41 OTU and 3 Tactical Exercise Unit from RAF Poulton as they trained up for their cross-Channel sweeps and armed tactical reconnaissance and ground support roles. These were essential preliminaries before moving on to Andover for a week's "live" practice on Salisbury Plain.

Had any incensed Whixall smallholder been in the habit of taking the numbers of offending aircraft he would surely have noticed, between March 1944 and February 1945, a constantly recurring BR372. The latter had come off the assembly line in April 1942 as a standard version of a Mark IV photographic reconnaissance Spitfire, but was immediately hi-jacked by the Controller of Research and Development (CRD) as an experimental aircraft. The RAF had been clamouring for some form of air brake to assist Spitfires decelerate and not overshoot during combat. After being fitted with double trailing-edge braking flaps, one section moving up, the other down, by Heston Aircraft, BR372 underwent trials at the Royal Aircraft Establishment (RAE), Farnborough. In July 1943 it was returned to Heston Aircraft for the installation of upper-surface dive brakes and for other drag reduction modifications. In October BR372 was returned to the RAE for further, successful, trials. Dive brakes were always used with flaps and although deceleration could peak at 5G at 400mph, pilots reported targets could be kept in gun-sight during combat manoeuvres. From March 1944, BR372 underwent service trials under the auspices of the Air Defence Development Unit, Boscombe Down, but until February 1945 field trials were actually held at 61 OTU, Rednal, on both Baggy Moor and Fenn's Moss ranges, the latter particularly after BR372 had been converted into an *ad hoc* fighter-bomber with the fitting of fuselage bomb racks. The Spitfire's dive bombing trials, squeezed in between the practice bombing runs of the never-ending stream of learner aircraft from the bomber OTUs proved the success of the specially-strengthened flaps in steepening dives onto ground targets. BR372 was flown up to Eshott, Northumberland, on 8 February 1945 for further trials with 57 OTU. It is doubtful if its presence was missed in the general cacophony that daily surrounded the Fenn's Moss range.

Between April-July 1945 the final users were the Spitfires Vs and IXs of 58 OTU, the last training unit at Hawarden and Poulton, producing fighter-bomber pilots for *Rhubarbs, Rodeos* and *Circuses* [39]. Whilst finding and shooting-up the Fenn's "train" was an integral part of intensive, low-level navigational exercises, it should be remembered that during their course pilots had also to drop at least sixteen practice bombs on the adjacent Fenn's bombing range so that the two exercises may have been linked. Surprisingly, despite adding to the congestion of the middle Dee low-flying area, there were no accidents whilst using this particular range.

On grounds of accuracy, perhaps, this might be re-phrased to read "... no accidents *on* this particular range...", for after September 1943 there is a subtle, yet discernible, shift in emphasis in 41 and 58 OTUs' aircraft crashes to the Whitchurch-Malpas area. The most spectacular was the fate of Spitfire IX NH437 of 58 OTU, which on Wednesday, 30 May 1945 had just shot up the "train" on Fenn's Moss. At full throttle and still at tree height the Polish pilot, Sgt. W. Polowancywk, adrenalin flowing, decided to beat up a moving target, namely a 3-tonner travelling from No.5 MT (Motor Transport) Squadron, Liverpool, to RAF Tilstock along the A41 at Edge Green, north of Malpas. He completely misjudged his attack and hit the lorry. NH437 carried on across the road, tore through a couple of hedges and ploughed up a field before coming to rest, a tangled wreck. Miraculously, Polowancywk was not killed, although critically injured. Unfortunately, two airmen in the rear of the lorry who had stood up to get a better view of the assault, were killed instantly. One of them, F/Sgt. J.A. Broadstock, lies buried in the Commonwealth War Graves Cemetery at Blacon, Chester.

The end of hostilities in Europe immediately reduced the demand for fighter pilots. 58 OTU closed down on 20 July 1945 with the passing out of No.6 Course. An unaccustomed silence descended upon Fenn's Moss, broken only by the occasional drone of high flying bombers and the crump of practice bombs on the North East Fenn's. Even this ceased on 10 August 1945. On the Moss aquatic beetles, dragonflies, large heath butterflies, raft spiders, bushcrickets and caddisflies regrouped!

Peat as Product

The potential of peat as a product for large-scale commercial utilisation was not recognised on Fenn's and Whixall Mosses until 1851, when "*a company of gentlemen*", one "*Vardy and Co.*", took a lease "*for a term of years of a considerable tract of the moss*". The reference records Vardy about to "*erect works for converting this hitherto comparatively useless commodity into articles of appliance for useful purposes. It is said to be superior to the Irish moss for some particular uses*". The "tract of moss" extended to some three hundred and eight acres on North East Fenn's Moss, abutting the English/Welsh border and in the ownership of the Hanmer Estate (Figure 14). Reference to the "company of gentlemen" reflects the nature of the early, experimental involvement of speculative companies in the development of peat as a commodity, a theme that was to continue up to and including the *Bettisfield Trust Company* in the early years of the 1920s (see Appendix One, p.173 for a tabulated summary of the key commercial and military activities on the Mosses).

On 5th May 1856 this area, together with an additional three hundred acres, was leased to Joseph Bebb of Argyle Street, St. James, Westminster by Sir John Hanmer for a term of twenty-one years [2]. The lease, in addition to the 608a.1r.28p. of Fenn's Moss, included 5a.27r.2p. of land then or lately belonging to one John Roberts. The plan accompanying this lease (refer Figure 14), clearly shows processing works (the "Old Moss Works" [3]) and the importance of John Roberts' land in enabling a tramroad link to the canal. That the works and tramroad are show on this plan suggests that they may be the works "about to be erected" by Vardy in 1851. The line of the tramroad may still be traced behind the modern sheds of English Nature's Manor House Nature Reserve base as a linear, hollow feature. At the point where it meets the canal [4], the towpath is seen to be raised and broadened into a simple wharf, the canal bank being faced

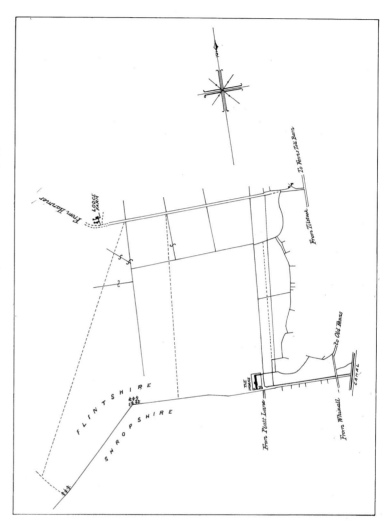

with dressed, sandstone masonry, now much overgrown.

The terms of the lease clearly express the Hanmer Estate's desire to develop the potential of the peat and to maximise returns from it. Clauses allow for reversion of the land to the Estate on failure to win peat for a consecutive period of six calendar months and of the right of the Estate to all buildings upon termination of the lease. The document also provides a valuable early insight into the form of the processed peat and its intended use.

Figure 14. Plan taken from the lease of 1856 [2], showing "The Old Moss Works" and the 308a. of North East Fenn's Moss leased to *Vardy and Co.*, together with the additional 300a. leased to Joseph Bebb and subsequently Richard Henry Holland and *The Moulded Peat Charcoal Company*. Note the tramroad link to the canal. Drawing: Timothy Morgan.

Royalty or tonnage rents were to be paid at rates of 6d. per ton for every ton of compressed or artificially consolidated peat, 3d. per ton for every ton of atmospherically dried peat and 4d. farthing per ton for every ton of peat converted to charcoal. Compressed and artificially consolidated peat is defined as intended for metallic or manufacturing purposes, with air dried peat for manure, fuel, charcoal making or distillation.

The weight of all peat was to be calculated in its natural state when dry and rents were to become due when the processed peat was sold or removed from the premises. In addition, a ground rent of 5s. per acre was payable, together with £8.14s. per year for land assigned for plant, works, buildings and tramroads. Rents were payable on the first of January and July each year and were to be substantiated by books of accounts lodged in an office at the works, and by a statement provided with each half-yearly rental payment.

Sadly, from the researcher's point of view, none of these records apparently survive and it is therefore not possible to give any accurate indication of the levels of production at this time. However, the lease states: "*that the total rents payable under this lease shall not in any one year exceed the sum of one thousand pounds and that Peat shall not be gotten which would cause the rents to be more than that sum in any one year*". This would allow for a maximum annual production of 67,024 imperial tons of atmospherically dried peat, or half that quantity of consolidated peat. Evidence discussed below, from later companies engaged in more intensive utilisation of the peat, suggest that this figure would have been substantially higher than the levels of production achieved.

Joseph Bebb was also required, before the 1st January 1858, to cause to be made, around the outside of the area of moss or turbary defined in the lease, a boundary ditch or drain at least two feet deep and one foot wide or one foot deep and two feet wide which he was required to keep open during the term of his lease. In addition, he was to make all other necessary drains and watercourses and to construct them in a manner so as not to damage the drainage of the remainder of the Moss.

On 12th September 1859[5], agreement was made between Sir John Hanmer and Joseph Bebb enabling the underletting of the lease to Richard Henry Holland, the Conservative Club, St. James Street, London for the residue of the term of twenty-one years less seven days. Within twelve months, on 3rd August 1860[6], this was further underlet by Richard Henry Holland to *The Moulded Peat Charcoal Company Limited*, of which Holland is recorded as being "*Resident Director*".

The Moulded Peat Charcoal Company Limited was incorporated on 25th May 1860[8] and stated as its aims the acquisition of peatlands "*to convert the peat into Charcoal or any other available commodity and to sell and dispose of the produce of the peat in its natural state for gain.....*" The Company purchased from Richard Henry Holland letters patent which he had acquired from Christopher Kingsford for "*improvements in the preparation of peat and charcoal for fuel, in the manufacture of coke there from, and in the machinery and apparatus employed for effecting the same*"[9].

Under this patent peat was to be mixed, whilst wet, with finely ground common pitch or a similar substance before being milled or "*pugged*" to produce a paste. The paste was then moulded and dried to produce a briquette suitable for fuel or for conversion into charcoal or coke. The patent also incorporated proposals for the manufacture of such briquettes from light peat charcoal dust, which was to be mixed with pitch, resin or other similar substance and heated before moulding. These processes were said to make a more homogeneous, solid and compact briquette superior in quality as a fuel; and, because of the pitch, when coked, a very hard and blast-resisting charcoal ideal for metallurgical purposes.

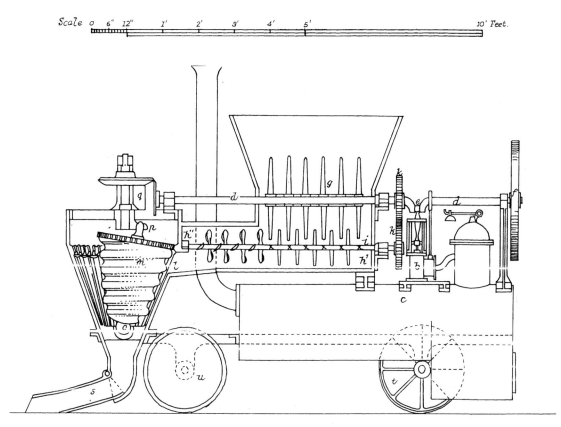

Scale 0 6" 12" 1' 2' 3' 4' 5' 10' Feet.

Retorts were specified for the production of peat charcoal and the patent also included designs for the improved machinery necessary to produce the required homogeneous milled paste, including a machine mounted on a carriage and worked by a portable steam engine, which combined the processes of mixing, kneading and moulding in one (Figure 15). The machine could run over the peat surface on a pair of wheels, with a roller to level the ground or, fitted with four flanged wheels, could run on trams or rails. In the latter case it was recommended that the rails be laid as an endless circuit, with wooden or wicker trays laid between the rails to collect the moulded peat as it was discharged. These loaded trays could then be removed to the drying house, to be replaced by others before the return of the "locomotive pugging and moulding machine".

There is apparently no surviving documentary material to enable evaluation of the nature of peat cutting operations or the levels of production of *The Moulded Peat Charcoal Company Limited*, or to substantiate whether any of the processes described in the patent were employed at Fenn's Moss.

Sir John Hanmer, in evidence to the Parliamentary committee on 17th April 1861 regarding the proposed Oswestry, Ellesmere and Whitchurch Railway, notes that he had had "*offers made for [the] Moss from a party who would make it like a Dutch meadow*"[10], whilst the process of moulding peat was evidently being used on the Moss as early as 1810:

"*In Fens Moss, in Flintshire, peat is so soft as to require being cast in molds. When it*

**Figure 15. "*The locomotive pugging and moulding machine*" shown in Christopher Kingsford's patent No.1671 of July 15th 1859[9] held by *The Moulded Peat Charcoal Company*.
Drawing: Timothy Morgan.**

hardens, it is highly inflammable; and is sold by the hundred in number to the townspeople of Whitchurch and Wem"[11]

This "softness" of the peat reflects the near-natural state of the mire at this time.

Whatever the impact of *The Moulded Peat Charcoal Company Limited* upon Fenn's Moss, the life of the company was short. On 12th December 1864 it announced that it had ceased trading and was in the process of winding up, although it was not formally dissolved until 7th March 1882[8].

George Wardle of Fenn's Hall commenced a peat moss litter business in 1884[12]. By 1886, and in partnership with William Henry Smith, ironfounder, of Whitchurch *The English Peat Moss Litter Company* was established, taking on a lease of North East Fenn's Moss from the Hanmer Estate. The Company was incorporated on 12th May 1888[12].

In 1889 Smith and Wardle purchased the Lordship of the Manor of Whixall from William Orme Foster[12], land which included the centre of Whixall Moss, now part of the Nature Reserve. With the Lordship of the Manor of Whixall came the obligation to maintain the network of drains established under the 1823 Inclosure for general drainage of Whixall Moss. The Inclosure gave the Lord of the Manor the right to levy a rate upon those holding allotments on the Moss for recovery of the costs of such maintenance. This was to be the cause of numerous disputes for Smith and Wardle as Lords of the Manor[13].

Many of the records of *The English Peat Moss Litter Company* survive, prior to its incorporation as a limited company[12]. From September 1886 through to November 1887 weekly records of expenditure record each workman, together with how he spent his time in each week and the relevant piece rate applicable to each activity.

At this time the method of peat cutting was the traditional indigenous method known as **Whixall Bible** cutting (see Fact Panel

Two, *Whixall Bibles*, p.105). The remains of Whixall Bible cuttings can still be picked out on the ground today, as rectangular "hollows" in the peat. This pattern is very obvious in the south of Whixall Moss, in the east of North East Fenn's Moss and on Fenn's Moss north of the disused railway line. These cuttings are often made into a previously "flayed"-cut surface, no doubt the result of the activities of the earlier peat companies on the Moss. Commercial cutting by *The English Peat Moss Litter Company Ltd* was restricted to Fenn's Moss, lands acquired by Smith and Wardle with the Lordship of the Manor of Whixall on Whixall Moss being rented out as **turf banks** on an "acre" by "acre" basis to local people, where again the peat was cut as Whixall Bibles.

1886 records of the *English Peat Moss Litter Company* document the amounts of peat cut by individuals. For example, in the week ending November 20th 1886 Edge, Green and Egerton cut ten roods, and Chidlow nine roods; a total of sixty-five roods was cut in the week at a piece rate of 2s.6d. per rood[12]. In the same week, at least sixteen men were employed, with work undertaken ranging from peat cutting, to grinding, stacking and carting out moss litter.

Records show that the firm was using a system of **tramroads** to transport cut peat from the Moss, with the wagons (or **trams**) pulled by horses - narrow gauge industrial locomotives not appearing on the Moss until October 1919 (refer Fact Panel Four, *The Peat Railway* p.108)[12, 14]. In the week beginning December 24th 1886, Challinor was paid for a quarter of a day's work during which he was "*carting into shed with tram*" and in the same week Bristow was paid for one day's work "*covering the stable with fern*"[12]. There is a local memory that George Wardle brought **irongrass** (purple moor-grass) to the Moss, which he sowed between the rails in order to consolidate the ground and increase traction for the horses pulling the trams of peat[15]. Irongrass is, in fact, an indigenous species of the Moss, but its growth could well have been encouraged along the tracks. Company records certainly mention "*sanding tram roads*"[12] which may have served a similar purpose in making the ground firmer for the horses.

The processing site for the *English Peat Moss Litter Company* was on Fenn's Moss in an area known today as "The Old Shed Yard" (N.G.R. SJ 5037 3682). The 1914 edition 25in. Ordnance Survey map provides the only evidence for the plan of these works (Figure 16 a, b and c). On the ground the area is now rapidly becoming overgrown, although it was used extensively by the later company, *L.S. Beckett*, for storing dried peat, and a large concrete machine base survived until a few years ago[16].

A note for the week ending August 6th 1887 records that one Beckett spent a quarter of a day "*opening watercourse to engine*"[12] Presumably this steam engine powered the grinding and baling machinery. Amongst the Wardle papers is an inventory of works machinery at Carrington Moss, dated December 21st 1891[12], a site owned by *The English Peat Moss Litter Company* which was "*sold to the Corporation for the sum of £2762*" in January 1892. The works comprised a storage shed, a workshop containing the grinding mill and engine, and a stable. Machinery included a portable engine on four travelling wheels, an improved peat breaking mill and specially-designed elevator to deliver the peat to the press box. The site also had twelve custom-made tram wagons carried on flanged iron wheels. It is perhaps reasonable to assume that the works at Whixall were similarly equipped.

Peat was cut and dried on Fenn's Moss by the Company, brought to the works by tram where it was ground and transported out as moss litter. Throughout the fifteen month period for which there are weekly records one man was employed delivering the finished product for the whole six day week. Other carts and horses were hired as and when needed. These generally seem to

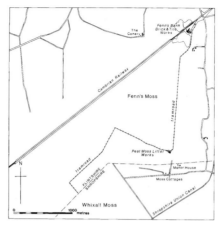

Figure 16a. *The English Peat Moss Litter Company Ltd* peat processing works in "The Old Shed Yard", showing tramroad links across Fenn's Moss to Oaf's Orchard and along the "Long Mile" to Fenn's Bank Brick and Tile Works. Based on the 1914 edition O.S. 25in. plan, Flintshire XXVI, sheets 7, 10 and 11, surveyed for Flintshire in 1872, revised in 1909.
Drawing: Timothy Morgan.

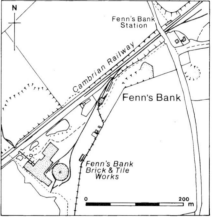

Figure 16b. Detail of *The English Peat Moss Litter Company Ltd* exchange siding with the Oswestry, Ellesmere and Whitchurch railway at Fenn's Bank Brick and Tile Works. Based on the 1914 edition O.S. 25in. plan.
Drawing: Timothy Morgan.

Figure 16c. Detail of *The English Peat Moss Litter Company Ltd* peat processing works at "The Old Shed Yard". Based on the 1914 edition O.S. 25in. plan.
Drawing: Timothy Morgan.

be for turf carting, a reference perhaps to peat blocks intended for burning as fuel. From the works peat was also taken by tramroad up the Long Mile to the Fenn's Bank Brick and Tile Works where the Company had a covered exchange siding with the Oswestry, Ellesmere and Whitchurch railway (N.G.R. SJ 5079 3893).

In 1889 *The English Peat Moss Litter Company Ltd* commenced building houses for its workers at Moss Cottages (N.G.R. SJ 5038 3641) and by 1898 seventeen such houses had been constructed[12]. The houses were built by Henry Williams of Whixall using bricks and tiles from the Fenn's Bank Brick and Tile Company[12], now the site of *H.H. Wardle Ltd*, manufacturers of Aluminium ingots (N.G.R. SJ 5064 3884).

The subsequent development of *The English Peat Moss Litter Company Ltd* is uncertain. At some stage George Wardle bought out William Smith's interest in the company. The *Whitchurch Herald*[17] reports a strike which affected the Company in 1914. No mention is made of William Smith and it may be that by 1914 his interest had been bought out. At this time the Company employed about fifty people of whom over half went on strike, and the local paper bemoaned the fact that the industrial unrest that was widespread across the country should have reached the rural areas around Whitchurch: "*The industrial troubles and labour unrest which have so far convulsed this country during the past few years, are at last, it seems, making themselves felt in our own unusually quiet and peaceful neighbourhood. There has been a great deal of talk lately about an effort being made, by the various classes of labourers and artisans in the district to gain better conditions - whether rightly or wrongly it is not for us to say - and there was a strike of bricklayers in the early part of last year, but that was brought to a peaceful termination, and there has been no further move until the news was received some weeks ago, that a portion of the Peat Moss Litter workers had 'downed tools'. The men are employees of the English Peat Moss Litter*

Company, formed some time ago for the purpose of manufacturing a horse litter from the peat and the company have about fifty employees. At first there were some dozen or so strikers, but the number gradually increased until about twenty were left at work, and the line taken by the strikers has necessitated the drafting of a special police force into the district to protect the property of the company, and to enable those who wish to follow their employment to do so, without hindrance from those who are differently minded"

"*It appears that some four or five weeks ago it came to the knowledge of the directors that the workmen who had recently joined the Workers' Union contemplated a strike during the summer - the most important part of the year from the company's point of view - and in consequence the chairman, Mr. G. Wardle of Fenns Hall, asked each of the men whether they were prepared to sign the following agreement: 'We, the undersigned, are quite willing to agree to continue turf cutting; also to carry out the harvesting of the turf on the terms we agreed upon when we commenced cutting (as last year)'. The terms are: For cutting 2s. 1d. per rood; rearing 4d. per rood; and stacking 1s. per rood. The men worked in sets of two, and six of the nineteen sets employed on the Moss refused to sign. Mr. Wardle consequently gave notice that no more turf was to be cut, on the ground that it would be ridiculous to cut turf if there was no likelihood of its being harvested within a reasonable time. The men who refused to sign the agreement accordingly left work, and were joined by three of the pickers. On April 3rd the strikers had a meeting with the non-strikers and, it is stated, threatened them when on their way to work. Subsequently, some twenty of the non-workers made their way to the works where the dried turves are crushed and pressed into bales by machinery, and, it is further alleged, stopped the engine and pulled up a portion of the tramline, heedless of the warning addressed to them by Mr. Wardle. Afterwards they proceeded to the bog, and there threatened the men at work and at the same time depriving them of their tools. To avoid further trouble, Mr. Wardle ordered the* temporary closing of the works. He re-opened them on April 6th, but only a couple of men turned up, being joined later by two or three others. The strikers numbers had increased by this time, and they again made their appearance, and in consequence of their conduct towards those at work Mr. Wardle was obliged to close down a second time. Work was resumed on April 14th, 21 men being allowed to follow their avocation until the following Saturday, on which day each Union man received strike pay at the rate of 5s. per week. On the Monday only 18 men turned up at work. In consequence of the threatening attitude of the strikers, it was found necessary to summon the police, and some twenty constables were drafted into the district during the day. During the night several more lengths of tramline were pulled up, and the following day the strikers marched in procession to the works, but becoming quarrelsome, it became necessary to eject them. On Tuesday week the ranks of the strikers were augmented, and by Thursday the number of men at work had been reduced to 17, and they were escorted to and from their work by the police. This week work on the bog is at a standstill, the directorate having found it necessary to close down the works until a mutual settlement is agreed upon. A couple of peat stacks were found to be on fire on Tuesday night, the outbreak, it is thought, being due to incendiarism, while one day last week one of the men who refused to cease work was stripped and splashed with tar".

"On Saturday the strikers marched to Whitchurch, and after parading the town held a meeting in Jubilee Park about nine o' clock, addresses being given by Mr. H.H. Laurie (district organiser of the Workers' Union), and Councillor J. Beard of Birmingham. The speakers explained the men's case to a fairly large, although not altogether sympathetic audience, and expressed the determination of the strikers to remain out until their terms are agreed to. They, it was stated, had not sought the fight, but it was now their intention to see that they had better conditions before they return. It was pointed out the men having only belonged to the Workers' Union about six weeks were not entitled to benefit, but that

the Union, in view of the special circumstances, had agreed to give the men 5s. each per week. A collection was taken on behalf of the strikers".

"There were considerable interruptions during the speeches and on several occasions there looked like being trouble, but the proceedings passed off without any disturbance".

The following week (9th May 1914) the newspaper was able to report: "that in the case of the Peat Moss Litter works trouble.....a settlement.....has materialised" [18], although, sadly, the terms of this settlement are not given.

Documentary material and surviving earthwork evidence described in the previous chapter (*The Military Takes Over*), suggest that *The English Peat Moss Litter Company Ltd* had, at least temporarily, relinquished its lease of North East Fenn's Moss by September 1915 when four new rifle ranges were constructed, although exploitation of the peat was certainly continued by the military authorities as discussed below. By the early 1920s Harold Wardle had established an aluminium business in Coventry taking with him several of the peat workers, including Wal Allmark who appears on an early photograph driving the first industrial locomotive to be used on the Moss (Plate 29). The Wardle family remain Lords of the Manor of Whixall,

Plate 29. MR&T locomotive No.1934 on the "Long Mile" c.1920, pulling trams loaded with baled peat litter. Reproduced with the kind permission of the Allmark family.

although their interest in the Manor House (now English Nature's Nature Reserve base) was sold in 1933 to Herbert Beckett for a market garden[19], and their holdings on Whixall Moss to Tom Allmark of the firm *L.S. Beckett* in c.1950 (discussed below). The aluminium business moved from Coventry to the site of Fenn's Bank Brick and Tile Works in 1941 *"because of what Adolf Hitler was doing to Coventry"*[19] and there is evidence in the form of letters and reports from the Department of Scientific and Industrial Research (Fuel Research Board) in 1941 which indicate that further exploitation of the peat was considered, although nothing ever came of this[12].

During WW1 peat was an extremely valuable commodity being used as bedding litter for the many horses of the cavalry and as a smokeless fuel in the trenches[20]. *Sphagnum* moss, because of its acidity and Iodine content, was also important as a sterile wound dressing. During the war years the qualities of peat were also promoted for use in deep litter housed poultry systems[21]. Although large parts of Fenn's and Whixall Mosses were commandeered by the War Department for emergency rifle ranges, evidence shows that the military authorities continued the cutting of peat, principally to supply the cavalry remount station at Bettisfield Park with bedding litter, where the condition in which the horses had first been kept had been a major cause for concern to the local people[22]. Peat cut on Fenn's Moss was apparently confined to military use, although some peat was evidently still being cut by local people for their own use on southern Whixall Moss: a letter to the editor of the local paper in 1918 asks: *"can anyone inform me where peat can be obtained? There is a large area of peat not far from Whitchurch, but I am informed that owing to the action of the military authority none has been cut for some time"*[23]. In similar vein another correspondent asks whether, in view of the coal shortage: *"we should consider it worth the while of the local authorities to approach the military authorities with a view to getting*

as much cutting and drying done as possible"[29]. Whilst an earlier article of July 1918 reports a fire which swept across the Moss and refers to: *"the peat in 'mows' and drying on the ground has been completely destroyed, occasioning an irreplaceable loss to the owners"*[24].

The War Department employed the expertise of local people. Isabella Sewell is recorded as working: *"for the Government on the Moss"*[25], and Tom Allmark, formerly works foreman for *The English Peat Moss Litter Company Ltd*, gained the military rank of Captain despite never leaving the Moss - a rank given in recognition of works carried out at the Moss works producing peat throughout the war[26].

An advertisement in *The Contract Journal* of 25th June 1919[27] for an auction sale by direction of the Surplus Government Property Disposal Board provide an insight into the nature of the peat processing works established by the War Department on the Bettisfield side of Fenn's Moss during WW1. Amongst *"the valuable machinery and equipment of the works"* is recorded a *"'giant' steam engine by Sir John Fowler Ltd; 'Bijoli' baling press with elevator, by Shirtliff Bros; peat grinding mill with elevator &c, by Nicholson; shafting, belting, &c, 2,874 yards of Decauville railway track, 103 various railway trucks, baling laths, wire, 68 tons of coal, electric light installation, &c."* On the ground there is evidence still visible of this peat processing works to the west of the surviving works of the later *Midland Moss Litter Company*. Concrete bases and metal engine fixings remain in this area referred to by many locally as "The Old Graveyard" (N.G.R. SJ 4776 3660)[15]. Local people remember the steam engine which was taken out across the fields and thence to a sawmills in Oswestry where it was still working until the 1960s[28].

A surviving plan[29] suggests that the War Department processing works was acquired by *The Bettisfield Trust Company*, a speculative company which was

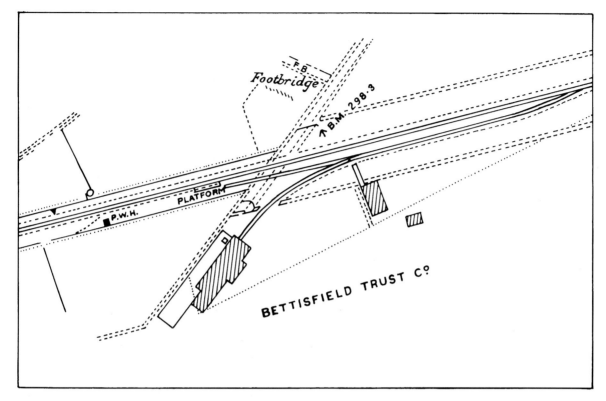

incorporated on 12th May 1921[30] (Figure 17). According to the Memorandum of Association, the objects for which the company was set up were varied, ranging from: "*to establish and finance companies and associations*", "*to negotiate loans of every description*", "*to transact business as capitalists, promoters and financial monetary agents both in England and elsewhere*", "*to purchase, lease or otherwise acquire brickfields, beds of clay, terra cotta, earth, peat, bogs.....*" and to "*purchase sell as merchants, agents, or on commission or otherwise, bricks, tiles, pottery, brick, or other earths, peat and peat charcoal.....*"[30]

In 1923 a lease was drawn up between the Hanmer Estate and *The Bettisfield Trust Company Ltd* for 948a. of Fenn's Moss to be used for the exploitation of **black peat**[12], that is, the basal or fen peat which was suited to distillation for the extraction of paraffinoid and other chemical products.

The 1923 lease also makes first reference to *The Midland Moss Litter Company* whose

interest lay in the upper layers of the peat, the **white**- and **grey peat**, which was used for packing, in the manufacture of molasses-based cattle feed and for livestock bedding. *The Midland Moss Litter Company's* interest evidently extended across the same 948a., as the lease requires *The Bettisfield Trust Company Ltd* to provide Midland Moss with plans showing the areas to be worked for black peat[12].

Interestingly, one of the directors of *The Bettisfield Trust Company Ltd* is W.H. Smith, partner of George Wardle when *The English Peat Moss Litter Company* was established[12]. The company accounts published in the Directors report of 1928 refer to: "*cash paid to W H Smith senior in connection with Purchase of Whixall Bog Property*". A sum of £500 is recorded[30].

Whilst the surviving plan referred to earlier clearly suggests acquisition of the former War Department works by *The Bettisfield Trust Company Ltd* this perhaps conflicts with an item in the company accounts,

Figure 17. Plan of peat processing works attributed to *The Bettisfield Trust Company* at "The Old Graveyard". Based on a railway plan in the possession of the Hanmer Estate.
Drawing: Timothy Morgan.

95

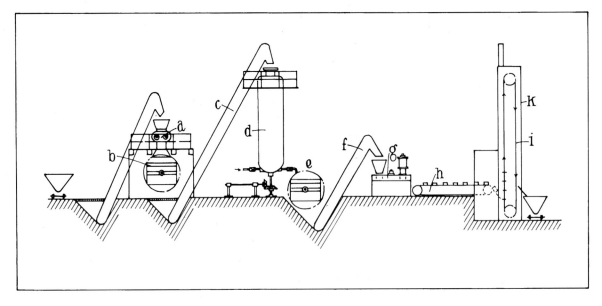

Figure 18. F.M. Perkin's patented (No.228,993) continuous peat briquetting process[31].
a- macerator, b- rotary vacuum filter, c- heated casing, d- autoclave, e- filter, f- cooled casing, g- briquetting press, h- conveyor, i- elevator/conveyor within k- finishing dryer.
Drawing: Timothy Morgan.

shown once again in the balance sheet for 1928 which refers to a payment of £5458.3s.3d. still outstanding to *W.H. Smith and Co.*, Whitchurch in respect of plant and machinery[30].

A sum of this magnitude suggests the construction of new works or, at least, substantial alterations to existing works. Indeed, the range of equipment known to have been in the War Department works would have been much more suited to the activities of *The Midland Moss Litter Company* than the perceived activities of *The Bettisfield Trust Company Ltd.*

The Bettisfield Trust Company Ltd held patents jointly with Dr. F.M. Perkins, who is listed along with directors of the Company as a creditor on the balance sheet of 31st December 1925[30]. The first patent (Number 228,993) dated November 14 1923 relates to a continuous briquetting process in which: " *peat is mascerated, subjected to treatment in a rotary vacuum or other moisture separator, conveyed within a heated casing to an autoclave then passed to a container in which the pressure is suddenly reduced to disrupt the peat cells.....Sawdust, finely divided coal, or other combustible material may be added before the peat is*

briquetted (Figure 18)[31]. The second patent (Number 232,358) relates to a process of *"destructive distillation"* and was lodged on January 31st 1924. "*This invention relates to the distillation and carbonising of coal, peat, and other carboniferous materials, and has for its object to improve upon such processes as hitherto proposed to be carried out, and upon the apparatus for carrying out such processes, the invention being applicable alike to high temperature processes for extracting the benzinoid products and to low or moderate temperature processes for the recovery of the paraffinoid products.....*[32] .

It is uncertain whether either of these processes were utilised by *The Bettisfield Trust Company Ltd* at their Moss works, although the Company's restricted interest in the black peat certainly indicates their intention to employ the patents. Evidence from the 1923 lease suggests that processing works concerned with briquetting or distillation may have been set up within the Fenn's Bank Brick and Tile Works rather than on the site of the former War Department works. Interestingly, in this context, there is a firm referred to locally as "The Black Firm" which apparently operated on the Moss in the 1930s and was linked with the manufacture of peat briquettes:

"the start of the nineteen thirties that ..... the Black Firm as we call it that was the German firm what they did they employed a lot of people and they cut a lot of peat and they had it in stacks on the Moss ..... and they took the peat up to Fenn's Bank and they made briquettes out of it"[33].

Although accounts for *The Bettisfield Trust Company Ltd* continued to be produced annually throughout the 1920s, records show that the Company had effectively ceased trading by 31st December 1925, being formally wound up on 18th February 1936[30].

The Midland Moss Litter Company, a Scottish company generally referred to by local people as "The Firm"[16], worked Fenn's Moss until August 1962, the longest period of any of the recorded companies. The Company's arrival on the Moss was to introduce a completely new system of peat cutting from Holland which involved the laying out of a system of flats and drains which are still very evident on the ground and, more than any other single element, define the landscape of the mire as it appears today (see Fact Panel Three, *Going Dutch,* p.106).

The surviving processing works, described in detail in the following chapter (*The Works*), were constructed by *The Midland Moss Litter Company* in 1938, replacing an earlier works destroyed in a fire (Plate 30). This earlier processing works was not that of the War Department, but rather a subsequent works standing more or less in the position of today's works. Jim Lindsay, Cambrian Cottage[28], recalled two factories working together, the one being abandoned and left to disintegrate to become what is today known as "The Old Graveyard" (the War Department's works), the other continuing in use by *The Midland Moss Litter Company.* Harry Hallmark whose father was the engine driver at the processing works remembers helping to rebuild the factory in 1938: *"it was a new shed put up a whole new building ..... new engine ..... mills, elevators and riddles ..... there must have been in the teens of men mixing concrete all done by hand ..... for a great big hole for that engine"*[34].

The Midland Moss Litter Company worked the peat on Fenn's Moss. Unfortunately, for a company that made such a lasting impact on the landscape, few documentary records remain. No company papers exist at the Public Record Office, nor apparently in the Hanmer Estate papers.

Plate 30. *The Midland Moss Litter Company* **peat processing works, which were destroyed by fire in 1938 and which stood on the site of the extant "Fenn's Old Works". From** *The Great Western Railway Magazine,* **March 1927**[40]. **By permission of The British Library.**

Herb Allmark remembers hearing that his grandfather, Joseph Allmark, helped to mark out the Moss two years prior to production commencing: "*I should think about 1926, me grandfather marked the Moss out for them two years before they were ready to go into production ..... he was Moss manager and he worked up there for two or three years while they were getting the mill built and in progress*"[15], and according to Albert Allmark: "*me dad got a job on the water mains at Prees until 1923 the Midland Moss Litter Company started on the firm and he started, one of the first to start with them*"[26].

The Midland Moss Litter Company already had interests in peat bogs on the Scottish borders. Personnel were brought down from Scotland to set up the works at Fenn's Moss. These included the Dekker family, Mr. Seurin, and Lodewyck Engelen, known locally as "Sandy England"[35]. All were of Dutch extraction and brought with them the Dutch pattern of cutting peat with its system of flats and ditches and a different assemblage of tools.

Cut and dried peat was transported from the Moss to the processing works by 2ft. narrow gauge railway, the loaded trams being pulled by a MR&T locomotive acquired originally by Jo Allmark in October 1919 (see Fact Panel Four, *The Peat Railway*, p.108)[14].

Throughout *The Midland Moss Litter Company*'s tenure of the Moss, peat was cut by hand, a gruelling and tough life: "*nothing has been got easy on the Moss*"[26], Men were paid piece rates, the more they worked the more they earned. Herb Allmark tells of his grandfather's disagreements with the firm over the wages paid in the early days of production: "*by the time they went into production they got large stocks of peat and a short time after my grandfather was supposed to tell the chaps that the piece work rate for cutting peat was to go down from 12s.3d. a chain to 8s.6d.*"[15]. This would be in the early days of the Company's involvement on the Moss: "*I'm talking about seventy years ago*

they were full up with peat on the Moss that they stopped 'em cutting.....the Midland Moss Litter they got that much peat there"[26]. This hints at the Company cutting peat on the Moss while a factory was being built or altered, thus a large stockpile of peat had built up. By the 1930s Charlie Starkey was able to report receiving wages of £3 a week for working a five and a half day week, 9am until 4pm, well-paid by contrast to farm work: "*the farm wage was 38s.6d. ..... when I got married [1936] ..... seven day a week starting at six in the morning*"[36], and by 1952, Mas Clorley was able to earn 42s. a **Dutch chain** for cutting peat [37].

Certain tasks on the Moss were paid at "day-rates". For example, a set time was allocated for moving the **shifting lines** of the peat railway for which a set sum was paid, the "day-rate". The rate was paid irrespective of the time taken: "*you had an allowance to do the shifting lines so if it was eight hours to take one out and put one in you get paid eight hours irrespective of how long it took you to do it ..... if it took you twelve it was tough luck you got paid for eight hours*"[16]. All men working in the processing works including the engine driver, were paid on piece rate. It was in everyone's interest to work hard: "*you wouldn't go up there and fool about you best fool about at home*"[28].

In 1931 *The Midland Moss Litter Company*, under the chairmanship of Sir John Train, joined a peat producers' consortium *London and Provincial Peat* (*L&P Peat*), through which the Company's peat products were co-operatively marketed[38]. Companies working under the banner of *L&P Peat* each supplied peat to quota for the consortium. Company minutes of a meeting of 28th April 1938 endorsed the Whitchurch (Fenn's Moss) quota at seven thousand tons per annum, in accordance with an earlier agreement of 1934[39].

The Midland Moss Litter Company principally produced milled peat, peat moss litter, although it did cut some peat for burning[40]. Extensive records remain of the transactions of *L&P Peat*, held in the offices of

Richardson's Moss Litter Company, Carlisle. It is known that peat litter was used extensively as a bedding material for horses and in deep litter housed poultry systems, although the latter market was to collapse with the advent of battery hen farming[26]. Records show that the *Crossfields Oil and Cake Company Ltd*, Liverpool was supplied through *L&P Peat* with milled peat from Fenn's Moss[39]. The peat was mixed with mollases in the manufacture of cattle cake.

During WW2 the peat industry was defined as a reserved occupation. Peat was used for packing munitions and large quantities were supplied to the *Magnesium Elecktron Company*, Manchester for use in the extraction of magnesium from sea water - the magnesium being desperately needed for the construction of military aircraft. The large surface area of the milled peat enabled precipitation of the magnesium, although some scientists argued that the peat had a more active catalytic effect[20]. Many men who were called up for military service but had previously been working for *The Midland Moss Litter Company*, were brought back to the Moss to work as part of their military duties. Part of this work was to help in the construction of the "strategic starfish" decoy site (see *The Military Takes Over*)[41]. Figures for *L&P Peat*, however, show *The Midland Moss Litter Company*'s peat litter production maintaining a rate of between 4.7 and 7.7 tons per year per man employed, throughout the war years[39] - and this despite the fact that a large part of North East Fenn's Moss had been commandeered for a bombing range!

It is reported in the obituary of Joseph Allmark, who died in February 1940 that he was employed on Government work "*somewhere in Wales*"[42]. Jo Allmark throughout his life worked on the peat. There are hints that men from other areas, particularly Ireland, were brought onto Fenn's and Whixall Mosses during WW2 to help cut peat. In a newspaper report of November 1943 two Whixall men, Albert Williams and Philip Clorley, were each fined £5 for failing to comply with a direction

given by a National Service Officer. Both men were sent to an East Midlands site to work. Neither stayed and in their unsuccessful appeal asked: "*why should they as married men be sent one hundred miles away from home and Irishmen were allowed to come from Ireland and stay on the site they had been working at*"[43]. Both men were peat cutters.

A newspaper article of 1954 reports *The Midland Moss Litter Company* processing three thousand tons of peat a year, an apparent drop from the pre-war levels of seven thousand tons. At this time the works was employing about fifteen men and Mr. Seurin, the works foreman of Dutch extraction who had come down with the Company from Scotland, had retired three years previously[44]. Towards the end of the Company's tenure the peat industry was in a lull, the demand for litter for both horses and poultry as well as other uses had fallen, and although peat's value for horticulture was recognised, this market had yet to become fully established. *The Midland Moss Litter Company* was one of the casualties of this decline. The Trade Report of *L&P Peat* reported that *The Midland Moss Litter Company* had gone into creditors voluntary liquidation in August 1962. The same report states that the Whitchurch (Fenn's Moss) site had been bought out by *L.S. Beckett*[39]. "The Firm" had gone, but the pattern of its workers' labours on the landscape remains.

Throughout the late nineteenth and twentieth centuries individuals have cut peat alongside the large-scale commercial companies both for their own use, predominantly for fuel, and for sale. Some individuals had rights to turf banks on the Moss. The Moss Cottages, constructed by Smith and Wardle to house workers of *The English Peat Moss Litter Company Ltd* all had turf banks associated with them, the concessions for which were removed in September 1945[12]. Several properties around Whixall continue to have allotments around the southern margin of Whixall Moss, assigned under the 1823 Inclosure, although most of these allotments have now been converted to agricultural land. The Wardle family continued to rent out the central portion of Whixall Moss as turf banks on an "acre" by "acre" basis until its sale to Tom Allmark of *L.S. Beckett* in November 1956. In the period between the two World Wars rents on these turf banks were collected for the Wardle family first by Joseph Allmark, who received 5% commission by way of remuneration[12], and later by his wife, known to everybody as "Aunt Sally" (Plate 31)[45], who lived in the former office of the *Moulded Peat Charcoal Company* (N.G.R. SJ 5039 3662). In a similar manner turf banks were rented by local individuals on the Welsh side on Fenn's Moss, "Aunt Sally" again acting as agent in collection of rents for the Hanmer Estate[46].

Much of the peat cut by individuals was used for burning, and peat is still burnt today in some local grates[47]. Many of the local peat cutters sold peat blocks in the area and there are many tales of peatmen taking their horse and cart on peat rounds[26]. In some instances men worked for "The Firm" during the weekdays and in the early mornings, evenings and weekends cut peat on their own turf bank: " *I got on The Firm and used to take a load of peat out on a Saturday morning, the first time round*

Nantwich I never sold a bag"[26]. The peat rounds covered a substantial area around Whixall: "*with a pony and cart round Malpas anything within about fourteen miles, Whitchurch, Marbury, Shawbury ..... Llay up Shrewsbury way*"[48]. Alf Bailey remembers as a fourteen year old, in 1934, going on the peat round when he worked with Jo Heath, who had a small peat cutting business. This was not a one man business as were many of the small peat cutting enterprises, but always employed one or two people. His son, Les Heath, succeeded to the business and began milling peat for horticultural use. It is only very recently that this business has ceased[33].

In the 1930s peat was sold at sixty pieces for a shilling, rising to 1s.6d. and then to half-a-crown (2s.6d.) just prior to WW2[48]. The peatmen have many tales to tell of ponies that could find their own way home following the peatman's celebrations at the local hostelry after a successful day selling peat! Raymond Heath remembers learning to drive the cart home when he was five or six. " *I been at Hanmer ten o' clock at night outside the Hanmer Arms ..... I wasn't left school then*", remembers Alf Bailey[48].

Plate 31. Sarah Allmark ("Aunt Sally") and her husband Jo Allmark, who collected turf bank rents on behalf of the Wardle family and Hanmer Estate. Reproduced with the kind permission of Mrs Millwood.

Local people exploited the Moss in many ways. The growing bogmoss itself was collected and used to make holly wreaths at Christmas time and to line hanging baskets in the spring (see Fact Panel Five, *Wreath Making*). Birch growing on the Moss was also made into laths for the peat bales in "The Old Shed Yard": "*they used to go and cut the birch and they had a little sawmill there and they used to cut laths for the bales of peat.....to sell to the Midland Moss Litter Works.....later.....all the laths came in by rail*"[34]. Many families also cut birch to be sold as pea and bean sticks[33].

For all the people who depended on the Moss for their living, whether large company or individual peat cutter, fire was a constant worry. The train as it crossed the Moss was not supposed to stoke up, but of course it did. Sparks very easily started fires and in particularly dry summers fragments of glass could also cause a fire. Peat cutters used fire to control surface growth and to protect their own peat banks. By controlled burning around a peat bank a fire break was formed which afforded some protection should a fire take hold later in the year. Controlled burning was carried out in the winter months when the ground was at its wettest[26].

When the peat is dry fire can spread through the body of the peat. The local newspaper contains many references to severe fires, most of which occurred in the summer months. The story seems to be the same each time. In August 1887: "*Whixall Moss was discovered to be on fire near the railway line. The flames spread with alarming rapidity ..... there is now probably a hundred acres of smouldering peat. We understand that a large quantity of stacked peat belonging to the Peat Moss Litter Company has been destroyed ..... Nothing but heavy rain will ultimately extinguish the fire*"[50]. Reference to this fire can be found in the records of *The English Peat Moss Litter Company* which show that during the week ending August 13th men worked overnight "*watching the fire*"[12]. Again, in July 1918: "*the extensive Moss fire ..... is said to have started*

on the evening of July 2nd, close to the Cambrian railways line ..... the fire spread with great rapidity ..... the peat in 'mows' and drying on the ground has been completely destroyed ..... Nothing less than a continuous and heavy downfall of rain ..... can extinguish the fire"[51]. Barbara Clorley remembers her father losing ten thousand blocks of peat in a particularly fierce fire[52]. Individual peat cutters could not afford to insure their peat stocks and a loss such as this could have devastating effects on the family income[16].

The fortunes of individual peat cutters mirrored those of the larger firms. By the 1950s demand for peat as fuel was falling, although its use for poultry litter was still popular: "*we sold a lot for deep litter until that went out and batteries started to come into popularity*"[33]

Peat rounds using horse and cart disappeared, although they were replaced to a certain extent with converted Austin 7 vans[26]. Horticultural use of peat was just beginning. *The Midland Moss Litter Company*, as early as the late 1930s was sending some milled peat to nurseries[20], but it was not until the 1960s that peat for gardening really took off: "*in the mean time Percy Thrower was giving us lots of cheap advertisement on the BBC gardening programme which helped to get peat so popular with gardeners*"[26].

In its early years, the firm *L.S. Beckett* was typical of the small-scale commercial enterprises of the local peat cutters. Len Beckett had started by renting a few "acres" for hand cutting like most local peatmen[15], operating his business on a small scale from Manor House, now the Nature Reserve base of English Nature (N.G.R. SJ 5054 3660), which Herbert Beckett, his father, had purchased for a market garden in 1933. Len Beckett had been crippled by poliomyelitis as a child and died in his early thirties, his business being bought from his widow by his brother-in-law, Tom Allmark, in c.1950. Under Tom Allmark *L.S. Beckett* was to anticipate the rapidly expanding demand for peat for horticulture.

In November 1956, Tom Allmark purchased 205a. of Whixall Moss from H.H. Wardle. The Wardle family had been owners of the centre of Whixall Moss since the purchase of Whixall manor by George Wardle and W.H. Smith in 1889, and had rented the area out as **turf banks** on an "acre" by "acre" basis to local individuals cutting peat by hand either for their own use, or as small-scale commercial enterprises. The Hanmer Estate similarly rented out parts of Fenn's Moss. Following the acquisition of Whixall Moss, Tom Allmark served notice on those local peat cutters who had been renting turf banks from H.H. Wardle. Some peat cutters vacated their banks, whilst others refused and continued cutting[16].

In November 1957, Tom Allmark purchased Manor House from his father-in-law, Herbert Beckett, to enable expansion of the factory base there. *L.S. Beckett* started: "*making a little bit of compost in a small way and renting a little bit of ground and getting various ones to do jobs*"[15] - many of the local peatmen cutting on Whixall Moss and North East Fenn's Moss sold their peat to *L.S. Beckett* for £1 per load[16]. The order by Cuthberts, Llangollen for bulb fibre for Woolworths was to trigger the expansion of *L.S. Beckett* and by the 1960s all the peat produced by *L.S. Beckett* was sold to Woolworths[16].

The running of *L.S. Beckett* was taken over in May 1960 by Tom Allmark's son, Herb Allmark and in 1962 the firm acquired *The Midland Moss Litter Company*'s lease on Fenn's Moss, together with their processing works. Peat continued to be baled at the former Midland Moss works, the baled peat being transported by rail to Fenn's Bank station from where it was transported by road using tractor and trailer to the factory base at Manor House. Here the dry, baled peat was mixed with "wet" **potting** peat, which had been brought directly off North East Fenn's Moss by tractor and trailer, to produce "sphagnum-moist" peat which was sold on for compost-making or made on site into compost for sale. Within a short period of time, the cost of rail transport from the former Midland Moss works to Fenn's Bank station came to equal the value of the baled peat - £8 per ton[16]. To overcome this problem *L.S. Beckett* laid a narrow gauge railway from the works across Fenn's Moss to bring the baled peat directly to Manor House and acquired additional locomotives secondhand to supplement the original MR&T locomotive purchased in 1919, which was still going strong!

Early in the 1970s *L.S. Beckett* moved the westernmost swing hammer dust mill from the former Midland Moss works to Manor House where all future peat processing was undertaken[16] (Plate 32).

Plate 32. The extant "Fenn's Old Works", still with original cladding, as they appeared in 1976 following abandonment by *L.S. Beckett*.
Reproduced with the kind permission of Trefor Thompson.

Plate 33. *Steba V* peat cutting machine on Fenn's Moss in 1968, manufactured by *Maschinenbau Hermann Backers*, Twist, Germany. Reproduced with the kind permission of Jenny Bellingham.

It was *L.S. Beckett* who first introduced mechanised peat cutting to Fenn's Moss. Sod cutting machines which cut peat in the same manner as hand cut **Dutch blocks**, were introduced from Germany. Herb Allmark first saw a machine in action near Glastonbury in 1965 and the first to be delivered to *L.S. Beckett* arrived Easter 1968, a *Steba V of Maschinenbau Hermann Backers*, Twist, Germany[53] (Plate 33). The machine was much quicker than cutting by hand but had the drawback of stacking the peat with the wettest peat at the bottom: *"put the very wet soggy peat out of the bottom back in the bottom whereas when you cut by hand you always put the top in the bottom and the bottom on the top so it made it better when you came to handle it"*[15]. This, of course, proved a problem as the peat still had to be stooled and walled by hand. The original machine was replaced before November 1969 by a *Steba 69* which cut a larger block, but stacked the blocks in exactly the same manner as hand cut peat with the wettest blocks to the top (Plate 34). For most of the period that a machine was used for peat cutting by *L.S. Beckett*, later by *Croxden Horticultural Products Ltd*, it was driven by Cliff Bellingham who had previously cut peat by hand. Initially he was a reluctant driver: *"the boss said to me will you have the job and I said no I don't want the job so he said will you do it for a week or two"*[54] - a replacement driver was still being sought twenty years later!

In May 1989, a fourfold increase in rents imposed by the Hanmer Estate resulted in *L.S. Beckett* selling its interests in Fenn's and Whixall Mosses to *Croxden Horticultural Products Ltd*, then part of the *Lands Improvement Group*[46]. *L.S. Beckett*'s records indicated that in the region of 20,000m³ of peat had been cut during the twelve

Plate 34. *Steba 69* peat cutting machine on Fenn's Moss in 1989. © Woodfall Wild Images

months prior to the sale of its interests to Croxden[55]. For the Company to meet the increased rental and continue to make a profit from peat would require a significant shift in working practice and a dramatic increase in production, something which *L.S. Beckett* was not prepared to do. Under Croxden, working practices were altered and clearing work began on drains which had been neglected for many years.

In August 1989 *L.S. Beckett*'s processing plant at Manor House was dismantled and replaced by Croxden with new Dutch-built machinery, operational by the end of that year. Only bagged horticultural peat was to be produced at Manor House, an increasing amount of peat being transported to Croxden's central works at Stoke-on-Trent for manufacture into a range of composts[55]. By December 1990, *Croxden Horticultural Products Ltd* was set up to extract between 40-50,000m³ *per annum*, although the actual total achieved in the two years to that date was only 65,000m³.

During the time that *Croxden Horticultural Products Ltd* were operating on the Mosses, the anti-peat lobby was at its height. Fenn's and Whixall Mosses had been designated a Site of Special Scientific Interest (SSSI) as early as 1953, and abortive discussions had taken place with *L.S. Beckett* regarding purchase of the Company's holdings for nature conservation. From the moment of acquisition of *L.S. Beckett*'s interests, *Croxden Horticultural Products Ltd* began talks with the then Nature Conservancy Council (NCC) with a view to areas of the Mosses being restored. In December 1990, all leases and land owned by Croxden's were purchased by the NCC and the era of large-scale commercial cutting came to a close. A new era of wetland conservation was about to commence, but for those who had known Mosses as a working environment all their life the change was to be a difficult one: "*it was a sad day when we had to walk away from this*

Fact Panel Two: Whixall Bibles

The traditional indigenous method of hand peat cutting known as **Whixall Bible** cutting takes its name from the shape of the peat block (refer Plate 72, p.160), which measured approximately 9in. × 7in. × 4in. The method of cutting may date back to at least the sixteenth century and continued to be used by one or two peatmen until 1960.

Whixall Bibles were cut by local peatmen from small, square/oblong pits (*c*.3-5m × 5-7m). Little or no drainage was attempted and the depth of the pits was dictated by the level of the water table. Where localised changes in surface topography permitted, cuttings would be progressively worked "uphill" to enable some degree of drainage. Once a pit filled with water it was abandoned and a new pit was opened nearby. Large-scale hand cutting of Whixall Bibles was undertaken by *The English Peat Moss Litter Company Ltd* from 1886 until the 1920s, and has created a characteristic "flayed"-cut or skimmed re-vegetated peat surface across extensive areas of North East Fenn's Moss. This method of cutting was succeeded under *The Midland Moss Litter Company* by the Dutch pattern of cutting with its intensive network of drains (see Fact Panel Three: *Going Dutch*, p.106), which in some areas overlays the earlier cut surface. Individual, later Whixall Bible pits, cut piecemeal by local peatmen, are also set into this "flayed" surface.

The Whixall Bibles were cut and lifted using a short handled spade (refer Figure 33, p.167). The peat cutter would slide the spade in and out of the cut face of peat horizontally so as to cut and lift three Whixall Bibles together[1]. Blocks would be placed on a peat barrow (Plate 35) to be wheeled to a drying area where they would be set on edge to part dry before being stacked into **windrows**, two Whixall Bible blocks in height (Figure 19). The "windrow" would be stabilised every 3 or 4 yards by alternating buttresses of peat blocks in an act known as **styching**. In circumstances where the peat had not dried sufficiently in the windrow to be brought off the Moss before the onset of winter, the Whixall Bibles would be stacked, with the driest blocks innermost, to form large beehive-shaped **cocks**.

Evidence of Whixall Bible cutting may be seen particularly on eastern North East Fenn's Moss and on Whixall Moss (refer Plate 67, p.149) as small, square depressions, now 0.5-1.m deep, the base of which is filled by bogmosses and other mire plants (refer Plate 4, p.13).

Plate 35. Alfred Heath removing Whixall Bibles from his turf bank. Photographed in 1960 during a visit to the Moss by the Denbighshire and Flintshire Rural Industries Committee. Photograph: Jim Parry, reproduced with his kind permission and that of the Daily Post Picture Library.

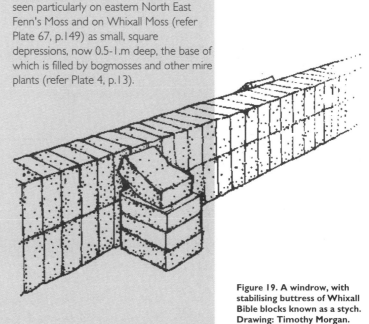

Figure 19. A windrow, with stabilising buttress of Whixall Bible blocks known as a stych. Drawing: Timothy Morgan.

Fact Panel Three: Going Dutch

The Midland Moss Litter Company became established on Fenn's Moss in the early 1920s and brought from its site on the Scottish borders, workers of Dutch extraction to set out a completely new pattern of hand peat cutting which was in widespread use in the Netherlands.

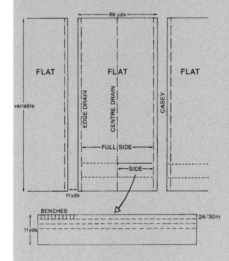

Figure 20. Schematic plan of the Dutch pattern of peat cutting on Fenn's and Whixall Mosses.
Drawing: Timothy Morgan.

This Dutch pattern of peat cutting comprised a system of **flats** and drains (Figure 20), each "flat" being 88 yards in width and of variable length, up to 550 yards on Fenn's Moss. The "flat" was divided from its neighbour by a **casey**, or trackway, approximately 11 yards wide, and was bounded by two edge drains. Each "flat" was also divided down the middle by a centre drain to create two blocks of peat 44 yards in width.

Each of these flats of peat was divided into strips 11 yard wide, known as the **side**, which were 44 yards long set at right angles to the "casey". One cut would be taken from each "side" per season and would be divided along its length into 100 **benches**. The "bench" comprised either 20 or 24 **Dutch blocks**, a "Dutch block" measuring 6in. x 6in. x 16in.

Peat cutters speak of cutting peat from the side a "yard" wide by a "yard" deep. This "yard" has no direct relationship with the imperial yard measuring 36in. The actual true width and depth of the "yard" was related to the number of Dutch blocks cut in each "bench". Cutting 4 Dutch blocks wide by 5 deep gave a "yard" width of 24in. and "yard" depth of 30in., whereas cutting 4 wide by 6 deep gave a width of 30in. and depth of 36in. The actual number of Dutch blocks cut from each "bench" along the "side" was often varied dependent on surface topography, so as to ensure that the peat cutting would serve as an effective drain in carrying water to the edge and centre drains on each "flat".

In cutting the Dutch pattern the hand peat cutter stood in the ditch and cut parallel to the "side". The peat cutter wore custom-made overshoes known as **pattens** (refer Plate 74, p.162) to prevent him from sinking into the soft peat in the ditch. The first operation was to remove the surface vegetation, or "fay", using a **fayer** (refer Figure 27, p.161). The "fay" would be thrown down into the ditch created by the previous season's cut or be placed on the surface of the adjoining "side" when first opening up the "flat". The bench would then be marked out on the exposed surface of the peat using a **sticker** (refer Figure 30, p.164), and the "sticker" would also be used to mark out and cut the sides of each Dutch block across the width of the "bench" (Figure 21). Where the peat was difficult to cut, the "sticker" would be replaced by a **nicker-out** (Figure 28, p.162). Each Dutch block would be separated from the underlying peat using an **uplifter** (refer Figure 32, p.166) and be placed on the

Figure 21. Diagram showing the Dutch blocks marked out on three successive benches, with the stepped effect favoured by the peatman for most efficient working.
Drawing: Timothy Morgan.

"side" alongside the cutting in three rows, with the blocks cut from the surface peat placed furthest from the cut face and those from the bottom of the cutting closest to the cut face, where they were known as the **pit row** (Plate 36). The hand peat cutter found it most efficient to work three benches together so as to create a stepped effect (refer Figure 21).

Once the rows of Dutch blocks had partially dried they would be made into **stools**, four blocks in height (Figure 22). Each stool would be linked to its neighbour for increased stability using two Dutch blocks in an act known as **spragging** (Figure 23). Following a period of further drying "spragged stools" would be used to construct **walls** (Figure 24), seven to eleven Dutch blocks in height, with up to ten walls on each "side".

Dried Dutch blocks from the "walls" would be carried by peat barrow (refer Figure 29, p.163) to the "casey" in an act known as **wheeling-out**. At the casey the blocks would either be loaded onto the trams on the **shifting line** of the peat railway for transport to the processing works, or would be built into large stacks, known as **maws** (refer Plate 73, p.162), for storage until required.

Hand peat cutters working for *The Midland Moss Litter Company* were paid piece rate, the rate being calculated on the **Dutch chain**, a cubic measurement of peat being 44 cubic imperial yards, equivalent to 3564 Dutch blocks. A good peat cutter would average a "chain" a day. In the 1920s the rate was 12s.3d. per Dutch chain, rising to 42s. per Dutch chain by 1952[2].

Peat continued to be cut in the Dutch pattern until the cessation of commercial cutting in December 1990, although mechanised cutting replaced the hand peat cutting under *L.S. Beckett* in Easter 1968. Some hand peat cutters still working the bog on a small-scale under licence from English Nature and the Countryside Council for Wales continue to use the Dutch method of peat cutting and its assemblage of hand tools.

Plate 36. George Heath poses for the camera with his sticker, his jacket and uplifter lying on the pit row. Photographed in 1960 during a visit to the Moss by the Denbighshire and Flintshire Rural Industries Committee. Photograph: Jim Parry, reproduced with his kind permission and that of the Daily Post Picture Library.

Figure 22. A stool. Drawing: Timothy Morgan.

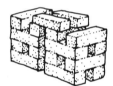

Figure 23. Adjoining stools linked using two Dutch blocks in an act known as spragging. Drawing: Timothy Morgan.

Figure 24. A wall, with diagrams showing the layout pattern and the way in which partially dried Dutch blocks were brought from the rows of spragged stools. Drawing: Timothy Morgan.

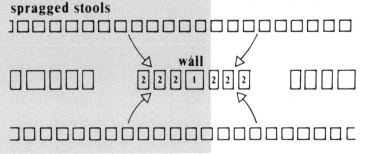

spragged stools

wall

Fact Panel 4: The Peat Railway

Plate 37. MR&T locomotive No.1934 on Fenn's Moss in 1966. Reproduced with the kind permission of Derrick Pratt.

A **tramroad**[1] , or narrow gauge "railway" upon which wagons or trams were pulled by horses, is first recorded from Fenn's Moss in 1856, but no doubt was in use from the commencement of commercial peat extraction in 1851. The extent of this early system is not known, although a tramroad certainly linked the then processing works ("The Old Moss Works" N.G.R. SJ 5039 3662) with a wharf on the canal (N.G.R. SJ 5113 3667), enabling distribution of peat products by barge (refer Figure 14, p.87)[2]. Under the *English Peat Moss Litter Company Ltd*, by 1909, tramroads extended from the processing works ("The Old Shed Yard" N.G.R. SJ 5037 3682) to Oaf's Orchard and provided a link for distribution of peat (the Long Mile) with a siding off the Oswestry, Ellesmere and Whitchurch railway at Fenn's Bank (N.G.R. SJ 5079 3893) (refer Figures 16a, b, c, p.91)[3]. Tramroads were sanded[4] and purple moor-grass may have been deliberately sown to improve traction for the horses pulling the laden peat wagons.

Industrial locomotives replaced horses in 1919. Four locomotives are recorded from Fenn's Moss[5]. The earliest, a 20hp petrol-driven locomotive of the *Motor Rail and Tram Company*, Bedford (No.1934), was delivered new to J.E. Allmark at the siding at Fenn's Bank station in October 1919 (Plate 37; and refer Plate 29, p.93) and continued in use on the Moss until *c.*1970. Much later it was joined by three further locomotives, all of which were acquired secondhand: a second 20hp MR&T (No.4023), rebuilt at Whixall in 1967 with a 22hp Armstrong Siddeley diesel engine, and two *Ruston and Hornsby* diesel locomotives (No's. 171901 and 191679), the former acquired from *Dowlow Lime & Stone Co. Ltd*, Derbyshire in spring 1968 and converted at Whixall from 2'3" gauge to 2'0" gauge; and the latter in September 1968 from the *Nash Rocks Stone & Lime Co. Ltd*, Radnor where it had been rebuilt in *c.*1966 with an air-cooled Lister diesel engine (Plate 38).

The peat wagons (Plate 39) were custom-made on the Moss and could be used as flatbed bogies for carrying baled peat and other loads, or with slatted timber side panels for carrying cut, dried peat blocks.

The railway, of 2ft. gauge, comprised a network of permanent line linking with the processing works, from which spurs, or **shifting lines**, were laid into each flat as the cut and stacked peat became dry and ready for processing. The permanent line was laid upon wooden sleepers to which it was affixed by flanged iron nails, or **dogs**. The shifting lines were permanently mounted to lightweight metal sleepers for ease and speed of installation and were connected to the permanent peat railway by points.

The peat railway continued in use until *c.*1970, from when peat was transported from the Moss by *L.S. Beckett* by Dexta tractors and Moss trailers.

Plate 38. Ruston and Hornsby locomotive No.191679 by Fenn's Old Works in 1989. Reproduced with the kind permission of Bill Hankers.

Plate 39. Peat wagons at Fenn's Old Works in 1966. Reproduced with the kind permission of Derrick Pratt.

Fact Panel Five: Wreath Making

Plate 40. Bill Allmark (foreground) and his father, Albert Allmark, wreath making. 12.1994. Photograph: André Q. Berry.

Holly wreaths have been made in Whixall for the Christmas market since c.1915. Mrs Jo Heath[1] recalls her father, James William Beckett, and mother, Elsie Beckett, making wreaths in the years following WWI. Mrs May Simcock[2], brought up on Wem Moss in the early years of this century, also remembers her father making holly wreaths.

Initially, the circular frames to hold the holly were made out of bound straw shaped around a bucket, and only plain holly was used in wreath making[1]. Straw frames were soon replaced with ones made of wire bought in ready-made, which continue to be used today. These are generally 10in. diameter circles, although some wreath makers make cross-shaped wreaths[3]. Bogmoss (*Sphagna*) is wrapped around the frame and bunches of holly are attached using thin florist's wire, ensuring that the glossy surface of the holly leaves are uppermost (Plate 40). Some families use **stabs** as a personal trade mark characterising their wreaths[4]. These are usually made of variegated holly, wired together with holly berries and pushed into the wreath as decoration. Many families now use artificial berries and stabs may include sprigs of other evergreen plants (Plate 41).

Holly for use in the wreaths is bought from local farmers and landowners, and wreath makers are always on the look out for suitable trees to harvest each season. Today bogmoss for wreath making is gathered on Fenn's and Whixall Mosses under restricted licence from English Nature. Growing bogmoss is collected from the ditches (ditch moss) or from the growing surface of the bog (**top moss**) in early autumn and left in piles on the Moss surface to drain. A week later the bogmoss, which by now is drier and lighter, is collected into sacks and taken off the Moss. Wreath making is carried out for about fifteen days in early December each year.

Moss has also been gathered in recent years for use in lining hanging baskets and many peatmen collected bogmoss to sell to local nurseries. None is now gathered for this purpose.

In the past, wreaths were sold to market traders in the Liverpool and Manchester areas[4] although today, with the increased popularity of Christmas wreaths, they are both made and sold across a much wider area. In the 1950s Jack Saywell acted as agent for many of the Whixall wreath makers and would despatch to market as many as 4,000 wreaths per year. Herb Beckett acted in a similar capacity for some families. Today around 10-20 families still make wreaths, producing several thousand each season.

Wreath making has been an important source of income for peat families, often tiding them over lean patches when sales of **burning peat** were poor. It has developed very much as a family activity - the men collecting the bogmoss and holly, the women making the stabs, and everyone helping in making the wreaths. Stan Clorley recalls as a child of eight or nine helping to make two or three thousand wreaths each season: "*oh heck, used to have terrible hands to go to school the next morning ..... you couldn't hold your pen* [5]"

Plate 41. Finished wreaths ready for market, with stabs of variegated holly and berries. 12.1994.
Photograph: André Q. Berry

The Works

The extant peat processing works, located at N.G.R. SJ 4780 3665, hold a unique place in our national heritage. Afforded legal protection as a Scheduled Ancient Monument by Cadw: Welsh Historic Monuments on 25th June 1991[1], the works are believed to be the last such works remaining in mainland Britain, featuring the only National Heavy Oil Engine still *in situ*.

The surviving works (Plate 42), of steel girder construction, formerly clad in corrugated iron with glass lights, comprises a main structure housing the peat processing machinery, together with two lean-to's - one to the west (re-clad in March 1994) housing the stationary engine which provided the motive force for driving the machinery; that to the south serving as off-loading bay over a loop of the narrow gauge peat railway. A third lean-to to the north, which served to protect the railway siding and loading bays from which the baled peat was transported, was removed to *L.S. Beckett*'s processing works at Manor House by Herb Allmark in the mid-1970s.

Immediately adjacent and to the west of the lean-to housing the stationary engine is a group of three (formerly four) 1,000 gallon cast-iron tanks, bearing the barely legible words "CORPORATION TRANSPORT". Two tanks held water acting as coolant for the stationary engine, whilst the remaining two held low grade fuel oil, the one now in the possession of Mr. Herb Allmark at East View Farm, near Wem, where it serves as a storage tank for central heating oil. Fuel oil was apparently delivered to site once per year[2].

To the south of the works stood a wooden and asbestos sheet building (Plate 43) providing site office and adjoining residential quarters. The derelict building was demolished by English Nature in 1993 on grounds of health and safety, although the remains of the "garden" created by the resident peatmen is manifest in the surviving apple tree and the spring show of primroses.

Interestingly, those peatmen involved in the building of the works complex place the date of construction in the *early* 1930s[3], spanning a nine month period between Easter and Christmas. However, the peatmen also recall that one of their number, John Hendricks Dekker, was tragically killed in Wem in a collision between his bicycle and a milk float one Sunday morning whilst on his way to work, as construction of the new processing plant neared completion - something which did not take place until the 11th December 1938[4].

Construction of the new works was necessitated by the destruction of the earlier works in a fire, allegedly caused by a spark from a railway locomotive on the adjacent Cambrian Railways line. Peatmen were employed in the fabrication of the building and construction of the concrete bases for the new machinery, the latter being installed by workers from the *Midland*

Plate 42. The surviving processing works. In the left foreground may be seen the top section from the swing-hammer mill, behind are the raised water and fuel oil storage tanks. The sheet-clad lean-to houses the National engine, whilst the processing shed containing mills, screens and balers is unclad.
Photograph: André Q. Berry. 02.1995.

Plate 43. The wooden and asbestos sheet former office and residential quarters demolished in 1993.
Photograph: J.L. Daniels. 10.1993.

bronze bearings, and the "salvage" for re-use elsewhere of some components has also occurred since abandonment in the late 1960s.

● The Stationary Engine

The stationary engine comprises a single cylinder, four-cycle cold starting, solid injection 110b.h.p. National Horizontal Heavy Oil Engine type NY of the National Gas and Oil Engine Co. Ltd, Ashton-under-Lyne (Plate 44)[6]. Of model type GADOG, drive was transferred by a 12in copper-stitched double leather drive belt to the principal drive shaft which ran the entire length of the adjoining processing shed (refer Plate 44; Plate 45). A clutch fitted to the belt wheel of the principal drive shaft enabled the drive to be disengaged whilst the engine remained running. Warning that the drive was about to be engaged was given to workers in the processing shed by the engine operator running an iron bar across the corrugated iron cladding[7].

The engine was started by compressed air. Ordinarily a storage cylinder, the "air receiver", would be charged to 300p.s.i. by a

Plate 44. The 110b.h.p. National Horizontal Heavy Oil Engine. To the right is the drive belt wheel which connects via a clutch to the principal drive shaft. Photograph: André Q. Berry. 02.1995.

Moss Litter Company's works on the Scottish borders[5]. In order to minimise the impact on peat production, peat cutting continued on the Moss whilst construction of the works was in progress, amassing a stockpile of drying peat ready for processing immediately the new works came "on stream" (refer p.98).

Today the works stand largely intact, although they have been subject to some limited vandalism. The theft of phosphor-

Plate 45. The principal drive shaft. To the right, a half-coupling and extension to the shaft are missing. Photograph: André Q. Berry. 02.1995.

compressor driven by belt from the main engine shaft whilst the engine was running - the air receiver holding the compressed air overnight ready to provide the starting stroke for the engine the following morning. The air receiver gave enough compressed air for one stroke only. Should the engine fail to "catch" or there be insufficient pressure for some reason, the air receiver could also be charged by a 5b.h.p. National Diesel Engine, still *in situ*. This, however, took several hours - much to the annoyance of all concerned, as workers in the processing works were on piece rate! This smaller engine was directly coupled to a 50 volt dynamo supplying the lighting for the works[8]. On the coupling shaft was a pulley, the belt of which could be put to work on the one side serving the compressor for the main engine and, on the other, to serve a water pump. This pump raised water from a well located under the processing shed to the two 1,000 gallon water tanks adjoining the engine lean-to, providing coolant for the main engine.

The engine operators had a method, although far from approved, for starting the engine in circumstances where there was insufficient pressure. Colin Clorley[9] recalls such an occasion when, at the age of 13, he had to stand in for his father who was unable to go and start the engine because of illness:

"[we] *used to have a trick if there was not enough air up.* [We] *would try it and when* [the engine] *come on the compression stroke it'd backfire. You'd knock the air off and as he went back again you'd hit it again. There was a terrible bang and if it went over it started*".

The resultant "cough" as the engine started was a characteristic sound well-known to the engine operator and obviously one which carried for some distance across the Moss, as Colin Clorley clearly recalls being in trouble with his father when he got home that day to Peartree House, Whixall - a distance of over $2^1/_2$ miles from the works!

The engine operator's responsibilities also extended to maintenance of the processing machinery whilst in operation; ensuring that oil reservoirs providing lubrication to certain bearings were regularly topped up, and re-filling grease caps on others. The operator would regularly go round and screw the caps down a half turn to force grease down into the bearing. The engine operator would also undertake repair of both leather and balata belting and would regularly sweep the underfloor area of the processing shed to keep it clear of peat "dust" which would accumulate at a steady rate during the course of processing. In a spare five minutes, he might also be called upon to assist in loading peat bales onto wagons on the railway siding, together with their sheeting prior to despatch!

● The Processing Shed

Machinery within the processing shed was arranged as processing units comprising three balers, two Webster and Bickerton (W&B) and one Shirtliffe baler, each served by associated peat mill, rotary screen and elevators. These could be operated individually, or when the rotary screens were in use, cross-feeding allowed the **throughs** and **tailings** from the screens to be baled in different presses.

In order to ensure that description of the machinery is comprehensible it is easiest to consider each of the component parts in turn before describing the baling operation itself.

• The litter machine/crusher and swing hammer mills

Peat blocks were delivered to the works via the southern lean-to. This stood over a loop off the narrow gauge peat railway and protected from the elements the timber hoppers (now missing) feeding into the three peat mills. Peat was fed manually from the wagons into the mills. Only the concrete base remains of the westernmost

Plate 46. The litter machine/crusher. Photograph: André Q. Berry. 02.1995.

mill, a swing hammer mill which was removed by *L.S. Beckett* for use in their processing works at Manor House in the mid-1970s and was subsequently scrapped. The two remaining peat mills comprise a litter machine or crusher (Plate 46) for the production of **litter**, and a swing hammer mill (Plate 47) for the production of **dust**.

The litter machine consists of two toothed drums, comprising disc sections assembled on 3in square shafts and bearing many hooked, blunt teeth. The shafts of the two drums are linked by large gears, arranged so as to enable each shaft to rotate at a different speed.

The remains of the extant swing hammer mill are not readily identifiable to any one manufacturer and it may be, as was often the case in the peat industry, that the mill was "home-grown" or custom built to suit its purpose. A horizontal shaft fitted with four discs, supported hammer spindles upon which the hammers swung. The upper half of the grinding chamber comprising the feed inlet section and breaker plate is no longer in position (refer Plate 42). The lower half of the grinding chamber housed an interchangeable grid unit, the "cross-vee grid". This grid comprised a frame carrying two rows of cast steel pieces, each steel piece being separated from its neighbours by spacer lugs. The spacing between the cast pieces could be varied by using different thicknesses of spacer lugs and with it the resultant coarseness of the milled peat. The two hanging rods which supported the grid assembly were mounted on adjustment frames which could move along two axes. The grid was adjusted so that the hammers travelled close to the inner face of the grid.

• The elevators

The three mills discharged onto elevators which carried the peat either directly to their respective balers or to one of two rotary screens. The elevators comprise a cog-driven demountable chain loop of the *Ewart Chainbelt Co. Ltd.*, Derby bearing wooden scraper boards mounted on carrier

Plate 47. The swing-hammer mill and its elevator. Photograph: André Q. Berry. 02.1995.

links. Scraper boards were usually of lime, poplar or beech.

• Rotary screens

The two rotary screens remain (Plate 48), although sections of the enclosing casing from one and the screw conveyors which carried the "throughs", or fine dust which had passed through the screen to the secondary elevators, from both are now missing. The rotary screens were driven by an open bevel gear mounted at their lower end.

As mentioned previously, the arrangement of the machinery was such that balers and their respective peat mills could be operated as discrete units or could be linked through the screens, a very comprehensive layout which could cope with diverse requirements simultaneously:

• The Shirtliffe baler could be fed from the westernmost (now missing) swing hammer mill directly, or with the "throughs" from the westernmost rotary screen;

• The westernmost W&B baler could be fed from the litter machine directly, or with the "tailings", that is coarser grained peat which could not pass through the rotary screen, from either or both screens;

• The easternmost W&B baler could be fed from the extant swing hammer mill directly, or with the "throughs" from the easternmost rotary screen.

This layout permitted a number of combinations of peat production:

• The production of "litter" in the westernmost W&B baler, with the production of unscreened peat (medium granulated) in the Shirtliffe and easternmost W&B baler;

• The production of "dust" or screened peat (fine granulated) in the Shirtliffe and easternmost W&B baler, with

"tailings" in the westernmost W&B baler;

• The production of unscreened peat in the Shirtliffe baler, "dust" peat in the easternmost W&B baler and "tailings" in the westernmost W&B baler.

Plate 48. One of two surviving rotary screens. Photograph: André Q. Berry. 02.1995.

117

Plate 49. One of the Webster and Bickerton balers, with weigh box above, fed by a secondary elevator. Photograph: André Q. Berry. 02.1995.

Plate 50. Press arm of W&B baler mounted on rollers on the press rails and linked to its companion arm by chain. Photograph: André Q. Berry. 02.1995.

Plate 51. W&B winch mounted on an extension of the press rails. To the left may be seen the linkage from the press operator's foot pedal and the vertical guide rods of the belt shifting mechanism. Behind are the three pulleys - "up" (right), "stopped" (centre) and "down" (left). Right of these is the brake band with its counterbalancing weight; note the "v"-notch in the rail which ensured positive engagement of the brake. In the background may be seen the principal drive shaft. Photograph: André Q. Berry. 02.1995.

- The balers

- Webster and Bickerton balers

The Webster and Bickerton balers (Plate 49), manufactured by Webster and Bickerton, Goole[10], are the older of the two types of baler at the Fenn's Moss peat processing works and were installed at the time of construction in 1938. The balers comprise two arms, coupled at their upper ends by toothed quadrants to ensure synchronous operation and pivoted on and supporting the press bottom which moved up and down in the pressing chamber. The lower ends of the press arms had roller wheels (Plate 50) riding on the press rails. A chain anchored by a large pin between the rails under the centre of the press, passed around a chain wheel on the one press arm and round a wheel on the other arm and back to a winch mounted on an extension of the press rails. When the winch was operated to wind in the chain, the arms were pulled together, causing the wheels to roll along the press rails and the press bottom to rise in the pressing chamber. The weight of the press bottom was sufficient to cause it to fall of its own accord and unwind the chain.

The winch gear (Plate 51) comprises three pulleys mounted on bearing on a common shaft. The centre pulley is free and is the "stopped" position for the drive belt, whereas the outer pulleys are geared. The "up" pulley drives the winch through an intermediate reduction gear shaft, reversing the rotation and increasing the ratio; whereas the "down" pulley's gear engages in the winch drum gear directly. The "up" pulley also has a brake drum which held the winch in the wound position.

The belt drive passed through a striking mechanism which was operated through a linkage from the operator's foot pedal on the floor in front of the press.

Four long shafts comprise the main structure of the baler. These pass through large lugs on the press rails up to the top of the structure and, in operation, contained the force generated as the arms moved closer. As the mechanical force applied to the contents of the baler increased substantially towards the end of the stroke, the massive rods were essential. As a consequence of the inter-relation between the position of the top of the stroke and the force exerted on the bale, any permanent adjustment to the finished bale dimensions had to be made by fixing timber packings to the bottom of the press.

The entire press structure is assembled on the four shafts, spacers supporting the press box section above the rails. The end faces and doors are also mounted on the shafts as well as the top of press structure, comprising two large castings front and rear. These latter castings are linked by two side pieces which carry the rails supporting the press top. The shafts were required here to contain the significant bursting forces to which the press was subjected when in use.

The top of the pressing chamber, which had to be rolled out of the way to let the peat drop from the weigh box, is a massive block suspended from two supporting rails.

The press chamber doors are also pivoted on the main shafts, the opposing shafts carrying the wrought iron door lock and catch mechanism, comprising a lever which drops into two catches mounted on the door.

Above the press is suspended a weigh box into which could be measured 2cwt. of peat fed from a secondary elevator. Upon reaching the required weight the weigh box would drop causing a linked steelyard to rise. This in turn would act through a striker mechanism so as to shift the drive belt serving the secondary elevator to its loose or "stopped" pulley, thereby disengaging its drive.

The weigh box was discharged manually by the press operator. The press top would be rolled forward, the weigh box being emptied into the press chamber by a counterbalanced lever opening two flaps on the weigh box bottom. Upon emptying, the

weigh box would rise causing the steelyard, again acting through the striker mechanism, to re-engage the drive to the elevator.

Plate 52. The Shirtliffe baler and weigh box above. Photograph: André Q. Berry. 02.1995.

• The Shirtliffe baler

The Shirtliffe baler (Plate 52) at Fenn's Moss is a more modern baler and was a later installation. It is believed never to have been used. The baler comprises two arms on each side, instead of the rail system used in the W&B balers. The shorter arms are joined to the press bottom as with the W&B baler, but the longer arms hang from pivots on the top of the baler structure, against which the press top bears. The lower ends of each pair of arms are joined and fitted with a three-sheave pulley. Because of the mechanical advantage given by the multiple sheaves, the tension is much less and a wire rope, pulled by a winch, is adequate to provide the compression rather than a more substantial chain. This rope pulls the arms together compressing the contents of the baler. As a result, the pressing forces are contained entirely within the structure of the baler. This arrangement reduces the lateral forces from the winch, allowing much lighter foundations to be used.

● Operation of the W&B balers

The bales were secured by three wooden laths, top and bottom, and three baling wires which were tied round the pack. The laths, 40in x 2in x $\frac{1}{2}$in were usually purchased in bulk, bundled in 50s. However, peatmen were occasionally employed in making laths from birch growing on the Moss[1].

Commencing at the end of the cycle with baling wires secured, the operator at the back of the press picked up three laths and operated the "down" side of the floor pedal. As the press descended, putting a foot against the bale, he waited for the bale to be released. As soon as it loosened, it was kicked clear of the baler to the front operator who rolled it away from the baler.

The front operator then closed his press door and pulled the press top out. The back operator cleaned off any loose peat from the press bottom and placed the laths as the press descended, before closing his press door. He picked up the three laths for the top of the bale. When the weigh box was filled, and the press had descended sufficiently to take the uncompressed peat, he pulled the discharge lever on the weigh box. Working through the press top opening, and after levelling any unevenness in the peat, the top baling laths were placed in position. Having placed the laths, the press top was pulled into position by the back operator, who then started the pressing cycle, using the "up" pedal on the floor.

It took about 15-20 seconds for the press to rise to the top of its stroke. Both doors were then opened and the back operator, who had picked up three securing wires, fed them through v-slots in the press top. The outer pair were fed, loop leading, right through to the front operator, who then fed them back through the press bottom v-slots. The centre wire was partly fed through the top, loop leading, the other end being fed through the bottom to the front. The front operator "tied" the wire: end through the loop, twice round the wire, then an open loop was made and passed under the wire to secure the free end. The back operator "tied" off the two outer wires similarly.

It was important that the wires were consistently tight, any excess slack resulting in the compressed peat being able to expand too much as the bale was released, giving a pack that was liable to disintegrate in storage or transport, leading to complaints from customers.

Ensuring that the doors were fully open to allow the bale to be ejected, the back operator picked up the three laths ready for the next bale, the "down" pedal was pressed, and the cycle repeated.

The normal rate of production was approximately 30-40 bales per hour, involving two press operators and an additional worker moving bales for storage or loading.

Roller-mounted doors on the northern side of the processing shed enabled loading of the baled peat onto railway wagons on the adjoining siding, and this was further assisted by a belt conveyor set at floor level between the Shirtliffe baler and westernmost W&B baler.

Mending the Mire

The large-scale expansion in commercial peat cutting on the Mosses which occurred in 1989-90 resulted in a major public campaign to acquire the site for nature conservation, spearheaded by the Fenn's and Whixall Mosses Campaign Group, a consortium of c.20 local organisations led by the Shropshire and North Wales Wildlife Trusts. The campaign culminated, in December 1990, in the then Nature Conservancy Council purchasing the freehold of 70ha of Whixall Moss and 45.3ha of Bettisfield Moss, together with the leasehold of c.260ha of Fenn's Moss. Since that date, major extensions to this landholding have enabled the positive management of the peat body and its flora and fauna to be secured, with English Nature having purchased an additional 22.4ha of Whixall Moss, and the Countryside Council for Wales having taken leases on a further 147ha of Fenn's Moss.

● General Problems in Rehabilitating Peatlands

The principles of rehabilitating lowland raised mires are straightforward: remove or retard smothering vegetation, provide propagules of the correct plants if necessary, and raise water tables to within 5cm of the peat surface all year round. However there are a number of factors, hydrological, hydrochemical, biological, archaeological/cultural and practical, which constrain what may be achieved[1].

From the hydrological perspective, various factors can impede the rapid restoration of ombrotrophic (rain-fed) bog vegetation. The peat may have been cut to such a thin residual thickness and regional ground water tables may have been lowered by abstraction so that loss of water through the peat base is increased. Also, the drained surface peat or the basal, more-compacted fen peat layers remaining after extraction may have a poor water storage capacity and thus may dry out to too great a degree during the summer months, preventing the survival of mire species. Loss of water may be further increased by the invasion of undesirable species such as birch. Such species transpire more water through their leaves than mire species and may cause summer water table levels to fall beyond the reach of mire species.

The irregular, residual shape of cut-away mires may leave a wide zone of dry peat around the margins of the peat body above the dome of water which the peat can support; the smaller the block, the greater this edge effect. The profile of the cut-over surface may also lead to water flow from one area to another giving a wide range of hydrological conditions in different parts of the mire, resulting in erosion as water levels in adjacent areas equalise.

From the hydrochemical perspective the peat body as a whole may have been cut so as to be level with surrounding mineral ground or so as to lie below the ground water table enabling mineral-rich water to affect the mire. In areas where the peat has been cut down to the underlying mineral substrate water can flow out through such cuttings, and in some cases peat may have been cut to such a depth that the loading of nutrient-poor bog water has been diminished enabling springs of mineral-rich water to emerge through the base of the peat up into the cuttings.

Also, decomposition of drained peat may lead to very high levels of acidity which can reduce the vigour of mire plants; or bog vegetation containing the nutrients essential for plant growth may have been scraped away leaving the surface too nutrient-poor even to support mire species.

From the biological viewpoint species may have become extinct from the site so that seed sources or propagules are not available to recolonise when suitable mire conditions are re-created. Dryland species which have invaded can also prevent the return of mire species by shading, through blanketing litter- or leaf-fall, or through the depression of the water table. The smaller the area of peat left, the greater also is the margin from which dryland plants and animals can invade.

Conflicts can also arise where extremely rare species of cut-over rather than intact mires are present. The continued survival of such species may be threatened by restoration of hydrological conditions suitable for mire rehabilitation.

Mire rehabilitation also has an uncertain impact on archaeological remains. Both drainage and re-wetting may adversely affect sub-surface preserved remains which have survived because of the nutrient-poor, anoxic, waterlogged conditions; and will almost certainly lead to the long-term loss of features associated with the more recent, industrial history of the site. Rehabilitation may also run contrary to the local cultural perception of the mire as a resource to be utilised, providing employment.

From the practical viewpoint difficulties may arise if the area has not been cut for some time, so that the workers who know the locations of drains and are familiar with the cutting patterns may not be available to help to plan rehabilitation work. Under such circumstances working on the site, particularly with specialist machinery, may be hazardous.

● Factors Affecting the Rehabilitation of Fenn's, Whixall and Bettisfield Mosses

In the context of the above, English Nature and the Countryside Council for Wales have been relatively fortunate at Fenn's, Whixall and Bettisfield Mosses.

On average three metres depth of peat remains on the cut-over areas. The central

areas are well above the ground water table and some areas are still domed so that ombrotrophic conditions generally prevail and the majority of the water flow is off rather than onto the mire. There is also relatively little depression of the ground water table locally by water abstraction from boreholes.

As substantial depths of peat remain, the mire still has a large capacity for water storage, and in general the surface has not been cut down to the basal fen peat, as it has in many continental mires. At Fenn's, Whixall and Bettisfield Mosses the surface peat is generally the middle, grey peat of moderately humified bogmoss.

The peat body of the Mosses is also large and relatively unfragmented, and the semi-natural areas lie centrally, with other better drained land-uses towards the margins. Consequently, edge effects are less than on smaller sites, although Wem and Cadney Mosses are more problematic in this respect.

From the hydrochemical perspective, only in relatively few locations in the central mire areas has the peat cutting broken through to underlying mineral ridges. The stripping of surface vegetation has been limited because the site was "sod-cut", so bare ground is restricted to a 3-4m wide strip every "11 yards" on the recent commercially cut areas. When water tables are raised, the acidity produced does not appear to retard bogmoss establishment, and nutrient limitations do not seem to create problems.

Practically, English Nature has been extremely fortunate in being able to employ several of the workers from the commercial peat cutting company, who have spent most of their working lives on the Mosses and who know the locations of the drainage network and how to operate safely with large and specialist machinery on this hazardous site. English Nature has also been able to purchase specialist plant from *Croxden Horticultural Products Ltd* for use in mending the mire:

• The Bigtrack bogmaster dumper, a 12 tonne 180° combined excavator and dumper with bogmaster tracks (Plate 53), was used by *Croxden Horticultural Products Ltd* to load dried peat onto the tractors and trailers to be transported to the Manor House processing site and also to load raw peat onto lorries. It is now used principally to dam the larger and deeper ditches and also to clear out peripheral drains in order to keep polluted water off the Moss. The Bigtrack is also used to remove and assist in disposal of the larger scrub as well as to load waste peat for repairing tracks;

• The Smalley excavator is a 4 tonne lattice-chassis 360° excavator with an extremely light footprint which can operate almost anywhere on the Mosses (Plate 54, p.127). It was formerly used to deepen and maintain the drains and is now used principally to dam up the small internal ditches, keep necessary drains open and to excavate small scrub;

• The Backer screw-leveller is a tracked auger with a front-mounted 1m diameter screw blade which cuts and removes the surface vegetation and peat, depositing it in a row to the side of the vehicle. It was previously used to scrape bare a 4m wide strip every "11 yards" ready for the peat cutting machine. It is now used to auger rows of dead vegetation or "rashes" of new birch seedlings back into the ditches (Plate 58, p.131). More recently, it has been used to row up linear storm-water dams along trackways where a higher flat has been leaking water onto an adjoining, lower flat;

• Two very old Dexta tractors and Moss trailers with twin axles, each fitted with twin wheels were also purchased. *L.S. Beckett* operated exclusively with these small tractors in bringing peat off the mire for processing so as to avoid cutting up the surface of the Moss. They are now used for carting brash, woodchippings and waste peat and for general transport.

Other equipment employed by English Nature includes specialist tracked and long wheelbase transport, fire fighting and winching equipment and herbicide applicators, including a converted boom sprayer fitted with two hand-lances and a carpet weed-wiper. The latter is designed to directly wipe herbicide onto those species to be controlled thus overcoming the problems of chemical spray drift which can arise from the more-or-less constant winds on the mire.

In rehabilitating Fenn's and Whixall Mosses there are, however, problems to be overcome. The Main Drain was deepened by *Croxden Horticultural Products Ltd* in two areas so as to divert water which used to flow off the Moss through Whixall into leaving via Bettisfield. This deepening of the drain has cut down into the sand below the peat, which may result in continual water-loss in the future through the base of the mire.

Also, the surface peats of the cut-over areas have been damaged and so do not function in the same way hydrologically as the uncut

Plate 53. The Bigtrack Bogmaster dumper carrying uprooted birch for burning.
Photograph: J.L. Daniels.

peat. The surface of the cut-over areas has also been left at a variety of different levels which causes difficulties with water flow and erosion.

Other land uses on the peat body which are not completely isolated hydrologically from the Nature Reserve, such as forestry, agriculture and domestic peat cutting will prevent rehabilitation work near the periphery of the Reserve until agreement has been reached with surrounding landowners.

Hydrochemically, much of the cut-over area is fairly level, enabling polluted waters to enter along ditches from surrounding ground, finding their way into the centre of the Mosses. Pig slurry has permeated along the central and marginal laggs of Wem Moss[2] and water from the canal has leaked onto both Fenn's and Bettisfield Mosses[3]. Earlier diversion of the phosphate-rich septic tank outfall water from Moss Cottages through Whixall Moss to the Main Drain[4] now means that such water passes right across Fenn's Moss and under the canal to Bettisfield. In one area of the mire, peat cutting appears to have permitted an upwelling of mineral-rich spring water.

Biologically, the majority of the surface of the Mosses is covered by non-mire vegetation. Fenn's Moss is covered by dry heath, acid grassland, bracken and birch scrub and woodland, commercial forestry and some pastureland; Whixall Moss has damp heath, dry heath with birch scrub and peripheral pastureland; Bettisfield Moss is covered by pine scrub and marginal woodland; Cadney Moss by commercial forestry and pastureland and Wem Moss by damp heath, dry heath with birch scrub and marginal woodland. Overall, trees, scrub, grasses and bracken have out-competed mire species except in the base of peat cuttings or on the few uncut areas

● The Condition of Fenn's, Whixall and Bettisfield Mosses Reserve following Acquisition in 1991

The uncut areas and each of the three cutting types, old hand cut and old and recent commercial cuts, has its own particular problems and advantages with regard to rehabilitation (refer Figure 1, p.11).

• Uncut areas

In general the uncut areas have the advantage that their peat is still "living" or functioning and they can maintain water levels better than cut-over areas.

Bettisfield Moss fortunately has few drains but its major challenge is the urgent need to remove the rapidly developing canopy of smothering pine trees, bushes and more marginal birch. Removal from the extremely fragile moss-covered surface must, however, be carefully executed so as not to cause damage to this internationally important community.

The Cranberry Beds and North East Fenn's Lake areas also have few drains and only required removal of short birch and pine scrub. The policy on the Cranberry Beds has been to not use herbicide for birch stump treatment so as to avoid any potential effect on those rare insects present.

Oaf's Orchard has a few old drains cut into it but suffers principally from being higher than the surrounding cut-over ground. Consequently, although some of the old cuttings around it had become partially blocked and had begun to regenerate bogmoss communities, the deep uncut peats on Oaf's Orchard were still deteriorating and were covered by dry heath vegetation with 1-2m high birch scrub. An obstacle to raising water levels in the uncut block has been the continued cutting operations of two hand peat cutters on Whixall Moss immediately adjacent to the south of Oaf's Orchard.

The canalside blocks and Cowberry Patch and a few other high lumps on Whixall and North East Fenn's Moss were all high and dry with bracken, birch scrub and trees and dry heath communities. The only way to raise their water tables is by damming the lower, surrounding cut-over areas.

• Hand cut areas

Hand cut areas comprise areas of old Whixall Bible cutting, old linear hand cuts and modern tractor-extracted hand cuts.

The hydrology of the northern dome of Wem Moss has been disrupted by the creation and deepening of the Border Drain; before this the dome would have continued into Cadney Moss. The creation of a drain to its north has also cut this dome off from Bettisfield Moss. In addition, the southern dome has been damaged by the creation and deepening of a southern marginal ditch as well as by the creation of the Border Drain. The surface of both domes has been affected by domestic Whixall Bible cutting and the drainage and cutting has resulted in deep, surface cracking across the entire site. This has encouraged the spread of purple moor-grass and 1-2m high birch scrub across both domes, together with the marginal spread of the lagg birch woodland and bog myrtle. The latter has also become very dense along the central lagg due to pollution arising from pig effluent from the adjacent farm. Whixall Bible cuttings on southern Whixall Moss have only a minor scrub problem in comparison with those on North East Fenn's Moss, and have the advantage that most of the cuttings lie in between tracks which are at a much higher level. This enables water to be raised to fill the cuttings, effectively drowning out the scrub. The southernmost areas of Whixall Moss lie adjacent to other ownerships in agricultural use and so cannot be dammed.

Areas of linear hand cuts have the advantage that they have a regular pattern

of peat baulks (ridges left after cutting) from which dams can be constructed across to higher adjacent tracks, and there are often only narrow drains leading out through the tracks which can be easily blocked. One complicating factor is that each "acre" only stretches halfway across from one track to another and may not correspond to the adjoining "acre", so that it often proves impossible to dam straight across from track to track.

By contrast, modern tractor-extracted hand cuts, when abandoned, leave large pools which cannot easily be dammed, except where a drain exits from the area under a track. Where such pools are located on sloping ground this may result in the lower end being full of water whilst the upper end is high and dry. Also wind action across the pools can generate waves and corresponding erosion and drive all regenerating bogmoss to one end. This erosion can be prevented by placing uprooted birch scrub in the pools, providing a neat disposal mechanism for a very effective method of scrub control.

• Commercial cutting areas

Areas of old commercial cutting have extensive dense birch scrub and bracken. In general, the cutting flats are at the same level as the tracks making it difficult to raise water levels sufficiently to eradicate undesirable plant species. As a consequence, scrub clearance is necessary. The Canal area of Fenn's Moss has a variety of different levels within it, all sloping down towards the canal. The Main Drain has created a valley through the area which lies at a higher level than the recent commercially cut areas to the north east. The Maelor Forest area has some of the oldest heather on the Reserve providing good spider habitat. To conserve the ground flora, scrub has to be removed by hand, which is labour intensive. Lundt's requires similar treatment.

The extensive area of the recent commercial cuttings were characterised by much bare ground and dense swards of 1m high birch with purple moor-grass. Alongside each ditch there was an augered row of dead vegetation, often with birch growing upon it. The ditches alongside the tracks are particularly hazardous, up to 3m in depth. Cutting flats lie at varying levels so that after damming, water in adjacent flats can be at markedly different levels and any low spots in the tracks can allow water to flow from the higher to the lower level creating erosion channels.

● Implementing the Fenn's, Whixall and Bettisfield Mosses Management Plan

On acquiring the site in 1991 English Nature and the Countryside Council for Wales drew up a five year management plan[5] for the Reserve. This plan was summarised in 1993 as the Synopsis Management Plan, which was circulated widely and is held in local libraries.

The eleven adopted management objectives for the site, and the progress made with these to date, has been as follows:

Objective 1. *Maintain and enhance the integrity of the entire peat body preventing further degradation to the peat body and its palaeoecological record.*

This has centred around works intended to prevent any further deterioration of the peat across the whole SSSI. To prevent this, no additional drainage must occur and, where possible, the mire must be re-wetted. The latter requires that English Nature/ Countryside Council for Wales acquire or secure management agreements on any area of peat likely to be affected by a rise in water tables. Management agreements have been entered into with several private landowners to maintain water levels on agricultural land, whilst other owners within the SSSI have entered the Countryside Stewardship Scheme, which enables them to receive payments for maintaining water levels and for management sympathetic to wildlife.

Legal protection for the peat body has been strengthened. The SSSI was extended upon renotification in 1994 to include much of the peat body and all of the semi-natural raised mire communities as identified in a survey carried out in 1992[6]. As noted in Chapter 2, the SSSI is also being notified as a *Wetland of International Importance* under the RAMSAR convention as part of the Midlands Meres and Mosses site and is a candidate *Special Area of Conservation* under the European Habitats Directive.

Large-scale mechanised commercial peat extraction ceased in December 1990 upon acquisition of the Reserve. Smaller-scale mechanised commercial extraction continues on 1.6ha until 1997 and ongoing small-scale hand peat cutting has been regularised. In 1991 there were several commercial hand peat cutters operating businesses on the site. English Nature acquired three annual licensees on Whixall Moss from the former site operator, one of whom still cuts peat on north east Whixall Moss. On Fenn's Moss peat cutters were operating outside the area of commercial planning permission. Several of the older peatmen have now ceased cutting, whilst the remainder have been transferred to areas on the Reserve with planning permission, identified as less damaging for cutting to continue.

Peat growth and shrinkage of the mire are measured across the site to determine whether damming works can halt deterioration. Two topographical surveys in 1980 and 1993 showed a shrinkage of 1-1.5m depth over that period. Data from 1993 to 1995 shows no further significant changes.

Objective 2. *Re-establish, as far as possible, the natural hydrological and hydrochemical integrity of the site.*

Progress towards this has involved works to re-establish the correct water tables and water quality for raised mire formation.

Surface heights across the SSSI were plotted from aerial photographs in 1993 to 0.5m contour intervals to enable the effects of raising water tables to specified heights at any location to be estimated, and permeability in different layers of the mire and trackways has been studied to determine the effectiveness of the tracks as barriers to water flow '.

The philosophy behind damming of the Reserve to raise water tables has been to start in the centre of the Moss radiating outward from the uncut areas of Oaf's Orchard and the Cranberry Beds to re-wet their irreplaceable peat profiles as quickly as possible and also to rapidly block-up the recent commercial cuttings. This recognises that areas may become less accessible to machinery once dammed and that the commercial cuttings supported many invasive dryland species which could spread rapidly if the correct water levels were not rapidly restored. Damming has been at frequent intervals (40-50m) so as to keep the water tables as near to the ground surface as possible despite the considerable local variation in surface contours.

At Fenn's, Whixall and Bettisfield Mosses damming is only carried out once all scrub

clearance has taken place. The main damming method used to block internal drains has been to fill the ditch with a 3-4m wide plug of peat, which is then compacted by excavator. Compressible "wet", dark peat excavated from the base of the drains is used to form the plug (Plate 54), as dams constructed from degraded surface peats are prone to leakage.

Where dams are on a slope, water gradually erodes a narrow channel across the dam. To prevent this, a 0.5m deep sheet of plastic-coated steel cladding is driven into the dam to the desired water level. In exceptional circumstances, where storm water has to pass below a track, U-shaped pipes will be used to prevent track erosion.

In situations where it is important to raise the water level above the ground surface bunding has been used, for example where the tracks between the cutting flats are lower than the peat baulks. A narrow channel is excavated from a peat baulk on one cutting flat, across the track to a peat baulk on the adjacent flat. Surface vegetation is scraped to form a 1m-wide mound parallel to the channel. A sheet of Visqueen plastic membrane is inserted to

Plate 54. "Wet" peat is extracted by the Smalley excavator from the base of a drain to form a peat plug dam.
Photograph: J.L. Daniels.

the base of the channel and up and over the mound, and is covered with surface vegetation (Plate 55). This creates a waterproof bund running from baulk to baulk, whilst minimising the amount of "wet" peat which must be dug from the area. This has been undertaken around Oaf's Orchard to maximise the water table rise in the adjacent, higher uncut area (Plate 69, p.152).

The screw-leveller has also been used to infill some of the peat cuttings once dams have been installed.

By the end of 1995/6 most of Whixall Moss hand cuttings, all of the commercially cut area, except the area on which peat cutters have been relocated, and about one third of the old commercially cut areas acquired in 1991 had been dammed.

Works have also been undertaken in order to measure the response of the water table to management and to determine the effects of pollution. Two transects of water level tubes were installed in June 1993, one running from the canal through Oaf's Orchard and up to the Lundt's cuttings on North East Fenn's Moss and one running from the railway line to the southern boundary of Whixall Moss. The level of water in the tubes is measured at fortnightly intervals. Water levels in the peat are

continuously recorded at one location on uncut ground and one on still-undammed recent commercially cut ground, and loss of water through the vegetation is also measured at both sites. Rainfall is also continuously logged and evaporation measured. Results from this work have recently been collated [8, 9, 10].

Water tables in the underlying substrate are also being recorded where sand occurs below the peat to investigate the effects of raising peat water tables on ground water tables [10].

Water quality across the Reserve has been measured in studies highlighting the pollution entering from the canal [3, 11], from Moss Cottages and adjacent fields, and from the spring below one area of Fenn's Moss [4, 11, 12, 13].

Objective 3. *Maintain areas of intact mire surface*

The locations of uncut mire surfaces have been identified, and all peat cutting has ceased near these areas. Scrub has been coppiced annually on Oaf's Orchard and less regularly on the Cranberry Beds. Clearing the scrub on the old commercial cuts around Oaf's Orchard was made a priority in 1992, with stumps treated with herbicides [14]. This enabled the old commercial cuts to be blocked with polythene bunds in 1993. The recent commercial cuttings to the north were dammed in 1994-95 and Whixall Moss hand cuts to the south in 1995, completing the raising of water levels all around this uncut block.

All internal drains and the hand cuttings on the southern side of the Cranberry Beds were dammed in 1995. The cuttings around the Cowberry Patch have also been dammed during 1992 and 1995. The uncut area behind the "Lake" on North East Fenn's Moss is partly blocked but requires systematic damming when scrub clearance is completed. No damming has yet been carried out on Bettisfield Moss as timber removal must be undertaken first.

Plate 55. Creating a waterproof bund using the Bigtrack and Smalley excavators. Photograph: J.L. Daniels.

Plate 56. The vegetation of the uncut Cranberry Beds has been recorded using permanent quadrats.
Photograph: J.L. Daniels.

The vegetation of all uncut areas was recorded during the general survey of 1991[15], and permanent 1sq.m. quadrats were set up in 1991, on the Cranberry Beds (Plate 56), Oaf's Orchard and the Cowberry Patch [16]. Together with the monitoring of water levels, records will ensure that the effects of management can be assessed.

Objective 4. *Maintain and enhance areas of quality raised mire communities (e.g. NVC M18a Sphagnum magellanicum - bog rosemary communities)*

This has involved maximising water levels and clearing scrub from areas where bogmoss carpets have begun to recolonise. Outside the uncut areas, this habitat is restricted to old commercial and old hand cut areas. These high quality areas were identified by the general vegetation survey in 1991[15] and permanent 1sq.m. quadrats were installed[17]. A subjective record of the abundance of mosses was also made across the whole SSSI[18]. The surveys helped to prioritise the old hand cut and old commercial cuttings for scrub clearance and damming once the treatment of uncut and recent commercial areas had been completed.

The fortnightly water-level monitoring will determine whether management aims to maintain water levels within 5cm of the surface throughout the year are being achieved. Damming to enhance this habitat will soon be completed on most of the hand cuts in the central area of Whixall Moss. Extension to the north east is dependent on resolution of pollution issues.

Half of the old commercial block by the Maelor Forest has been dammed up, but blocking the remainder of this habitat awaits completion of scrub clearance.

The old hand cuts and old commercial cuttings in particular supported extensive scrub cover. Scrub clearance is carried out by a variety of methods dependent on the sensitivity and accessibility of the site. It is possible to drown birch if water levels can be raised high enough above the peat surface by damming against high tracks, as on the south of Whixall Moss, otherwise the scrub must be cut and/or herbicide treated to prevent regrowth.

Plate 57. Brush cutting and herbicide treatment of birch scrub.
Photograph: J.L. Daniels.

In areas where sensitive vegetation would be damaged by machines, birch and pine has been cleared using hand-held brush cutters and stump treatment (birch only) undertaken using Krenite or Roundup herbicides (Plate 57). Where tractors can be used, small birch has been sprayed by hand-lance or weed-wiped. On areas of birch too tall for this treatment a tractor-mounted hedge-trimming power arm, fitted with a 1m diameter circular saw blade has been used to cut the birch off at the base and this has then been removed for burning using a tractor-mounted buck-rake. Stumps have either been immediately recut and treated with herbicide or allowed to regrow to the correct height for weed-wiping or spraying.

Birch scrub has also been uprooted by the Smalley excavator working with a tractor and trailer or by the Bigtrack, but this has been abandoned on all areas except where it can be tipped into large cuttings because of the inordinate length of time it took to burn the stumps. If labour permits, dense pine and birch brash is removed for disposal because otherwise the brush smothers underlying vegetation, causes enrichment, and makes subsequent management difficult. Pine can be disposed of through a

wood-chipper and the chippings are then sold or used to fill the tracks. Birch does not chip easily, so is generally burnt on-site on metal plates, and the ash is removed to prevent enrichment.

The removal of large volumes of timber from the Mosses is problematic as conventional tree harvesting techniques are likely to damage the sensitive ground flora. Trials are to be undertaken in the extensive pine woodland on Bettisfield Moss to evaluate the most suitable method for large-scale extraction. Here, a marginal fringe of pine will be retained in accordance with the wishes of the local community so as to minimise the visual impact of clearance works.

Objective 5. *Provide conditions conducive to the future rehabilitation of the site as a raised mire system*

This requires scrub clearance and the restoration of suitable water levels on severely damaged areas. On the recent commercial cutting area on Fenn's Moss any heaps of augered-off vegetation have been put back into the drains. Birch has been dug up and dumped in the drains or removed for burning if particularly thick. Rashes of small birch have been rotovated and also augered-off into the drains (Plate 58) and all drains have been dammed by mid-1995.

The vegetation of recent commercial cuttings was recorded during the general survey[15], and the moss survey[18], and was assessed by random quadrats in 1991[19]. These quadrats were reset as permanent quadrats after management works had taken place in 1994[20].

Experiments have been carried out on some other sites to determine methods of "re-seeding" with missing species, using transplants from other parts of the site. Trials were proposed to re-introduce bogmosses onto the bare, recent commercial cuttings, but this has not proved necessary. However, some lesser bladderwort has been transplanted[21].

Objective 6. *Tolerate seral habitats until it becomes clear whether their presence interferes with Objective 1, or until they are identified and accepted as important seral habitats in their own right*

Damp fields, heathlands, fens and woodlands on the boundaries of the Mosses all support different species from the central mire communities. The decision as to whether to retain these habitats or return them to mire is dependent upon their conservation and aesthetic value. The extent of marginal habitats was mapped in 1992 [6], and their value for wildlife has been in part assessed through the moss survey[18], numerous invertebrate surveys, the RSPB breeding bird transects of 1995[22], and plant surveys of marginal fields and the canal lagg. A study has also been conducted of changes in ground beetle species from the Moss out onto surrounding farmland [23]. Hydrological information is being collected in the tall scrub near the railway line and in the pine trees at Bettisfield Moss and in the north of North East Fenn's Moss. This data will be drawn together in the 1996 management plan revision to determine the extent of seral habitats to be maintained. Meanwhile, management of these areas focuses on maintenance of particular '

marginal animal groups, for example the opening out of scrub along the railway line and tracks leading up to the Moss for butterflies.

Objective 7. *Safeguard populations of all significant species characteristic of raised mire habitats described in Objective 1*

The insect and rare plant surveys described in Chapter 2 have provided data as to the distribution of significant raised mire species, and more information has been gained about their habitat requirements. Where possible, and where the species requirements are clear, management aims to accommodate these species. Clearly, many of the raised mire species will

respond positively to the general scrub removal and increase in water levels. The specific habitat requirements of the rare caddisfly *Hagenella clathrata* have been accommodated and damming in areas where this species occurs has been restricted to permit the base of tussocks to dry out in the summer.

Similarly, scrub clearance has not been carried out on the main areas used by the northern footman moth.

Plate 58. Rows of dead vegetation and "rashes" of small birch are augered back into the drains by the screw-leveller. Photograph: J.L. Daniels.

Plate 59. Many parties enjoy guided walks on the Mosses. Photograph: W. Allmark.

been developed with the Fire Service, including provision of fire pools and fire procedure cards.

Three further objectives are specified in the management plan:

Objective 9. *Provide for controlled visitor access.*

Objective 10. *Provide for controlled educational use of the site.*

Objective 11. *Promote and provide facilities for research, particularly into experimental management techniques in the rehabilitation of raised mire systems, which will help realise but not compromise Objectives 1 and 2. Ensure the demonstration and dissemination of the resulting information.*

The occurrence of deep drains and the high potential fire risk in dry periods make the Mosses a hazardous environment. English Nature and the Countryside Council for Wales have, however, been keen to enable the visitor to experience the special habitat and landscape of the mire and through an extensive programme of lectures, guided public and school group visits, have been able to address the need to ensure the safety of all visitors (Plate 59). General public access to the Reserve is managed by a system of annual permits which ensure that visitors can explore the Mosses in safety whenever they wish.

● Progress Towards Mending the Mire

The extension of the SSSI, and the progress towards European and international recognition for the site have imposed additional restrictions on further damage to the mire. Large-scale mechanised commercial peat cutting has ceased and the remaining commercial cutting has been regularised. The Mosses fortunately have been acquired with substantial depths of peat remaining to aid successful rehabilitation. Further land acquisitions now mean that most of the semi-natural mire

The transfer of commercial hand peat cutters onto the Nature Reserve may also accommodate certain rare invertebrates associated with peat cuttings.

Objective 8. *Fulfill all legal and other obligations*

These obligations have been particularly onerous with regard to upgrading the safety of the site both for workers and for the general public, to comply with all aspects of the Health and Safety at Work Act, Occupier's Liability Act and English Nature's and the Countryside Council for Wales' requirements. The many sleeper bridges have been upgraded and signed, substantial improvements have been carried out to trackways and a fire-fighting strategy has

community is under the direct management of the Countryside Council for Wales and English Nature and the additional land will enable better management of the central mire communities.

The changes caused to the mire vegetation by the leakage of water of high nutrient status and pH, transforming it into alder/willow carr with fen and swamp plants such as rushes and bulrush, is now well-recorded and the sources of hydrological pollution have been traced. British Waterways have carried out a programme of extensive deep-piling where the canal crosses the Moss, to prevent the leakage of the canal water onto the Moss and surrounding farmland. The nutrient-rich spring on Fenn's Moss has been blocked by a network of dams and it is expected that the increased head of water will prevent continued upwelling. Action to resolve problems arising from enriched waters from Moss Cottages and surrounding fields is to be initiated.

Techniques have been developed for damming, bunding and controlling erosion in the wide variety of drainage situations present on the site, using available machinery and the expertise of retained workers. Three-quarters of the 1991 landholding has already been dammed. This work has been supported by the detailed mapping of contours, drain levels and drain locations and, together with peat depth studies, has increased understanding of which land in the SSSI will be affected by raising water tables at different locations.

The geology underlying different areas of the Mosses has been investigated indicating that major bands of sand underlie much of Fenn's Moss and some parts of Whixall and Wem Mosses[10]. However, the extensive peat depth studies undertaken by English Nature show a much greater extent of clay in the surface few centimetres immediately below the peat all across the Mosses, with sand rarely being found. This, together with the fact that the extremely decomposed lower peats also conduct water very slowly, will restrict any effects of raised heads of bog water on the underlying ground water table.

Hydrological results have indicated that the summer water tables in 1993 in Oaf's Orchard were within 30cm of the ground surface before any damming commenced; this level was at least a metre above the surface of the marginal fields, indicating that the mire was still retaining in part a dome of water. However, hydrological data have not been collected for long enough to enable other than general conclusions to be drawn. The peat water table has been shown to closely follow the surface contours across the Moss so that there is no one general water level, and even small, uncut lumps of peat such as the Cowberry Patch (150m x 200m) draw the water table to a height well above the surface of surrounding cuttings. Uncut ground or cut-over ground without regular (11 yd) drains retains water much closer to the ground surface than regularly drained, cut-over areas even if they are situated at a higher level; and they also respond much more rapidly to rainfall after droughts.

The damming has been extremely successful at retaining water on the Moss, providing the correct conditions for mire species to re-establish, and substantial areas of open water now occur. Damming enables water to be retained nearer to the ground surface for longer periods. For example, in the recent commercial cuttings in 1993/4, in an undammed area, water-levels never reached the top 20cm of peat, and lay between 20-30cm for only 13% of the year; for the remainder of the time they lay at a deeper level. By contrast, in a low part of the dammed commercial cuttings water-levels remained permanently in the top 20cm of the peat, the same as in the uncut peats of Oaf's Orchard and better than in a poorly drained hand cut, both of which have mire vegetation. Thus the damming should enable the re-establishment of mire communities.

Plate 60. The expansion of hare's-tail cotton-sedge into dammed cuttings will greatly increase the food available for larvae of the large heath butterfly. Photograph: J.L. Daniels.

Monitoring the ditch water levels at the wettest and driest times of year shows clearly that the extent of surface water in the summer droughts mirrors the extent of the damming. Even in the unprecedented drought of 1995 there was still standing water for dragonflies in some of the dammed areas.

Extensive winter flooding occurred in 1992 and 1993 on surrounding farmland within the peat basin. This has been a regular occurrence on the peaty fields in very wet years, when the drainage network leading away from the Mosses backs-up. Extensive opening-up of drains by the peat companies in the past has allowed storm water to immediately flow off the Moss onto surrounding farmland. It is anticipated that the recent damming may give a more gradual release of water, so helping the surrounding culverts and drainage channels to cope with storm water. The longer the peat is dammed, the better it seems able to retain water and so may be able to absorb and then gradually release more water than the damaged peats of the drained mossland.

Detailed vegetation monitoring will not be repeated until 1996, but a subjective assessment of the effects of damming is that the mosses are clearly returning to the Mosses!

The polythene-bunding of Oaf's Orchard has already changed the vegetation of the area, with much more water being held in the old cuttings, giving sheets of flowering cotton-sedges in spring and a change on the uncut surface to wet heath and mire communities and an increase in the extent of bogmosses. The annual scrub clearance has killed many of the birch stumps and the site is now open, as are the Cranberry Beds.

On the south of Whixall Moss, because of the high tracks, it has been possible to retain water at ground surface for most of the year. In flooded areas, the bogmoss and liverworts which originally lay in the base of the cuttings have risen up as floating carpets. Bogmoss has spread out from these across the surface of the peat, between the large tussocks of hare's-tail cotton-sedge which have begun to develop (Plate 60). These tussocks should greatly increase larval foodplant availability for the large heath butterfly.

In general, scrub clearance on the 1991 landholding has opened up all except part of the old commercial cuttings of Fenn's

Moss. Although the birch has been cut down on a large proportion of Fenn's Moss, studies have shown that 30% is likely to regrow[14], although growth rates will be retarded by high water levels. This percentage can be reduced in the future by retreatment should it prove necessary.

Bogmosses have appeared in what were dry ditches all across Fenn's Moss soon after they had been dammed (Plate 61). The residual strip of mire species left every 11 yards after peat cutting is thriving because of the higher water levels and cotton-sedges and bogmosses are colonising bare areas. On higher, cut-over areas where damming cannot retain as much water, purple moor-grass and heather are spreading onto bare areas, but bogmoss still thrives in and alongside the drains.

The results of pine clearance on Bettisfield Moss have been spectacular. Cotton-sedges have spread and flowered on all of the cleared areas and the cleared bogmoss carpet of the cut-over area has been coloured red with cranberries, amongst which can be found the starry flowers of the rare white beak-sedge.

There has been a rapid and immediate expansion of the populations of many damselflies, darters and dragonflies across the Mosses in response to works, with species such as four-spotted chaser, emerald- , common blue- and large red damselflies and black darters thriving on newly-dammed cuttings. The site's particular rarity, the white-faced darter, has spread to new areas. Areas of tall scrub have been shown by the invertebrate studies (see *The Nature of the Place*) to be important for a number of species and, consequently, areas of this habitat are to be retained. Butterflies such as the dingy skipper, common blue, small skipper, meadow brown and small heath have responded well to the opening up of scrub along the railway trackbed.

Birds too have responded dramatically to the greater availability of water, with lapwing nesting in the centre of the site for the first time in many years. The number of

Plate 61. Bogmoss appears in dammed ditches within six months.
Photograph: André Q. Berry.

pairs of breeding curlew has increased and spread out across the site[22]. New species such as spotted redshank use the Mosses on autumn passage and in 1995 the mire was even visited by a red-necked phalarope.

Hobby are now present, reflecting not only their northward spread across the country but also the increased availability of dragonflies and damselflies on the Mosses. Marsh- and hen-harrier are also beginning to use the site.

Breeding birds have shown marked responses to scrub clearance. Scrub species such as tree pipit have declined[22], but there has been a large increase in the numbers of meadow pipit and skylark. The importance of this should not be understated, as ground

135

nesting species such as skylark have suffered major, recent declines in their populations with the advent of silage production and the sowing of winter wheat.

In winter the Mosses abound with wildfowl and waders, with mallard, teal and snipe replacing species of scrub.

In our increasingly intensively-managed countryside, the seemingly remote wilderness of Fenn's and Whixall Mosses is a landscape to be experienced, an intricate tapestry of peat cutting patterns reflecting the changing seasons - from the haunting, bubbling call of curlew in the spring; the smell of warm peat and the constant darting flight of dragonflies on balmy summer days; through the myriad rich autumnal hues of the bog vegetation and the "jinking" flight of silver snipe flushed from the ditches in winter. The conservation management of this important wetland site will ensure that this evocative landscape is secure for future generations to explore and enjoy.

A Bird's Eye View

Plate 62. Fenn's, Whixall and Bettisfield Mosses from the south west, looking north east. The standing water visible across the centre of the mire highlights the success of English Nature's damming works undertaken as part of their rehabilitation programme.
© **Crown Copyright: Royal Commission on the Ancient and Historical Monuments of Wales. Ref. 95-CS-0117. 12.03.1995.**

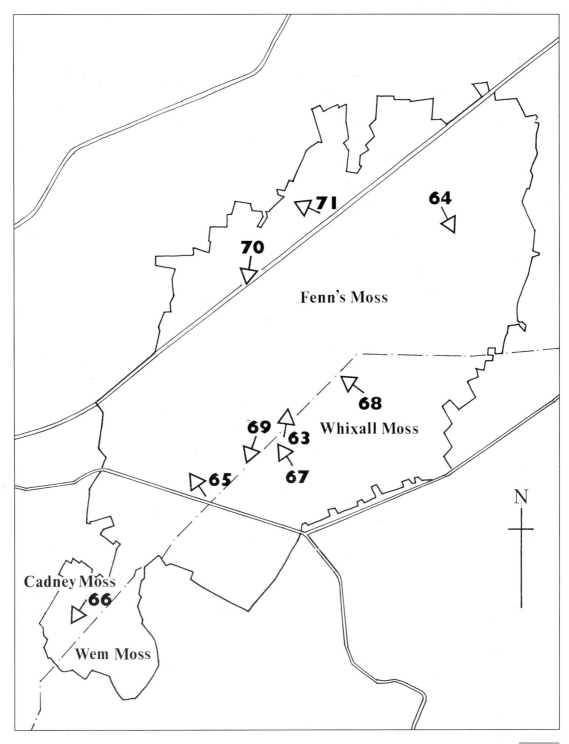

Figure 25. Approximate centre and orientation of Plates 63 to 71. Drawing (and accompanying annotation diagrams): Timothy Morgan.

Plate 63. A comparison between the hand cut "acres" of Whixall Moss (foreground) and the regular commercial cutting on Fenn's Moss.
© Crown Copyright: Royal Commission on the Ancient and Historical Monuments of Wales.
Ref. 95-CS-0118*. 12.03.1995.

1. Agricultural land on surrounding higher mineral soils.

2. Old hand peat cuttings (pre-1960s) and fields reclaimed from the Moss.

3. Recent commercial hand peat cuttings (Abbie Austin's) *cf.* Plate 70.

4. Recent commercial mechanised peat cuttings (Mr. Lloyd's) *cf.* Plate 71.

5. Maelor Forest pine plantations on Fenn's Moss (planted 1960s).

6. Former Oswestry, Ellesmere and Whitchurch railway (dismantled).

7. North East Fenn's uncut peat.

8. North East Fenn's Mezzina.

9. Old commercial hand peat cuttings (pre-1950s).

10. Old commercial hand peat cuttings (pre-1950s) with recent commercial machine cuttings (1989-91).

11. The Eighteen Chain.

12. Recent commercial machine cuttings showing standing surface water arising from dam construction as part of English Nature's rehabilitation programme.

13. Old commercial hand peat cutting (pre-1960s).

14. Cranberry Beds (uncut).

15. The Batters WWI rifle ranges target butts.

16. Polythene lined dams forming part of English Nature's rehabilitation programme on old commercial peat cuttings.

17. Oaf's Orchard (uncut).

18. English/Welsh Border Drain.

19. Recent hand peat cuttings (ongoing).

20. Old hand peat cuttings (pre-1980).

21. Fields reverting to mossland.

22. Shropshire Union Canal.

23. Fields on peat.

24. Billy Furber's scrapyard.

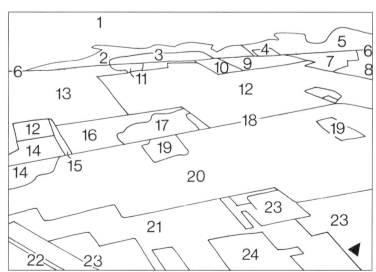

Plate 64. North East Fenn's Moss, showing the WW1 rifle range butts and WW2 bombing range target centre.
© Crown Copyright: Royal Commission on the Ancient and Historical Monuments of Wales.
Ref. 94-CS-1715*. 04.10.1994.

1. Agricultural land on surrounding higher mineral soils.

2. Fenn's Wood pine plantations on peat (planted 1960s).

3. Line of former tramway linking 1850/56 peat processing works with canal.

4. Manor House, now English Nature's Nature Reserve base, formerly *L.S. Beckett's* and *Croxden Horticultural Products Ltd* peat processing works.

5. House, formerly office for *Moulded Peat Charcoal Company* processing works.

6. "The Old Shed Yard".

7. Old hand peat cuttings (pre-1940).

8. Recent commercial machine peat cuttings (*Croxden Horticultural Products Ltd* 1989-90).

9. Long Mile, tramroad/peat railway linking with Fenn's Bank station on the former Oswestry, Ellesmere and Whitchurch railway.

10. Old Whixall Bible hand peat cuttings (pre-1940s) recolonised by heather, purple moor-grass, bracken and birch scrub.

11. Recent commercial hand peat cuttings (to 1994) showing tractor extraction patterns.

12. WW1 rifle range target butts and sites of WW2 air-to-ground machine gun targets (including 12a).

13. WW2 bombing range target centre.

14. Drain dating to 1777 inclosure award.

15. Self-sown pine/birch woodland.

16. Old hand peat cuttings (various 1960-1994).

17. Recent commercial machine peat cuttings (1970-1988).

18. Earlier hand and more recent commercial peat cuttings (1960-1988).

19. Mezzina (pre-1940s).

20. Lundt's old commercial machine peat cuttings (pre-1975).

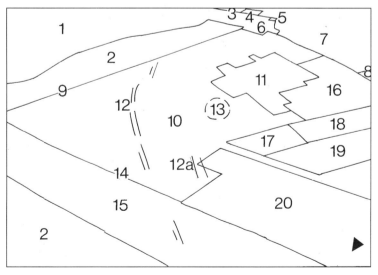

Plate 65. Bettisfield Moss, showing clearance work.
© **Crown Copyright: Royal Commission on the Ancient and Historical Monuments of Wales.**
Ref. 94-CS-1706*. 04.10.1994.

1. Agricultural land on surrounding higher mineral soils.

2. Former Oswestry, Ellesmere and Whitchurch railway (dismantled).

3. The Batters WWI rifle ranges target butts.

4. Line of spine track and shooting butts associated with The Batters rifle ranges.

5. The Cinder Track (a cinder "enriched" rifle range spine track) through the Cranberry Beds.

6. English/Welsh Border Drain.

7. The Quob, alder carr/birch woodland.

8. Shropshire Union Canal.

9. Bettisfield Moss (uncut) colonised by self-sown pine woodland.

10. Old commercial hand peat cuttings now colonised by self-sown pine woodland.

11. Remnant of 1777 inclosure award shelter belt (birch woodland).

12. Probable source of self-sown pine.

13. The Duck Pool, dynamite used in an attempt to construct a lake!

14. English Nature cleared *Sphagnum* "lawn".

15. Birch/pine woodland over old commercial hand peat cuttings.

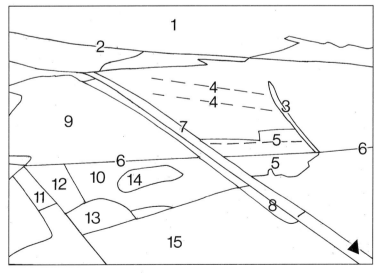

Plate 66. Wem and Cadney Mosses.
© Crown Copyright: Royal Commission on the Ancient and Historical Monuments of Wales.
Ref. 94-CS-1705*. 04.10.1994.

1. Limit of peat body (dashed line).

2. Agricultural land on surrounding higher mineral soils.

3. English/Welsh Border Drain.

4. Bettisfield Manor Drain.

5. Head of River Roden.

6. Wem Moss Shropshire Wildlife Trust nature reserve, showing marginal tree invasion and the
    results of recent scrub clearance work.

7. Agricultural land reclaimed from Cadney Moss.

8. Forestry plantations on Cadney Moss.

9. Agricultural land reclaimed from Wem Moss.

10. Recent commercial hand peat cuttings on tree covered mossland link between Cadney and
    Bettisfield Mosses.

11. Agricultural land reclaimed from Bettisfield Moss.

12. Bettisfield Moss colonised by self-sown pine.

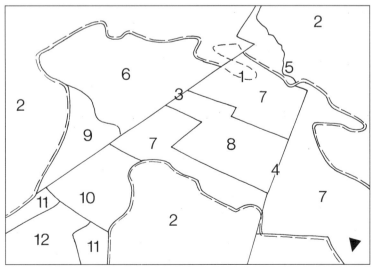

Plate 67. Whixall Moss, showing Whixall Bible cuttings (foreground) and hand cut "acres" (centre).
© Crown Copyright: Royal Commission on the Ancient and Historical Monuments of Wales.
Ref. 94-CS-1734*. 04.10.1994.

1. **The Batters WWI rifle ranges target butts.**

2. **Old commercial hand peat cuttings, dammed using polythene lined bunds as part of English Nature's rehabilitation programme.**

3. **Oaf's Orchard (uncut).**

4. **English/Welsh Border Drain.**

5. **Old hand peat cuttings (various to 1980).**

6. **Recent hand peat cuttings (various to 1994).**

7. **Old hand peat cuttings, Whixall Bibles (pre-1940s).**

8. **Standing surface water and regenerating bogmoss arising from English Nature's rehabilitation programme.**

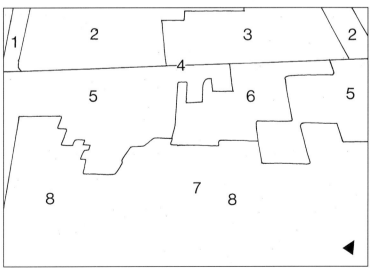

**Plate 68. The contrast between hand cut "acres" on Whixall Moss (foreground) and recent
commercial cutting on Fenn's Moss (background).
© Crown Copyright: Royal Commission on the Ancient and Historical Monuments of Wales.
Ref. 94-CS-1735*. 04.10.1994.**

1. **Arterial Main Drain.**

2. **Standing surface water and regenerating bogmoss arising from English Nature's rehabilitation
   programme.**

3. **Recent commercial machine peat cuttings (to 1990).**

4. **WW2 "Starfish" site.**

5. **English/Welsh Border Drain.**

6. **Old hand peat cuttings (various to 1980), showing standing surface water arising from English
   Nature's rehabilitation programme.**

7. **Recent hand peat cuttings (ongoing).**

8. **Area of uncut peat.**

9. **Old hand peat cuttings, black peat (pre-1970s).**

10. **Drain bringing nutrient enriched water from Moss Cottages, bordered by willow/alder trees.**

11. **Area of Whixall Bible peat cuttings.**

12. **Turfed area (pre-1940s), with some recent hand cut trenches.**

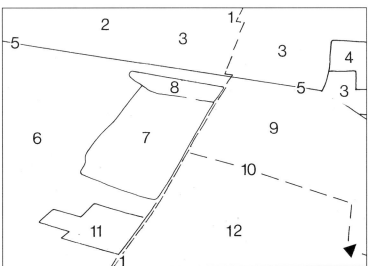

Plate 69. The uncut peat of Oaf's Orchard (foreground) and the Cranberry Beds (background).
© Crown Copyright: Royal Commission on the Ancient and Historical Monuments of Wales.
Ref. 95-CS-1416*. 18.05.1995.

1. **Agricultural land reclaimed from the Moss.**

2. **Bettisfield Moss hand cuttings recolonised by self-sown pine woodland.**

3. **Bogmoss "lawn" cleared of pine by English Nature.**

4. **Shropshire Union Canal.**

5. **The Quob, alder carr/birch woodland.**

6. **Reclaimed fields now with regenerating scrub.**

7. **Old hand peat cuttings (pre-1985, mainly pre-1950).**

8. **Cranberry Beds, uncut bogmoss carpet.**

9. **The Cinder Track, enriched spine track of The Batters WWI rifle ranges.**

10. **The Batters WWI rifle ranges target butts.**

11. **Old commercial hand peat cuttings (pre-1940).**

12. **Polythene lined peat dams installed in 1993 by English Nature as part of their rehabilitation programme.**

13. **Oaf's Orchard (uncut crown of the Moss).**

14. **Recent hand peat cuttings (to 1994).**

15. **Recent commercial machine peat cuttings (to 1990).**

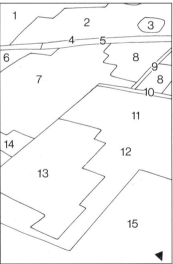

Plate 70. Recent, commercial tractor-extracted hand cuttings north of the dismantled railway line. © Crown Copyright: Royal Commission on the Ancient and Historical Monuments of Wales. Ref. 95-CS-0111. 12.03.1995.

1. **Recent commercial machine peat cuttings (*Croxden Horticultural Products Ltd*), showing standing water resulting from damming undertaken as part of English Nature's rehabilitation programme.**

2. **Old commercial machine peat cuttings (pre-1960), showing darker due to heather growth, with some recent machine peat cuttings.**

3. **Former Oswestry, Ellesmere and Whitchurch railway (dismantled), surrounded by scrub.**

4. **Recent commercial hand peat cuttings, showing tractor extraction pattern (Abbie Austin's).**

5. **Area of old hand peat cuttings recolonised by pine, birch, bracken and heather.**

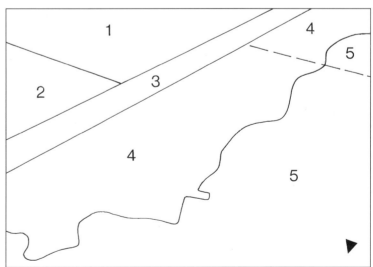

Plate 71. Recent, excavator-extracted commercial cuttings north of the dismantled railway line.
© Crown Copyright: Royal Commission on the Ancient and Historical Monuments of Wales.
Ref. 95-CS-0115. 12.03.1995.

1. Burnt area of forestry recolonised by self-sown pine.

2. Area cleared ready for commercial mechanised peat cutting, showing linear forestry drains (Mr. Lloyd's).

3. Recent commercial mechanised peat cuttings (Mr. Lloyd's).

4. Fay thrown into bottom of wet, peat excavations.

5. Former Oswestry, Ellesmere and Whitchurch railway (dismantled).

6. Fire break pool cut by Mr. Lloyd.

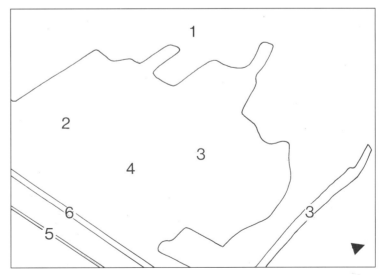

Peat Speak

- a glossary of
peatmen's terms

The peatmen of Fenn's and Whixall Mosses have had little cause to describe their day-to-day activities in written form. Consequently, in the case of those terms whose spelling is not immediately identifiable from the spoken word, the editors have had to impose a spelling which best seems to reflect the pronunciation of the term concerned. These terms are highlighted in **bold italics** and, where necessary, an aid to pronunciation is given in simple form.

Readers should note that all hand tools illustrated were custom-made. As a consequence, the pattern may vary considerably from tool to tool of the same type where different blacksmiths were employed or where users had particular requirements, although the function remains the same. Tools of the firm *L.S. Beckett* were used extensively across both Fenn's- and Whixall Mosses and were made to a standard pattern, many by the Scottish *Bar Blues Forge*. The Ellesmere blacksmith Alf Strange made Whixall Bible tools for some local people[1]. Accordingly, these tool patterns have been taken as "typical" of those used on the Mosses.

Bat (Dutch method) see **Uplifter**.

Bench (Dutch method) A **yard** width of peat (in fact 24in. or 30in. in width dependent on whether cutting four or five blocks wide) was taken from a **side** at each cutting. Each "yard" width was divided into one hundred "benches" along its length, each "bench" being 16in. in length and comprising either 20 or 24 **Dutch blocks** dependent on whether blocks were cut 5 wide by 4 deep or 4 wide by 6 deep (refer Figure 21, p.106).

24 blocks were the maximum number of blocks which could be stacked on a side without the cut face collapsing.

Black Peat The lowest layer of peat, of well-humified swamp or fen peat. *cf.* **Grey Peat**, **White Peat**.

Burning Turf Well-dried **Dutch blocks** intended for fuel. *cf.* **Potting**.

Casey Apparently a corruption of "causeway". Also called ***mawing*** roads. Used to describe the areas of uncut peat dividing and giving access to the cutting **flats**: Peat would be stacked in ***maws*** on the "caseys" and the **shifting rails** of the peat railway would be laid along them.

Chatty Pale straw-like peat usually found near the base of the peat body. *cf.* **Black Peat**, **Grey Peat**, **White Peat**. e.g. *Chatty Bottoms Drain* (N.G.R. SJ 4990 3660 to SJ 5045 3667).

Coal The gyttia or lake deposits at the base of the peat.

Cock (traditional indigenous method) A bee-hive shaped stack of **Whixall Bible** peat blocks. The "cock" was only constructed if the peat was not dry enough to be taken off the Moss by the onset of winter. Blocks were stacked with the driest innermost and the wettest to the outside and arranged with spaces between each block, alternating on each row, so as to enable air to circulate both through and around the stack.

Cut-out (Dutch method) Cutting **flats** were progressively worked a **yard** wide by a "yard" deep across the width of each side. The last "yard" or two width left on a layer of peat was called the "cut-out", because the next operation would be to cut it out and then, in the following season, cut the "yard" of peat immediately below it to create the first new drain in the underlying next layer of peat.

Figure 26. A dog. Drawing: Timothy Morgan.

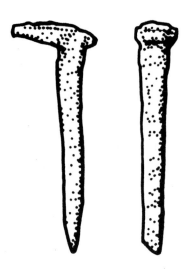

Dog Iron flanged nail used to secure the lengths of rail of the **permanent peat railway** to their wooden sleepers (Figure 26).

Dust Fine granulated dry peat processed through the swing hammer peat mills, or derived as **throughs** from the rotary screens. Used for packing and in cattle feed. *cf.* **Litter**, **Tailings**, **Throughs**.

Dutch Block (Dutch method) A peat block measuring approximately 6in x 6in x 16in (Plate 72).

Dutch Chain (Dutch method) A cubic measurement, being 44 cubic imperial yards of peat. A **side** of peat (44 imperial yards in length) cut 5 blocks wide (30in.) by 4 blocks deep (24in.) comprised half a chain of peat (22cu.yd.), whilst cut 4 blocks wide (24in.) by 6 blocks deep (36in.) comprised 27cu.yd.

Dutch Method 6in x 6in x 16in **Dutch blocks** are cut out horizontally from the peat body by the peatman standing in the cutting, as opposed to the Irish method where the peatman stands on the peat surface to cut the blocks out vertically.

Fay The surface vegetation of the peat body, which would be cut away using a *fayer* to expose the bare peat surface ready for cutting. Although the term is today associated with the Dutch method of peat cutting it appears to have been assimilated from a traditional indigenous term. At Whixall Moss "*fleeinge* [believed pronounced "*flaying*"] *the greene sward uppon the wast*" is first described in 1626[2], with "*flawe turves*" in 1653[3]. In 1716[4], such turves are described as "*greensward **flaes** or green turves*". At a time when construction of drains upon the Moss was limited, the water table lay close to the surface and peat could only be cut to a very limited depth before the cuttings flooded and became unworkable. Under such circumstances most of the peats or turves referred to would have been cut from the greensward and immediate surface layers of the peat body.

Plate 72. Mr. Dick Tinsley and Mrs Joan Heath compare Dutch block and Whixall Bible, c.1955. C10070, Geoff Charles Collection. Reproduced with the kind permission of The National Library of Wales.

Fayer (Dutch method, but see **fay** above) Spade-like hand tool (Figure 27) used to remove the surface vegetation or **fay** to expose the bare peat surface ready for cutting. Today, the "*fayer*" is often a modified standard pattern spade.

Fettling (Dutch method) A generic term encompassing all the operations between the act of cutting the peat and transporting it for processing, i.e. **stooling**, **walling**, *mawing*, **wheeling out**.

Fiarn (pronounced *fee-yarn*) Bracken (*Pteridium aquilinum*). Derived from "fern".

Flae see **Fay**.

Flats (Dutch method) With the arrival of the Dutch at Fenn's and Whixall Mosses in the 1920s, the peat body was marked out and divided up by drains into oblong cutting fields or "flats" each eighty-eight yards wide and of variable length up to 550 imperial yards on Fenn's Moss, divided from the next "flat" by a track or **casey** eleven yards wide (refer Figure 20, p.106).

Fleeinge see **Fay**.

Full Side see **Side.**

Grey Peat The intermediate peat layer of moderately humified bogmoss and other mire species. Describes the colour of the peat when dry. *cf.* **Black Peat**, **White Peat**.

Grig Heather (*Calluna vulgaris*). Derived from the Welsh word for heather, *grug* (pronounced *grig*).

Irongrass Purple moor-grass (*Molinia caerulea*). Describes the tough, wiry nature of the stem bases and roots which made cutting difficult. It is commonly held that "irongrass" was deliberately introduced to Fenn's and Whixall Mosses alongside the sections of **tramroad** to improve traction for the horses pulling the laden peat wagons. "Irongrass" is a

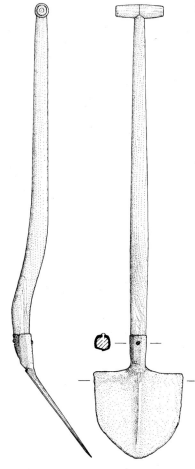

Figure 27. Fayer.
Drawing: Timothy Morgan.

naturally occurring species of wet or damp peaty areas, usually abundant and frequently dominating large areas. It is therefore probable that rather than being introduced to the mire the species may well have been encouraged to grow in desired areas. Also known as **sniddle**.

Kipe (Archaic) **Burning turf** is recorded as being served out in a **whisket** or a "kipe" by the peatman on his delivery rounds in c.1900 [5]. The "whisket" is described as a wide, shallow basket with a hand space on each side underneath the rim, whilst a "kipe" is a deeper basket of smaller circumference with a handle each side.

161

Plate 73. A maw, showing the vertical blocks known as "sergeant majors".
Reproduced with the kind permission of Ted Clorley.

Figure 28. Nicker-out.

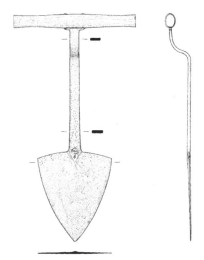

Plate 74. Pattens.
Photograph: André Q. Berry.
07.10.1994.

Lift (Archaic) The upper layer of the peat or **white peat** is described as "*lift*" in 1889[6]. The term is no longer used by peatmen.

Litter Coarse/medium granulated dry peat processed through the litter machine and used for livestock bedding and deep litter housed poultry systems. *cf.* **Dust, Throughs, Tailings**.

Mawing (Dutch method) (pronounced *mao*-ing) The act of stacking peat for storage in **maws**.

Mawing Road see **Casey**.

Maws (Dutch method) (pronounced *mao-z*) Peat once it had been dried in the **wall**, and if not immediately required for processing, would be stacked along each **casey** in large stacks or "maws" (Plate 73).

Mossing The act of collecting bogmoss from the drains. Moss would be pulled from the drains to be left to dry alongside before being collected for use in making holly wreaths and in recent years for commercial sale for hanging baskets. See **Top Moss**.

Mullocks see **Tailings**.

Nicker-out (Dutch method) Similar in form to a **fayer** (Figure 28). Used to mark out the **side** for the next cut, for cutting the **fay** and in place of the **sticker** for marking out the **benches** and top **Dutch blocks** in areas where the peat is difficult to cut.

Nog The remains of cotton-sedges (*Eriophorum* spp.), particularly their rhizomes, found in the peat. Tough and fibrous in nature, such remains rendered peat cutting difficult. Used in the past as a tobacco substitute by some peatmen.

Pattens Custom-made large, flat "overshoes" worn over working boots to spread the peatman's weight and prevent sinking into the wet peat whilst cutting (Plate 74).

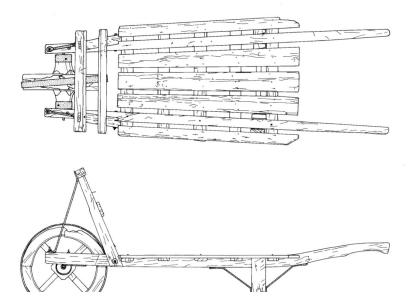

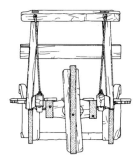

Figure 29. Peat barrow.
Drawing: Timothy Morgan.

Peat Barrow Wooden barrow (Figure 29) used for **wheeling-out** the dried **Dutch blocks** from the **wall** to the **shifting line** of the peat railway.

Permanent Peat Railway A 2'0" gauge track system traversed the Moss and enabled transport of the dried peat from the cutting **flats** to the peat processing works. The majority of the system was "permanent", with track laid on wooden sleepers to which it was affixed by **dogs**. Flexibility was, however, required in track layout at the cutting **flats**, as areas of cutting moved and stacked peat in new areas became dry. In the latter case temporary **shifting line** was employed and linked into the "permanent peat railway" using points.

Piking The act of re-stacking the **ruins** from the *maws* to dry.

Pit Row The row of cut **Dutch blocks** placed nearest to the edge of the peat cutting during the hand cutting process. These blocks would be those cut from the base of each **bench**.

Platt Wooden bridge over a drain. e.g. *Platt Lane* (N.G.R. SJ 5140 3640)

Potting 9in × 12in × 6-9in peat blocks. Used in the production of horticultural composts and therefore only partially dried so that the core remains moist to give a damp granulated peat when milled. In winter production, when such blocks were too wet they would be mixed with **dust** derived from dry **Dutch blocks**. *cf.* **Burning Peat**.

Rearing (traditional indigenous method) The initial act of stacking **Whixall Bible** peat blocks on edge to dry.

Ruck A heap of peat.

Ruins The uppermost layer of **Dutch blocks** forming the domed top to the *maws* would often become wet in storage, for example where lying snow had melted. When the "maw" was dismantled for processing, this uppermost layer of blocks would be haphazardly thrown to one side to be known as "ruins".

Figure 30. Sticker. Drawing: Timothy Morgan.

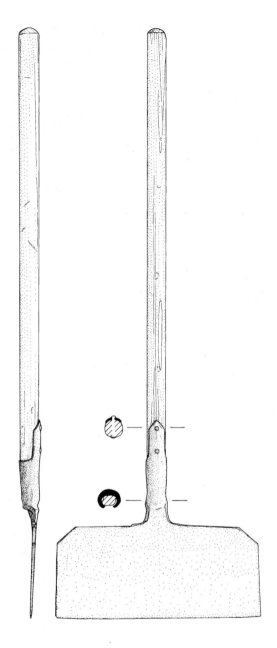

of the stack to form a water-shedding, domed top to the stack (refer Plate 73).

Sheeding (holly wreath making) The act of shedding leaves by holly when in the wreath, as a consequence of frost damage or drying out.

Shifting Line (Dutch method) Temporary 2'0" gauge peat railway line laid along the **casey** between each cutting **flat** as peat became dry ready for processing, enabling the locomotives and peat wagons to approach close to the peat cuttings and so minimise the distance for **wheeling-out**. Shifting lines were rigid-mounted on metal "sleepers" for ease and speed of installation and were connected into the **permanent peat railway** by points.

Side (Dutch method) Each **flat** was divided into eleven imperial yard wide "sides" lying at right angles to the **casey**. One cut of peat was taken from each "side" each year. A "side" was 44 imperial yards in length, a **full side** 88 imperial yards in length (refer Figure 20, p.106).

Siggle Cranberry (*Vaccinium oxycoccus*).

Sniddle see **Irongrass**.

Spragging (Dutch method) The act of linking two adjoining **stools** together using two **Dutch blocks** so as to increase stability (refer Figure 23, p.107).

Stabs (holly wreath making) Decorative variegated holly, foliage or (today) artificial flowers, etc. bound with florist wire and used to enhance holly wreaths. The nature, position and number of "stabs" is used as a trademark by individual wreath-makers.

Stanking The act of lining cut drains with clay and timbers to prevent collapse[7].

Sticker (Dutch method) Flat-bladed hand tool (Figure 30) used to mark out the **bench** (the width and length of the **Dutch blocks**) on the **side**. Each block would then be cut and separated from

Sergeant Major (Dutch method) **Dutch blocks** once dry were stockpiled in *maws* along each **casey** until required for processing. Blocks were carefully stacked horizontally to around head height and then a row of blocks were stacked vertically, the "sergeant majors", before blocks were thrown onto the top

the underlying peat and placed to the side of the cut to dry using the **uplifter**. A standard pattern hay knife (Plate 75; Figure 31) has also traditionally served the function of the "sticker" and is the dominant such tool in use today. A **nicker-out** can replace the sticker, particularly where the peat is difficult to cut.

Stool (Dutch method) Small, individual stacks of **Dutch blocks** comprising two spaced blocks in each layer, each successive layer set perpendicular to the last (refer Figure 22, p.107). Usually no more than four layers in height. Stability was increased by **spragging**, the linking of one "stool" to its immediate neighbour using two peat blocks (refer Figure 23, p.107).

Stooling (Dutch method) The act of stacking cut peat blocks in a **stool** to partially air dry.

Stych (traditional indigenous method) (pronounced sty-ch) A number of **Whixall Bible** peat blocks piled so as to form a buttress against the **windrow** and arranged on alternating sides, thereby increasing stability of the stacked, drying blocks (refer Figure 19, p.105).

Styching The act of constructing a **stych**.

Tailings Medium granulated dry peat processed through the litter machine, or that would not pass through the rotary screens. Used for livestock bedding and deep litter housed poultry systems. Also known as **mullocks**. cf. **Dust**, **Litter**, **Throughs**.

Throughs Fine granulated dry peat that had passed through the rotary screens. Used for packing and in cattle feed. cf. **Dust**, **Litter**, **Tailings**.

Plate 75. The modern hand peat cutter's tools - (from left to right) pattens, hay knife, sticker, uplifter and standard pattern spade serving as a fayer.
Photograph: André Q. Berry. 07.10.1994.

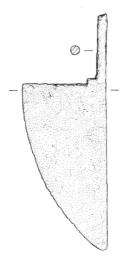

Figure 31. Blade of hay knife, from Lindow Moss.
Drawing: Timothy Morgan.

Figure 32. Uplifter.
Drawing: Timothy Morgan.

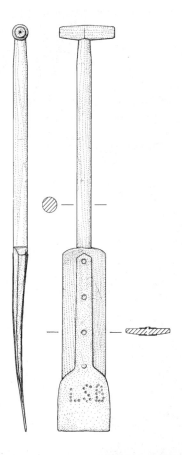

Plate 76. A wall.
Photograph: André Q. Berry.
07.10.1994.

Top Moss (holly wreath making) *Sphagnum* mosses growing on the surface of the peat, as opposed to in the ditches or cuttings. "Top moss" was, in more recent times, sold for hanging baskets and has been traditionally harvested annually to supply the local industry of Christmas holly wreath making. This latter use by peatmen is still permitted under licence from English Nature.

Tramroad Prior to 1919 peat wagons on the 2'0" gauge track were pulled by horses, subsequent to that date by light industrial locomotives. In accordance with Bradley[8], the term "tramroad" is used to describe the horse-drawn track system and "railway", that operated with locomotives.

Trams The wooden peat wagons used to transport peat on the narrow gauge peat railway.

Turf Bank An "acre" of peat rented for hand peat cutting.

Uplifter (Dutch method) Long, narrow, wooden-bladed, metal-tipped hand tool (Figure 32) used to separate from the underlying peat the **Dutch blocks**, which had been marked out using the **sticker**, and to lift and move the blocks to alongside the cutting face for drying. Also known as a **bat** because of its shape, or **uplegger** from the Dutch *oplegger*.

Wall (Dutch method) The cut **Dutch blocks** if not drying quickly enough in the stool, would be stacked to form a "wall" to fully air dry (Plate 76). The "wall" comprised a sequence of individual stacks of spaced peat blocks to form an open structured stack through which air could pass to accelerate drying of the blocks (refer Figure 24, p.107).

Walling (Dutch method) The act of stacking peat from a **stool** to form a **wall** to fully air dry.

Wheeling-out (Dutch method) The act of moving the dried peat from the **stool** or the **wall** to the **casey** using a **peat barrow**, where it would be stacked in *maws* or be loaded onto **trams** on the **shifting line** for transport for processing.

Whinrowing see **Windrowing**.

Whisket (Archaic) see **Kipe**.

White Peat The uppermost layer of peat comprising mostly little-humified *Sphagnum* moss. Describes the colour of the peat when dry. *cf.* **Black Peat**, **Grey Peat**.

Whixall Bible (traditional indigenous method) A peat block for burning measuring approximately 9in x 7in x 4in (refer Plate 72). "Whixall Bibles" were cut from more-or-less square, shallow peat cuttings. Little or no drainage was attempted and cuttings were abandoned once the water table was reached and flooding of the cuttings occurred. The indigenous method of cutting, probably little changed from methods employed in the 16th century. Persisted in use alongside the Dutch method on Whixall Moss until the 1960s (refer Fact Panel Two, p.105).

Whixall Bible Cutter (traditional indigenous method) Spade-like hand tool (Figure 33) used to cut the **Whixall Bible**.

Windrowing (traditional indigenous method) The act of stacking **Whixall Bible** peat blocks on edge in rows to dry (refer Figure 19, p.105). If not adequately dry by the onset of winter, the **Whixall Bible** peat blocks would be stacked from the "windrow" to form a bee-hive shaped stack known as a **cock**. Also known as **Whinrowing**.

Yard (Dutch method) Peat cutters speak of cutting peat from the **side** a "yard" wide by a "yard" deep. This "yard" has no direct relationship with the imperial yard measuring 36in. The actual true width and depth of the "yard" was related to the number of blocks cut in each **bench**. Cutting 4 **Dutch blocks** wide by 5 deep gave a "yard" width of 24in. and "yard" depth of 30in., whereas cutting 4 wide by 6 deep gave a width of 30in. and depth of 36in.

Figure 33. Whixall Bible cutter. Drawing: Timothy Morgan.

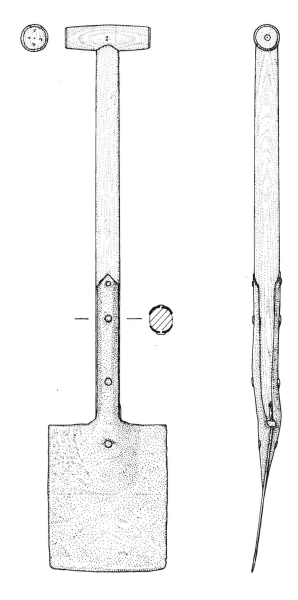

Damselfly, Whixall Moss. Photograph: André Q. Berry

Scientific Names of Species Referred to in the Text:

Plants[1]

Alder *Alnus glutinosa*

Alder buckthorn *Frangula alnus*

Beech *Fagus sylvatica*

Birch *Betula* spp.

Bog asphodel *Narthecium ossifragum*

Bogbean *Menyanthes trifoliata*

Bog myrtle *Myrica gale*

Bog pondweed *Potamogeton polygonifolius*

Bog rosemary *Andromeda polifolia*

Bracken *Pteridium aquilinum*

Bramble *Rubus* spp.

Bulrush *Typha latifolia*

Cotton-sedge, Common *Eriophorum angustifolium*

Cotton-sedge, Hare's-tail *Eriophorum vaginatum*

Cowberry *Vaccinium vitis-idaea*

Cranberry *Vaccinium oxycoccus*

Cross-leaved heath *Erica tetralix*

Crowberry *Empetrum nigrum*

Deer-sedge *Trichophorum cespitosum*

Elm *Ulmus* spp.

Fern, Lady *Athyrium filix-femina*

Fern, Royal *Osmunda regalis*

Hazel *Corylus avellana*

Heather *Calluna vulgaris*

Lesser bladderwort *Utricularia minor*

Lime *Tilia* spp.

Many-stemmed spike-rush *Eleocharis multicaulis*

Marsh cinquefoil *Potentilla palustris*

Marsh pennywort *Hydrocotyle vulgaris*

Meadow thistle *Cirsium dissectum*

Oak *Quercus* spp.

Orchid, Early marsh *Dactylorhiza incarnata*

Orchid, Lesser butterfly *Platanthera bifolia*

Pine *Pinus* spp.

Pine, Scots *Pinus sylvestris*

Poplar *Populus* spp.

Purple moor-grass *Molinia caerulea*

Rosebay willowherb *Chamaenerion angustifolium*

Rush, Rannoch *Scheuchzeria palustris*

Rush, Soft *Juncus effusus*

Sheep's sorrel *Rumex acetosella*

Slender sedge *Carex lasiocarpa*

Sundew, Great *Drosera longifolia*

Sundew, Oblong-leaved *Drosera intermedia*

Sundew, Round-leaved *Drosera rotundifolia*

Violet, Marsh *Viola palustris*

Violet, Water *Hottonia palustris*

White beak-sedge *Rhynchospora alba*

Willow *Salix* spp.

Willow, Creeping *Salix repens*

Lepidoptera
Butterflies[2]

Blue, Common *Polyommatus icarus*

Blue, Holly *Celastrina argiolus*

Brimstone *Gonepteryx rhamni*

Brown, Meadow *Maniola jurtina insularis*

Brown, Wall *Lasiommata megera*

Clouded yellow *Colias crocea*

Comma *Polygonia C-album*

Fritillary, Dark green *Argynnis aglaja*

Fritillary, Small pearl-bordered *Boloria selene selene*

Gatekeeper *Pyronia tithonus britanniae*

Hairstreak, Green *Callophrys rubi*

Hairstreak, Purple *Quercusia quercus*

Heath, Large *Coenonympha tullia davus* and *cockaynei*

Heath, Small *Coenonympha pamphilus pamphilus*

Orange tip *Anthocharis cardamines*

Peacock *Inachis io*
Red admiral *Vanessa atalanta*
Ringlet *Aphantopus hyperantus*
Skipper, Dingy *Erynnis tages*
Skipper, Large *Ochlodes venata faunus*
Skipper, Small *Thymelicus sylvestris*
Small copper *Lycaena phlaeas phlaeas*
Small tortoiseshell *Aglais urticae*
Speckled wood *Pararge aegeria tircis*
White, Green-veined *Pieris napi sabellicae*
White, Large *Pieris brassicae*
White, Small *Pieris rapae*

Moths [3]

Common Heath *Ematurga atomaria*
Dingy Mocha *Cyclophora pendularia*
Eggar, Northern *Lasiocampa quercus callunae*
Eggar, Oak *Lasiocampa quercus*
Eggar, Small *Eriogaster lanestris*
Emperor moth *Pavonia pavonia*
Forester *Adscita statices*
Manchester treble-bar
Carsia sororiata anglica
Northern footman *Eilema sericea*
Plain clay *Eugnorisma depunctata*
Purple-bordered gold *Idaea muricata*
Silver-Y *Autographa gamma*
Waved black *Parascotia fuliginaria*
Waves *Cabera* spp.
Wood tiger *Parasemia plantaginis*
Yellow-tailed moth *Euproctis similis*

Odonata [4]

Black-tailed Skimmer *Orthetrum cancellatum*
Chaser, Broad-bodied *Libellula depressa*
Chaser, Four-spotted
Libellula quadrimaculata
Damselfly, Azure *Coenagrion puella*

Damselfly, Blue-tailed *Ischnura elegans*
Damselfly, Common blue
Enallagma cyathigerum
Damselfly, Emerald *Lestes sponsa*
Damselfly, Large red *Pyrrhosoma nymphula*
Damselfly, Red-eyed *Erythromma najas*
Damselfly, White-legged
Platycnemis pennipes
Damselfly, Variable *Coenagrion pulchellum*
Darter, Black *Sympetrum scoticum*
Darter, Common *Sympetrum striolatum*
Darter, Ruddy *Sympetrum sanguineum*
Darter, White-faced *Leucorrhinia dubia*
Darter, Yellow-winged *Sympetrum flaveolum*
Demoiselle, Banded *Calopteryx splendens*
Demoiselle, Beautiful *Calopteryx virgo*
Downy Emerald *Cordulia aenea*
Dragonfly, Emperor *Anax imperator*
Dragonfly, Golden-ringed
Cordulegaster boltonii
Dragonfly, Scarce blue-tailed
Ischnura pumilio
Hawker, Brown *Aeshna grandis*
Hawker, Common *Aeshna juncea*
Hawker, Migrant *Aeshna mixta*
Hawker, Southern *Aeshna cyanea*

Other Invertebrates [5]

Beetle, Flower *Luperus longicornis*
Beetle, Green tiger *Cicindela campestris*
Beetle, Leaf *Lochmaea suturalis*
Beetles, Leaf *Chalcoides* spp.
Bog bushcricket *Metrioptera brachyptera*
Common backswimmer *Notonecta glauca*
Fly, Horse *Chrysops relictus*
Fly, Sweat *Hydrotaea irritens*
Great raft spider *Dolomedes fimbriatus*
Weevils *Phyllobius* spp., *Polydrusus* spp.

Herptiles[6]

Adder *Vipera berus*

Common frog *Rana temporaria*

Common lizard *Lacerta vivipara*

Common toad *Bufo bufo*

Grass Snake *Natrix natrix*

Newt, Common *Triturus vulgaris*

Newt, Great crested *Triturus cristatus*

Newt, Palmate *Triturus helveticus*

Slow-worm *Anguis fragilis*

Birds[7]

Blackcap *Sylvia atricapilla*

Black-headed gull *Larus ridibundus*

Buzzard *Buteo buteo*

Chiffchaff *Phylloscopus collybita*

Curlew *Numenius arquata*

Dunlin *Calidris alpina*

Goldcrest *Regulus regulus*

Goose, Canada *Branta canadensis*

Goose, Greenland white-fronted *Anser albifrons flavirostris*

Goose, Greylag *Anser anser*

Goose, Pink-footed *Anser brachyrhynchus*

Greenshank *Tringa nebularia*

Green sandpiper *Tringa ochropus*

Grouse, Black *Lyrurus tetrix*

Grouse, Red *Lagopus lagopus*

Harrier, Hen *Circus cyaneus*

Harrier, Marsh *Circus aeruginosus*

Hobby *Falco subbuteo*

Kestrel *Falco tinnunculus*

Lapwing *Vanellus vanellus*

Mallard *Anas platyrhynchus*

Merlin *Falco columbarius*

Nightjar *Caprimulgus europaeus*

Peregrine *Falco peregrinus*

Pipit, Meadow *Anthus pratensis*

Pipit, Tree *Anthus trivialis*

Plover, Golden *Pluvialis fulva*

Plover, Little ringed *Charadrius hiaticula*

Redshank *Tringa totanus*

Redshank, Spotted *Tringa erythropus*

Reed bunting *Emberiza schoeniclus*

Robin *Erithacus rubecula*

Ruff *Philomachus pugnax*

Short-eared owl *Asio flammeus*

Snipe *Gallinago gallinago*

Sparrowhawk *Accipiter nisus*

Skylark *Alauda arvensis*

Stonechat *Saxicola torquata*

Swallow *Hirundo rustica*

Swift *Apus apus*

Teal *Anas crecca*

Treecreeper *Certhia familiaris*

Twite *Carduelis flavirostris*

Warbler, Garden *Sylvia borin*

Warbler, Willow *Phylloscopus trochilus*

Wheatear *Oenanthe oenanthe*

Whinchat *Saxicola rubetra*

Whitethroat *Sylvia communis*

Woodpecker, Great spotted *Dendrocopos major*

Woodpecker, Green *Picus viridis*

Wren *Troglodytes troglodytes troglodytes*

Mammals[8]

Badger *Meles meles*

Brown hare *Lepus europaeus*

Fox *Vulpes vulpes*

Mink (Feral) *Mustela vison*

Polecat *Mustela putorius*

Shrew, Common *Sorex araneus*

Shrew, Pygmy *Sorex minutus*

Shrew, Water *Neomys fodiens*

Vole, Bank *Clethrionomys glareolus*

Vole, Field *Microtus agrestis*

Fenn's Old Works. Photograph: André Q Berry

Appendix One:
Tabulated Summary of Key Commercial/ Military Activity

Date	Company	Activity	Location of Processing Works
1851	*Vardy and Co.*	Lease 308a. of N.E. Fenn's Moss	?"The Old Moss Works" N.G.R. SJ 5039 3662
05/05/1856	Joseph Bebb	Lease above 308a. together with an additional 300a. of N.E. Fenn's Moss. Tramroad link to Shropshire Union Canal.	"The Old Moss Works" N.G.R. SJ 5039 3662
12/09/1859	Richard Henry Holland	Underleases Joseph Bebb's interest in N.E. Fenn's Moss	"The Old Moss Works" N.G.R. SJ 5039 3662
25/05/1860	*The Moulded Peat Charcoal Company*	Underlease Richard Henry Holland's interest in N.E. Fenn's Moss. Holland is recorded as Resident Director of the Company. Ceased trading 12/12/1864.	"The Old Moss Works" N.G.R. SJ 5039 3662
1884	George Wardle	Commences peat moss litter business.	?
1886	George Wardle and William Henry Smith establish *The English Peat Moss Litter Company*	Lease area of N.E. Fenn's Moss. Become a limited company in 1888. Tramroad link to Oswestry, Ellesmere and Whitchurch railway along "Long Mile" to Fenn's Bank.	"The Old Shed Yard" N.G.R. SJ 5037 3682
1889	William Henry Smith and George Wardle	Purchase Lordship of the Manor of Whixall from William Orme Foster.	
WWI	Military	Construct rifle ranges on Fenn's Moss. Produce peat litter for bedding of cavalry horses from new processing works set up on Fenn's Moss. Siding link into Oswestry, Ellesmere and Whitchurch railway.	"The Old Graveyard" N.G.R. SJ 4776 3660
16/10/1923	*The Bettisfield Trust Company Ltd*	Lease 948a. of Fenn's Moss for extraction of black peat. Ceased trading 31/12/1925.	?"The Old Graveyard"; Fenn's Bank Brick and Tile Works N.G.R. SJ 5079 3893
by 10/1923	*The Midland Moss Litter Company*	The Company, with an interest in the white and grey peat for production of peat litter for livestock bedding, is noted in the lease of *The Bettisfield Trust Company Ltd.*	?
before 1927	*The Midland Moss Litter Company*	Construct new processing works adjoining "The Old Graveyard" works to the east.	On site of "Fenn's Old Works" N.G.R. SJ 4780 3665

Date	Company	Activity	Location of Processing Works
1930s	"The Black Firm"/ *The Peat Supply Company*	"The Black Firm" is remembered by local peatmen as producing peat briquettes at Fenn's Bank. Pencil alterations to 10/1923 lease of *The Bettisfield Trust Company Ltd,* dated 1931, suggest this company may be *The Peat Supply Company.*	Fenn's Bank Brick and Tile Works N.G.R. SJ 5079 3893
1931	*The Midland Moss Litter Company*	Join *London and Provincial Peat (L&P Peat),* a co-operative peat marketing consortium.	
1938	*The Midland Moss Litter Company*	Fire destroys processing works. New works constructed on same site. These works survive to this day and are protected as an ancient monument.	"Fenn's Old Works" N.G.R. SJ 4780 3665
WW2	Military	N.E. Fenn's Moss commandeered for practice bombing range.	
13/11/1956	Tom Allmark for *L.S. Beckett*	Purchases 205a. of Whixall Moss from H.H. Wardle.	
11/11/1957	Tom Allmark for *L.S. Beckett*	Purchases Manor House from Herbert Beckett.	"Manor House" N.G.R. SJ 5054 3660
1962	Tom Allmark for *L.S. Beckett*	*The Midland Moss Litter Company* go into voluntary liquidation. *L.S. Beckett* acquire their interest in Fenn's Moss, together with their peat processing works.	"Fenn's Old Works" N.G.R. SJ 4780 3665 and "Manor House" N.G.R. SJ 5054 3660
21/12/1964	Tom Allmark for *L.S. Beckett*	Purchases Alf Millwood's house and land, with one-time tramroad link to the canal. Formerly "The Old Moss Works" and the office of *The Moulded Peat Charcoal Company*	
1968	*L.S. Beckett*	Mechanised peat cutting commences on Fenn's Moss with the purchase of a *Steba V.*	
early 1970s	*L.S. Beckett*	Move the westernmost swing hammer mill from "Fenn's Old Works" to the processing site at Manor House.	"Manor House" N.G.R. SJ 5054 3660
05/1989	*Croxden Horticultural Products Ltd.*	Purchase L.S. Beckett's interests in Fenn's and Whixall Mosses.	"Manor House" N.G.R. SJ 5054 3660
12/1990	Nature Conservancy Council	Purchase *Croxden Horticultural Products Ltd* interests in Fenn's and Whixall Mosses. "Manor House" peat processing works becomes Nature Reserve base.	

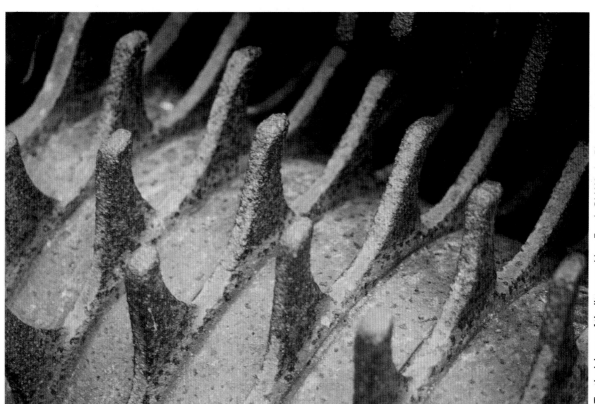

Toothed drums of the litter machine, Fenn's Old Works. Photograph: André Q Berry

Acknowledgements, Notes and References

● About Mires

• References

[1] Bellamy, D. (1995) *A Celebration of (Mires) Peatlands.* Proceedings of the Peatland Convention, 1995. Scottish Wildlife Trust.

[2] Wheeler, B.D. and Shaw, S.C. (1995) *Restoration of Damaged Peatland.* Department of the Environment.

[3] Reiley, J., Page, S. and Shepherd, P. (1995) *Tropical Bog Forests of South-East Asia.* Proceedings of the Peatland Convention, 1995. Scottish Wildlife Trust.

[4] Lindsay, R.A., Everingham, F., Fanden-Lilja, Y., Mayer, P., Nicholls, R., Reid, E., Rowell, T.A. and Ross, S. (1992) *Raised Bogs in Great Britain - The National Peatland Resource Inventory (NPRI).* Scottish Natural Heritage.

[5] Rodwell, J.S. (1991) *British Plant Communities* Vol.2. *Mires and Heaths.* Cambridge University Press.

[6] Bragg, O.M. (1989) The Importance of Water in Mire Ecosystems in, Fojt, W and Meade, R. (eds) *Cut-over Lowland Raised Mires.* Research and Survey in Nature Conservation No 24. Peterborough: Nature Conservancy Council. 61-82.

[7] Ingram, H.A.P. (1983) Hydrology in Gore, A.J.P. (ed) *Mires, Swamp, Bog, Fen and Moor.* General Studies, Elsevier Scientific (Ecosystems of the World 4A). 67-185.

[8] Anon. (1993) *Out of the Mire - a Future for Lowland Peat Bogs.* RSPB and Plantlife.

[9] Scottish Raised Bog Conservation Project. (1995) *A Conservation Strategy for Scotland's Raised Bogs.* A discussion draft for the Peatlands Convention, Edinburgh, 1995. Scottish Wildlife Trust.

[10] Foss, P. (1995) *Ten Years of the "Save the Bogs" Campaign.* Proceedings of the Peatland Convention, 1995. Scottish Wildlife Trust.

[11] Ryan, J. and Streefkerk, J. (1995) *Problems and Possible Solutions for Conserving Irish Raised Bogs.* Proceedings of the Peatland Convention, 1995. Scottish Wildlife Trust.

[12] Clymo, R.S. (1995) *The Roles of Sphagnum in Peatlands.* Proceedings of the Peatland Convention, 1995. Scottish Wildlife Trust.

[13] Breeman, N. van. (1995) How *Sphagnum* Bogs Down Other Plants in, *Trends in Ecology and Evolution,* 10, No.7. Elsevier. 270-275.

● The Nature of the Place

• References

[1] Thomas, G.S.P. (1989) The Late Devensian Glaciation along the Western Margin of the Cheshire-Shropshire Lowland. *J. Quaternary Science,* 4(2). 167-181.

[2] Gyopari, M.C. (1990) *Why is Wem Moss Drying Out?* Unpublished M.Sc. thesis, University of Birmingham.

[3] Pringle, A. (1994) *The Hydrology of Fenn's, Whixall and Bettisfield Mosses.* Unpublished M.Sc. thesis, University of Birmingham.

[4] Lindsay, R.A. (1989) *Fenn's and Whixall Moss SSSI, Clwyd/Shropshire. Morphology and Management Prescriptions.* Unpublished report of the Nature Conservancy Council.

[5] Burton, R.G.O. and Hodgson, J.M. (1987) *Lowland Peat in England and Wales.* Special Survey No.15 of Soil Survey of England and Wales. Harpenden.

[6] Daniels, J.L. (1995) *Peat Depth Report.* English Nature internal report.

[7] Sinker, C.A. (1962) The North Shropshire Meres and Mosses: A Background for Ecologists. *Field Studies,* 1. 101-138.

[8] Prestwood, W.V. (1977) *Whixall Moss.* Nature Conservancy Council internal report.

[9] Day, P. (1978) *Survey of Fenn's, Whixall and Bettisfield Mosses on the Clwyd/Shropshire Border.* Nature Conservancy Council internal report.

[10] Russell, J. (1989) *A Baseline Vegetation Transect at Wem Moss, Shropshire.* Unpublished Honours project. Wolverhampton Polytechnic.

[11] Betts, C. (1990) *A Plant Community Survey of Fenn's and Whixall Moss.* Land Improvement Group Ltd unpublished report.

[12] Joy, J. (1991) *Fenn's and Whixall Mosses: General Survey.* Nature Conservancy Council internal report.

[13] Phillips, J. (1992) *Fenn's, Whixall and Bettisfield Mosses, SSSI: Evaluation of Land which may Affect National Nature Reserve Management.* Countryside Council for Wales internal report.

[14] Karpouzli, E. (1994) *An Investigation into the Water Pollution and its Effects on the Vegetation Distribution of Whixall Moss, Shropshire.* Unpublished B.Sc. Honours project, Wolverhampton University.

[15] Seddon, A. (1991) *Fenn's, Whixall and Bettisfield Mosses NNR: Management Plan 1991-1995.* Nature Conservancy Council.

[16] Ellis, R.G. (1983) *Flowering Plants of Wales.* National Museum of Wales, Cardiff.

[17] Wynne, G. (1993) *Flora of Flintshire.* Denbigh: Gee & Sons.

[18] Newton, M. (1993) *Fenn's, Whixall and Bettisfield Mosses NNR: Bryophyte Survey.* Countryside Council for Wales internal report.

[19] Bellamy, D. (1986) *Bellamy's Ireland: The Wild Boglands.* Christopher Helm.

[20] The rarity of species is measured by the number of 10km squares or tetrads in Britain in which the species occurs. The rarest species are listed as Red Data Book species of different grades depending on rarity. RDB1 species are nationally endangered, occurring in 5 or fewer tetrads; RDB2 species are vulnerable, being likely to move into the endangered category, and RDB3 species are rare, occurring in 15 or less tetrads. Species which are not quite so threatened, but are nationally restricted in distribution, are called nationally notable. Of nationally notable species, Notable a (Na) species are found in between 15 and 30 10km squares in Britain, and Notable b (Nb) species occur in between 31 and 100 10km squares.

[21] Joy, J. (1991) *Survey and Monitoring of the Large Heath Butterfly on Fenn's, Whixall and Bettisfield Mosses.* English Nature internal report.

[22] Joy, J. (1992) *Transect Records and Butterfly Surveys Undertaken on Fenn's, Whixall and Bettisfield Mosses in 1992.* English Nature internal report.

[23] Joy, J. (1992) *Observations on the Large Heath Butterfly* (Coenonympha tullia) *in Shropshire and Clwyd in 1990 and 1991.* Occasional Paper No.3, Butterfly Conservation.

[24] Boardman, P. (1993) *Fenn's, Whixall and Bettisfield Mosses 1993 Butterfly Survey.* English Nature/ Countryside Council for Wales internal report.

[25] Boardman, P. (1993) *Fenn's, Whixall and Bettisfield Mosses 1993 Odonata Survey.* English Nature/ Countryside Council for Wales internal report.

[26] Lockton, A.J. *et al.* (1996) *Dragonflies of Shropshire*. Wildscan Ecological Consultants.

[27] Joy, J. (1992) *A Survey of the Odonata of Fenn's, Whixall and Bettisfield Mosses in 1992, with Particular Emphasis on the White-faced Dragonfly*. English Nature internal report.

[28] Judd, S. (1993) *Liverpool Museum 1992-1993 Invertebrate Survey of Fenn's, Whixall and Bettisfield Mosses SSSI*. Countryside Council for Wales report - contract No.NW/11/92/93.

[29] Riley, A.M. (1991) *A Natural History of the Butterflies and Moths of Shropshire*. Swan Hill Press.

[30] Clayson, P. (1994) *The Coleoptera of Whixall Moss*. B.Sc.(Hons) Applied Biology thesis, Nottingham Trent University.

[31] Davies, P. (1988) *Fenn's, Whixall and Bettisfield Mosses SSSI Breeding Bird Survey May-June 1988*. Nature Conservancy Council internal report.

[32] Groome, D. (1995) *Fenn's, Whixall and Bettisfield Mosses - Report on Breeding Bird Survey 1995*. English Nature internal report.

● The Palaeoenvironmental Record

• Acknowledgements

Thanks are due to Dr. Joan Daniels and Mr. Bill Allmark (both English Nature) for advice and assistance in locating subfossil pine stumps, for the provision of vehicular access and for equipment and personnel used in sampling by chainsaw. A small research grant from the Countryside Council for Wales funded the initial work; studentships from the Department of Geography, Keele University (for M.E. Grant) and the Department of Geography and Geology, Cheltenham & Gloucester College (for L.J. Roberts) helped fund the postgraduate research. Thanks to Cathy Groves, University of Sheffield, for assistance in dating the medieval oak timbers, and to David Brown, Queen's University, Belfast for assistance in the absolute dating of prehistoric oak timbers. NERC granted radiocarbon dates on samples of peat and of pine from Whixall Moss. Andrew Lawrence (Keele University) drew Figures 2 and 4, based on maps and data supplied by Dr. Joan Daniels and from field survey during the course of the research.

• Note

Radiocarbon dates are in uncalibrated years BP (Before Present, where "present" is AD 1950); calibrated dates are in cal. BC; any tree-ring, absolute (i.e. calendar years) ages are BC.

• References

[1] Godwin, H. (1981) *The Archives of the Peat Bogs*. Cambridge: Cambridge University Press.

[2] Barber, K.E. (1995) Peat Bog Archives of Past Climates. *NERC News*, January 1995, 4-6.

[3] Birks, H.J.B. and Birks, H.H. (1980) *Quaternary Palaeoecology*. London: Arnold.

[4] Barber, K.E., Chambers, F.M., Maddy, D., Stoneman, R. and Brew, J. (1994) A Sensitive High-resolution Record of late Holocene Climatic Change from a Raised Bog in Northern England. *The Holocene*, 4, 198-205.

[5] Godwin, H. and Willis, E.H. (1960) Cambridge University Radiocarbon Measurements II. *American Journal of Science, Radiocarbon supplement*, 2, 62-72.

[6] Haslam, C.J. (1987) *Late Holocene Peat Stratigraphy and Climatic Change*. Unpublished Ph.D. thesis, University of Southampton.

[7] Lageard, J.G.A., Chambers, F.M. and Grant, M.E. (1992) *Study of Vegetational History at Fenn's and Whixall Mosses based on a Study of Pine Remains and Pollen in Peat Strata* (Interim Report to Countryside Council for Wales). Keele: Environmental Research Unit, Keele University.

[8] Grant, M.E. (1995) *The Dating and Significance of* Pinus sylvestris *Macrofossil Remains at Fenn's/Whixall Moss: Palaeoecological and Comparative Modern Analyses.* Unpublished Ph.D. thesis, Keele University.

[9] Godwin, H. (1975) *History of the British Flora,* 2nd edn. Cambridge: Cambridge University Press.

[10] Hardy, E.M. (1939) Studies of the Post-glacial History of British Vegetation. V. The Shropshire and Flint Maelor Mosses. *New Phytologist,* 38, 364-396.

[11] Turner, J. (1964) The Anthropogenic Factor in Vegetational History. I. Tregaron and Whixall Mosses. *New Phytologist,* 63, 73-90.

[12] Tallis, J.H. and Birks, H.J.B. (1965) The Past and Present Distribution of Scheuchzeria palustris in Europe. *Journal of Ecology,* 53, 287-298.

[13] Godwin, H. (1934) Pollen Analysis. An Outline of the Problems and Potentialities of the Method. Part I. Technique and interpretation. *New Phyologist,* 33, 278-305.

[14] Godwin, H. (1940) Forest History in England and Wales. *New Phytologist,* 39, 370-400.

[15] Granlund, E. (1932) De Svenska Hogmossarnas Geologi. *Sveriges Geologiska Undersokning Arsb.,* 26, i, 1-193.

[16] Chitty, L.F. (1933) Bronze Looped Palstave from Whixall Moss, North Shropshire. *Transactions of the Shropshire Archaeological and Natural History Society,* 47(i), 73-7.

[17] Turner, J (1962) The *Tilia* Decline: An Anthropogenic Interpretation. *New Phytologist,* 61, 328-341.

[18] Turner, J. (1965) A Contribution to the History of Forest Clearance. *Proceedings of the Royal Society of London* B, 161, 343-354.

[19] Barber, K.E. (1981) *Peat Stratigraphy and Climatic Change.* Rotterdam: A.A. Balkema.

[20] Twigger, S.N. and Haslam, C.J. (1991) Environmental Change in Shropshire During the Last 13,000 years. *Field Studies,* 7, 743-758.

[21] Chambers, F.M. (1994) Peatlands - Evolution, Heritage and Conservation, in Stevens, C., Gordon, J.E., Green, C.P. and Macklin, M.G. (eds) *Conserving our Landscape, Proceedings of the Conference, Conserving our Landscape: Evolving Landforms and Ice-age Heritage, Crewe, May 1992.* Peterborough: English Nature, 163-167.

[22] Lageard, J.G.A. (1992) *Vegetational History and Palaeoforest Reconstruction at White Moss, South Cheshire, UK.* Unpublished Ph.D. thesis, Keele University.

[23] Lageard, J.G.A., Chambers, F.M. and Thomas, P.A. (1992) Palaeoforest Reconstruction from Peat Exhumations at White Moss, South Cheshire, UK, in Bartholin, T.S., Berglund, B.E., Eckstein, D. and Schweingruber, F.H. (eds.) *Tree Rings and Environment, Proceedings of the International Dendrochronological Symposium, Ystad, South Sweden (1990),* Lundqua Report Vol. 34. Lund: Lund University, Dept. Quaternary Geology, 172-176.

[24] Lageard, J.G.A., Chambers, F.M. and Roberts, L.J. (forthcoming) A Prehistoric Pine Woodland at Lindow Moss, near Wilmslow. *Cheshire Past,* 6 (in press).

[25] Lageard, J.G.A. and Chambers, F.M. (1993) The Palaeoecological Significance of a New, Subfossil-oak (*Quercus* sp.) Chronology from Morris' Bridge, Shropshire, UK. *Dendrochronologia,* 11, 25-33.

26 Hillam, J., Groves, C.M., Brown, D.M., Baillie, M.G.L., Coles, J.M., and Coles, B.J. (1990) Dendrochronology of the English Neolithic. *Antiquity,* 64, 208-220.

27 Brown, D.M. and Baillie, M.G.L. Construction and Dating of a 5000 year English Bog Oak Chronology, in Bartholin, T.S., Berglund, B.E., Eckstein, D. and Schweingruber, F.H. (eds.) *Tree Rings and Environment, Proceedings of the International Dendrochronological Symposium, Ystad, South Sweden (1990),* Lundqua Report Vol. 34. Lund: Lund University, Dept. Quaternary Geology, 72-75.

28 Brassil, K., Silvester, R. and Tosteven, P. (1991) *An Archaeological Assessment of Fenn's and Whixall Mosses, Clwyd and Shropshire* (Report to English Nature/CCW). Welshpool: Clwyd-Powys Archaeological Trust.

29 Lindsay, R. (1989) *Fenn's and Whixall Moss SSSI, Clwyd/Shropshire. Morphology and Management Prescriptions* (Internal Report). Peterborough: English Nature.

● Bog Bodies

• Acknowledgements

This is an edited version of Turner, R.C. and Penney, S. (1996) Three Bog Bodies from Whixall Moss, Shropshire. *Shropshire History,* 71. Thanks are due to the Shropshire Archaeological and Historical Society for allowing this pre-publication.

• References

1 Vol.1, second series, 217.

2 Chitty, L.F. (1933) Bronze Lopped Palstave from Whixall Moss, North Shropshire. *Transactions of the Shropshire Archaeological and Historical Society,* 47(i), 73-7.

3 Turner, R.C. (1993) Lindow Man and Other British Bog Bodies in, Carver M (ed) *In Search of Cult: Archaeological Investigations in Honour of Philip Rahtz.* York. 9-15.

4 Housley, R.A., Walker, A.J., Otlet, R.C. and Hedges, R.E.M. (1995) Radiocarbon Dating of the Lindow III Bog Body in, Turner, R.C. and Scaife, R.G. (eds) *Bog Bodies, New Discoveries and New Perspectives.* London: British Museums Press. 39-46.

5 Hardy, E.M. (1939) Studies of the Post-glacial History of British Vegetation V., the Shropshire and Flint Maelor Mosses. *New Phytologist,* 38. 364-96.

6 Twigger, S.N. and Haslam, C.J. (1991) Environmental Change in Shropshire During the Last 13,000 Years. *Field Studies,* 7. 754.

7 Turner, J. (1964) The Anthroprogenic Factor in Vegetational History, I. Tregaron and Whixhall Mosses. *New Phytologist,* 63. 73-90.

8 Glob, P.V. (1967) *The Bog People.* London: Faber and Faber.

9 Munksgaard, E. (1984) Bog Bodies - A Brief Survey of Interpretations. *J. Danish Arch.,* 3. 120-3.

10 Briggs, C.S. (1995) Did they Fall or were they Pushed? Some Unresolved Questions about Bog Bodies in Turner, R.C. and Scaife, R.G. (eds) *Bog Bodies, New Discoveries and New Perspectives.* London: British Museum Press, 168-92.

11 Turner, R.C. (1995) Recent Research into British Bog Bodies, in Turner, R.C. and Scaife, R.G. (eds) *Bog Bodies, New Discoveries and New Perspectives.* London: British Museum Press, 108-22.

12 De la Pryme, A. (1694) Of Trees Underground in Hatfield Chase, *Phil. Trans. Roy. Soc.,* No 275 and Leigh C. (1700) *The Natural History of Lancashire, Cheshire and the Peak of Derbyshire,* Oxford.

[13] Turner, R.C. (1989) A Cumbrian Bog Body from Scaleby. *Trans. Cumb. and West Antiqu. and Arch. Soc*, xxxix. 1-7.

[14] O'Floinn, R. (1995) Recent Research into Irish Bog Bodies, in Turner, R.C. and Scaife, R.G. (eds) *Bog Bodies, New Discoveries and New Perspectives.* London: British Museum Press, 137-45.

[15] Sanden, W.A.B. van der (1990) *Mens en Moeras,* Assen: Drents Museum.

[16] Savory, H. (1980) *Guide Catalogue to the Bronze Age Collections.* Cardiff: National Museum of Wales.

[17] Pryor, F. (1991) *Flag Fen.* London: English Heritage.

[18] Fox, C. (1946) *A Find of the Early Iron Age from Llyn Cerrig Bach, Anglesey.* Cardiff: National Museum of Wales.

[19] Jensen, J. (1982) *The Archaeology of Denmark.* London: Thames and Hudson.

[20] A gold coin of William I reportedly found in the course of peat cutting in the 19th century (John Lord Hanmer [1877] quoted in Owen, T.M. [1969] Historical aspects of peat-cutting in Wales, in Jenkins, G. [ed] *Studies in Folk Life* London: RKP. 123-155) referenced by Brassil, K., Silvester, R. and Tosteven, P. (1991) *An Archaeological Assessment of Fenn's and Whixall Mosses, Clwyd and Shropshire* (Report to English Nature/CCW). Welshpool: Clwyd-Powys Archaeological Trust.

[21] Gill-Robinson, H. (in prep) *A Comparative Evaluation of Factors Contributing to Soft Tissue Preservation in Human and Animal Peat Bog Bodies.* Ph.D. thesis - University of York.

● Framing the Landscape

• Acknowledgements

Thanks are due to Mr. Edward Wardle for access to family papers concerning the Lordship of the manor of Whixall and to Mr. W. Fancourt for donating copies of the Whixall manorial court rolls and other historical documents; to Miss Eileen Simpson, Archivist, for her sterling work in undertaking selective translation of the Latin texts of the Whixall manorial records and to Dr. Paul Stamper, Shropshire Records and Research, for references to medieval assart and the early 18th century Whixall Inclosure.

• References

[1] *La Rede Broc* is the area known today as Red Brook (N.G.R. SJ 515 408). 8th June 1282, Deed 1630. Schedule of the Bettisfield Documents. National Library of Wales (1947). Also the Calendar of Welsh Rolls in Calendar of Chancery Rolls, Ed.I-II 1277-1326, Public Record Office (1912), p.253. William le Botiler was captain of Edward I's garrison at *de Albo Monasterio Warenn'* (Whitchurch).

[2] 28th June 1283. Calendar of Welsh Rolls in Calendar of Chancery Rolls Ed.I-II 1277-1326, Public Record Office (1912), p.274.

[3] Deed 350, 17th December 1284. Schedule of the Bettisfield Manuscripts and Documents. National Library of Wales (1947).

[4] e.g. Grant of mid-13th century referring to *Madoc son of Yareford's assart,* Shropshire Record Office, Sutherland Collection, 972/224/3/1. Also reference to assart dated c.1310, Shropshire Record Office, Sandford of Sandford Collection, 2/39.

[5] Housebote and haybote - respectively, the right to take timber for the repair or construction of houses and hedges/fences. Pannage - the right for swine to take oak mast in the appropriate season. Grant of c.1260-80. Shropshire Record Office, Sutherland Collection, 972/224/3/2.

[6] Leah, M. Personal communication. North West Wetlands Survey. The moated sites are located at N.G.R. SJ 4993 3530 and SJ 4980 3503. The former site is recorded on the 1841 Tithe map for Prees parish, Whixall township as *Moat Field* (parcel 490), Shropshire Record Office.

[7] Pratt, D. (1964) Moated Settlements in Maelor. *Journal of the Flintshire Historical Society*, 21. 110-120.

[8] The Whixall manorial records covering the period AD1407-1928 are in the possession of Mr. Edward Wardle, Fenn's Cottage, Fenn's Wood. Copies, on microfilm, are in Shropshire Record Office, 5811. Photocopies supplied by Mr. W. Fancourt are lodged in English Nature and Clwyd Archaeology Service site archives.

[9] *le holynwood* is the area known today as Hollinwood (N.G.R. SJ 523 364). 5th February 1476/7, court book 1, 1407-1557. p.11.

[10] 21st April 1545, court book 1, 1407-1557. p.27. Also 6th May 1547, court book 1, 1407-1557. p.32.

[11] 11th July 1555(?), court book 1, 1407-1557. p.39.

[12] 31st October 1572, court book 2, 1559-1601. p.13.

[13] Vinogradoff, P. and Morgan, F. (1914) *Survey of the Honour of Denbigh 1334*. London: British Academy. p.305.

[14] Vinogradoff, P. and Morgan, F. (1914) *Survey of the Honour of Denbigh 1334*. London: British Academy. p.192.

[15] 24th January 1348 (Westminster). *The Register of Edward the Black Prince Preserved in the Public Record Office* (1930), Part I, AD1346-1348. London: HMSO. p.161.

[16] 15th August 1357 (London). *The Register of Edward the Black Prince Preserved in the Public Record Office* (1932), Part III (Palatinate of Chester) AD1351-1365. London: HMSO. p.272.

[17] 22nd August 1359 (London). *Ibid.*, p.358.

[18] 24th March 1351 (London). *Ibid.*, p.8

[19] 23rd January 1348 (Westminster). *The Register of Edward the Black Prince Preserved in the Public Record Office* (1930), Part I, AD1346-1348. London: HMSO. p.160.

[20] 2nd November 1351 (London). *The Register of Edward the Black Prince Preserved in the Public Record Office* (1932), Part III (Palatinate of Chester) AD1351-1365. London: HMSO. p.47.

[21] e.g. Grant to Hugh de Mulyngton of turbary on Rudheath, 24th May 1357 (London). *Ibid.*, p.240; Representation by Robert de Ward regarding his grant of turbary in the forest of La Mare, 24th May 1357 (London). *Ibid.*, p.240.

[22] e.g. 15th June 1357 (London), Ibid., p.250; 30th November 1364 (London), *Ibid.*, p.472; 4th February 1365 (London), Ibid., p.473.

[23] Grant to John de Stokton, for life, of "*sufficient turbary on the moss of Bikkelegh for the expenses of his house*", and to David de Wodehull, for life, "*sufficient pasture on the moss of Pecforton for the expenses of his house, - to cause plots for digging turves to be delivered to them on the said mosses in places where the least damage to the prince will be involved*". 15th May 1357 (Sherborne Castle), *Ibid.*, p.239.

[24] 28th August 1359 (London). *Ibid.*, p.364.

[25] 6th November 1582, court book 2, 1559-1601. p.34.

[26] Indenture granting turbary and peatrye, 20th February 1608. Shropshire Record Office, Sandford Collection, 3607/III/A/40.

[27] 11th April 1590, court book 2, 1559-1601. p.48.

[28] 11th October 1600, court book 2, 1559-1601. p.82.

[29] 30th October 1630, court book 4, 1613-1659. p.61A.

[30] 26th October 1626, court book 4, 1613-1659. p.46.

[31] 15th April 1637, court book 4, 1613-1659. p.81.

[32] 22nd October 1638, court book 4, 1613-1659. p.84.

[33] e.g.18th April 1628, court book 4, 1613-1659. p.56.

[34] e.g. 8th November 1655, court book 4, 1613-1659. p.101.

[35] e.g. 27th October 1652, court book 4, 1613-1659. p.88.

[36] 4th May 1702, court book 7, 1702-1777. p.2.

[37] 5th July 1715, court book 7, 1702-1777. p.35.

[38] 27th July 1710. Shropshire Record Office, Lady Curteis' Collection, 741/1.

[39] Copyhold land is land held at will of the lord of the manor. Enfranchisement served to render the tenure of such land freehold.

[40] Stamper, Dr. P. Personal communication. Head of Records and Research, Shropshire County Council.

[41] Shropshire Record Office, 731/5/10/213 and 214.

[42] 2nd June 1711. Shropshire Record Office, Lady Curteis' Collection, 741/2.

[43] Whitfield, J.R.W. (1939-42). The Enclosure Movement in North Shropshire. *Caradoc and Severn Valley Field Club Transactions,* 11. 53-62.

[44] Shropshire Record Office, 731/5/10/213 and 214.

[45] 27th July 1710. Shropshire Record Office, Lady Curteis' Collection, 741/1.

[46] *Ibid.*

[47] Deed of Admeasurement, Shropshire Record Office, 731/5/10/215.

[48] *Ibid.*

[49] Shropshire Record Office, 731/5/10/220.

[50] *"Hossage"* appears as a fieldname associated with parcels 76, 134 to 140 of the Prees parish, Whixall township tithe map, Shropshire Record Office.

[51] Stamper, Dr. P. Personal communication. Head of Records and Research, Shropshire County Council.

[52] Particulars of Sale, 22nd April 1829, comprising the manor of Whixall totalling *c.*1067 acres to be sold by auction by order of the assignees of Messrs. Corser, Naylor and Hassall, bankrupts. Shropshire Record Office, 611/744

[53] 23rd October 1729, court book 7, 1702-1777. pp.60-64.

[54] e.g. Shropshire Record Office. 26th March 1712/13, 731/5/4/25; 24th June 1713, 731/5/4/2; 13th February 1715/16, 731/5/4/16; 18th March 1722/23, 731/5/4/27.

[55] e.g. 17th October 1720, court book 7, 1702-1777, p.42.

[56] Chapman, J. (1992) *A Guide to Parliamentary Enclosures in Wales.* Cardiff: University of Wales Press. 10.

[57] *Ibid*. p.91. 52006 Hanmer. Act 15 Geo. III c.16 1775. Award 1777 and 1779. The inclosure encompassed *Fens Heath* [Fenn's Moss], *Stemmy Heath, Bronington Green, Little Green, Rhos Poeth Green, Horse Moss Green, Talwrn Green, The Arrowry, Braden Heath, Bermoss Green* and *Bettisfield Moss*. See Flintshire Record Office, Hawarden QS/DE/1 and 2.

[58] *Ibid*. Earlier inclosures: 52003 Dee Estuary (White Sands) Act 26 Geo. II c.35 (Public) 1753, p.89; 53010 Swansea (Town Hill and Burroughs) Act 2 Geo. III c.7 1762, p.106; Welshpool (Pool Common or Gwern y go) Act 1 Geo. III c.36 1760, p.132. Of some 229 Parliamentary inclosures in Wales, only 13 were enacted prior to 1790, with over 50% after 1840, p.4, 5.

[59] Shropshire Record Office, QE/1/2/44.

[60] e.g. 1892-1897, various documents. Mr. Edward Wardle, Fenn's Cottage, Fenn's Wood. Photocopies are lodged in English Nature and Clwyd Archaeology Service site archives.

[61] Paragraph XXIII Act 54 Geo. III c.92 1814. Photocopies are lodged in English Nature and Clwyd Archaeology Service site archives.

[62] Schedule K of inclosure award QE/1/2/44.

[63] Schedule A, QE/1/2/44, parcels 62, 83, 85-91, 131-133.

[64] Schedule G, QE/1/2/44, parcels 30 and 141.

[65] Schedule H, QE/1/2/44, parcels 1, 28, 29, 74, 84.

[66] Stamper, Dr. P. Personal communication. Head of Records and Research, Shropshire County Council.

[67] Chapman, J. (1992) *A Guide to Parliamentary Enclosures in Wales*. Cardiff: University of Wales Press.

● Fact Panel One: Peat Houses

• References

[1] Whixall manorial records: 11th April 1590, court book 2, 1559-1601. p.48; also, 17th October 1601, court book 2, p.85.

[2] e.g. houses at 1-3 Church Street, Whitchurch. Stamper, Dr. P. Personal communication. With reference to a transcript of an interview with Mrs Penlington, Nantwich supplied by Mrs M. Moran.

[3] Birch, M.J. Personal communication. Whixall. Shropshire.

[4] *Whitchurch Herald*, 13/07/1918.

● Crossing the Moss

• References

References to the *Oswestry Advertiser and Montgomeryshire Mercury* relate to the collection held on microfilm at Oswestry library unless otherwise stated.

[1] PRO Rail 827/1 and Shropshire Record Office, Shrewsbury G25.7

[2] Wilson, E.A. (1975) *The Ellesmere and Llangollen Canal: An Historical Background*. Chichester: Phillimore. 19-20.

[3] PRO Rail 827/8 Report to the General Assembly of Ellesmere Canal Proprietors, 25th November 1801. Quoted in Wilson, E.A. (1975) above, p.20 but source not referenced.

[4] PRO Rail 827/7, Part 1.

[5] Personal communication. British Waterways.

[6] Strange, J. Personal communication. Formerly foreman and member of Moss gang on canal.

[7] Personal communication. British Waterways.

[8] *Oswestry Advertiser and Montgomeryshire Mercury,* 17/10/1860.

[9] *Oswestry Advertiser and Montgomeryshire Mercury,* 3/10/1860.

[10] Letter to Rt. Hon. Lady Marian Alford and the Hon. Col. Peregrine Francis Cust - Guardians of the earl Brownlow, from the Provisional Committee of the O,E&W Railway Co. 09/10/1860. Shropshire Record Office, Shrewsbury. Bridgewater Collection 611/773.

[11] *Oswestry Advertiser and Montgomeryshire Mercury,* 17/10/1860.

[12] First subscription list, Shropshire Record Office, Shrewsbury. Bridgewater Collection 611/774. A copy schedule to subscription contract, in addition, gives subscribers occupations and places of abode (SRO, Shrewsbury. Bridgewater Collection 611/777).

[13] for reference to O,E&W as 'Independent Line' see e.g. *Oswestry Advertiser and Montgomeryshire Mercury,* 23/04/1862; *The Shrewsbury Chronicle,* 25/04/1862; *Oswestry Advertiser and Montgomeryshire Mercury,* 30/04/1862 all under Shropshire Record Office, Shrewsbury. Bridgewater Collection 2013/269-282.

[14] *Oswestry Advertiser and Montgomeryshire Mercury,* 3/04/1861

[15] Petition against the O,E&W Railway in the House of Lords by certain inhabitants and ratepayers of Ellesmere and its vicinity. 230 signatories giving place of residence, occupation and extent of ownership with value of holding. Shropshire Record Office, Shrewsbury. Bridgewater Collection 611/775.

[16] *Oswestry Advertiser and Montgomeryshire Mercury,* 16/04/1862. Shropshire Record Office, Shrewsbury. Bridgewater Collection 2013/271.

[17] Extract from *Eddowes's Shrewsbury Journal* reporting evidence given before the Parliamentary Committee of the House of Commons 24/04/1861. Shropshire Record Office, Shrewsbury. Bridgewater Collection 2013/17.

[18] O,E&W Railway, plans and sections. Flintshire Record Office, Hawarden QS/DR/61.

[19] *Oswestry Advertiser and Montgomeryshire Mercury,* 6/03/1861. Shropshire Record Office, Shrewsbury. Bridgewater Collection 2013/270.

[20] *Oswestry Advertiser and Montgomeryshire Mercury,* 27/03/1861. Shropshire Record Office, Shrewsbury. Bridgewater Collection 2013/12.

[21] Manchester and Birmingham Continuation Railway, plans and sections. Flintshire Record Office, Hawarden QS/DR/30.

[22] Bailey, W.H. (1889) Prehistoric Chat Moss, and a New Chapter in the History of the Manchester and Liverpool Railway, *Trans. Manchester Geol. Soc.,* 5. 119-127. The London and North Western Railway Company's Manchester and Liverpool line was commenced in 1828 and opened in 1830.

[23] *Oswestry Advertiser and Montgomeryshire Mercury,* 27/03/1861. Shropshire Record Office, Shrewsbury. Bridgewater Collection 2013/12.

[24] *Oswestry Advertiser and Montgomeryshire Mercury,* 2/07/1862. Shropshire Record Office, Shrewsbury. Bridgewater Collection 2013/279.

[25] *Oswestry Advertiser and Montgomeryshire Mercury,* 17/04/1861.

[26] For comments re: costs of crossing Fenn's Moss see e.g. *Oswestry Advertiser and Montgomeryshire Mercury*, 24/04/1861; *Oswestry Advertiser and Montgomeryshire Mercury*, 27/03/1861. Shropshire Record Office, Shrewsbury. Bridgewater Collection 2013/12.

[27] *Oswestry Advertiser and Montgomeryshire Mercury*, 24/04/1861.

[28] Extract from *Eddowes's Shrewsbury Journal* reporting evidence given before the Parliamentary Committee of the House of Commons 24/04/1861. Shropshire Record Office, Shrewsbury. Bridgewater Collection 2013/17.

[29] *Oswestry Advertiser and Montgomeryshire Mercury*, 26/06/1861.

[30] *Oswestry Advertiser and Montgomeryshire Mercury*, 3/07/1861.

[31] *Oswestry Advertiser and Montgomeryshire Mercury*, 28/08/1861.

[32] *Oswestry Advertiser and Montgomeryshire Mercury*, 31/08/1861.

[33] Open Column article dated 28/10/1861 in *Oswestry Advertiser and Montgomeryshire Mercury*, 30/10/1861.

[34] *Oswestry Advertiser and Montgomeryshire Mercury*, 26/02/1862.

[35] Baughan, P.E. (1980). A Regional History of the Railways of Great Britain, Vol.11, North and Mid Wales. Newton Abbot: David and Charles. 154.

[36] *Ibid*. 154.

[37] *Ibid*. 155.

[38] *Ibid*. 167.

● The Military Takes Over

● References

[1] e.g. see agreement made between War Department and Lords of the Manor of Whixall dated 15th October 1915 for 218 acres of Whixall Moss in the area of "The Batters", Clwyd Archaeology Service and English Nature site archive; The *Whitchurch Herald*, 3/04/1915, p.3, Whitchurch library; letter dated 25th February 1942 from Lucas, Butter and Creak, solicitors, to James Heath, senior re: compensation for loss of profit following requisition of the Moss by the Air Ministry, Clwyd Archaeology Service and English Nature site archive.

[2] At Sealand (N.G.R. SJ 330 700), Flintshire; Shawbury (N.G.R. SJ 550 220) and Tern Hill (N.G.R. SJ 645 310), Shropshire.

[3] At Hawarden (N.G.R. SJ 350 650), Flintshire; Tilstock (Prees Heath) (N.G.R. SJ 560 375) and Sleap (N.G.R. SJ 480 265), Shropshire.

[4] The *Whitchurch Herald*, 24/06/1916, p.6. Whitchurch library.

[5] The *Whitchurch Herald*, 1/07/1916, p.6. Whitchurch library.

[6] See Ordnance Survey Six-inch plans, Edition of 1914, Flintshire Sheets XXVI NE, SE, NW and SW, originally surveyed 1872 and revised 1909. Shropshire Sheets VII SE, SW cover only the eastern part of the Moss but were surveyed in 1878-9 and revised in 1899. Not surprisingly for such rural areas, neither the wartime *Provisional Edition* nor their recasting on the National Grid (Sheets SJ 43NE, 53NW incorporating revisions of 1949 and 1954) show the later, but ephemeral, range and decoy developments.

[7] *Whitchurch Herald*, 25/09/1915, p.4. Whitchurch library.

[8] *Whitchurch Herald*, 25/09/1915, p.4. Whitchurch library.

[9] Allmark, W. Personal communication. Former peatman and currently Lead Hand Estate Worker, English Nature, Whixall. Shropshire.

[10] Copies in Clwyd Archaeology Service (CAS) and English Nature site archive. Original lodged by CAS in Flintshire Record Office, Hawarden. It seems to be former War Office Drawing F.W.1 No.59 with detail from F.W.1 Prints 37C (Target Gallery) and 45A (Target Shed).

[11] Otherwise RAF Form 540 upon which station and unit diaries were compiled. ORBs are preserved in the PRO under AIR 28 (Stations) and AIR 29 (Miscellaneous Units).

[12] They are AMWD drawings numbered 1948/40, 11765/41, 9061/43 and 2840/44. They may have been destroyed as one superseded the other.

[13] Both English Nature and Clwyd Archaeology Service hold vertical coverage (black and white) for the Fenn's and Whixall Mosses area taken on an approximate 6 inch (1:10,000) and 25 inch (1:2500) scales by the RAF and CUCAP (Cambridge University Committee for Aerial Photography) in 1946, 1983, 1988 and 1990. Coloured obliques were specially-commissioned from Chris Musson, Royal Commission on the Ancient and Historical Monuments of Wales, in 1994/1995 by Clwyd Archaeology Service.

[14] For squadron histories and movements see Halley, J (1988) *Squadrons of the RAF & Commonwealth 1918-1988*. Tonbridge: Air-Britain (Historians). For station histories see Smith, D. (1981) *Action Stations 3: Military Airfields of Wales and the North-West* Wellingborough: Patrick Stephens.

[15] Case studies such as this are made up from many sources, but researchers start at the RAF Museum, Hendon, with the two enormous collections of index cards containing the service history of almost every RAF aircraft and the accidents that befell them.

[16] Pre-war the public were kept posted as to developments in pilot training by means of local press coverage of Empire Air Day displays at local airfields, e.g. for the first held by 10 FTS at Tern Hill on 28 May see the *Shrewsbury Chronicle*, 21 May 1937 or the *Newport & Market Drayton Advertiser*, 4 June 1937.

[17] Decoys were codenamed K (daylight use) or Q (night time use). The latter were further differentiated as L (using electric light), or F (using controllable fires) to create the desired deception effect.

[18] There were three types of air raid warning: *Yellow*, a blanket preliminary issued by Fighter Command to all areas over which raiders might pass; *Purple*, issued at night to areas in the path of raiders - exposed lights in factories, sidings, etc. to be extinguished; *Red*, a public warning followed by sirens.

[19] For details see County Record Office (Hawarden) FP/5/21, register of air raids in Flintshire 1940-1942, collated in Jones, I.W. (1977) The Air War over Denbighshire and Flintshire, *Denbighshire Historical Society Transactions*, 26, 95-140.

[20] Ferguson, A.P. (1977) *A History of RAF Shawbury*. Liverpool: Merseyside Aviation Society. 13-14.

[21] Home Security War Room Reports are to be consulted in PRO HO 202/1-10 and consist of: Part I - Summary; Part II - precise times of area air raid warnings; Part III - special damage reports to services, buildings, communications, etc. Even more detailed Home Security Daily Intelligence Reports, prepared 12-hourly, are to be found in HO 203/1-16. A further set of daily reports was prepared by the Key Points Intelligence Directorate, HO 201/1-23, covering air raids on establishments of national importance with assessments and reviews of defence measures.

[22] Evans, E. Personal communication. Former Private, King's Shropshire Light Infantry. Cosford.

[23] PRO AIR 20/4352 begins with document Serial 27 for 01/08/1941. Half of this file is therefore missing. Thanks to Roger J.C. Thomas, RCHME, York, for initial computer printouts of this information.

[24] AMWD Drawing 1030/45, C. Andrews, surveyor. Clwyd Archaeology Service and English Nature site archive.

[25] Swindell, A. Personal communication. Former Sergeant, RAF. Platt Lane, Whixall. Shropshire.

[26] Letter dated 25th February 1942 from Lucas, Butter and Creak, solicitors, to James Heath, senior re: compensation for loss of profit following requisition of the Moss by the Air Ministry, Clwyd Archaeology Service and English Nature site archive.

[27] Details of practice bombs as used on Fenn's Moss range supplied by the RAF Armament Support Unit, RAF Wittering (Cambs). Clwyd Archaeology Service and English Nature site archive.

[28] Insley, J. Personal communication. Curator, Environmental Sciences, National Museum of Science and Industry.

[29] Carter, I. Personal communication. Photograph Archive, Imperial War Museum.

[30] Churchill, W.S. (1953) *Second World War: II Their Finest Hour.* London: Reprint Society. 316-7, 319.

[31] Dodgson, J.McN. (1972) *The Place-names of Cheshire: Part IV.* Cambridge: Cambridge University Press. 164.

[32] On 20/21 December 1940 some 205 German aircraft bombed Merseyside; 299 were over target the following night. On 22/23 December 270 enemy bombers pounded Manchester, with a repeat visitation from 171 bombers on 23/24th.

[33] Undertaken by Clwyd Archaeology Service as part of the Fenn's and Whixall Mosses Historic Landscape Project. Clwyd Archaeology Service and English Nature site archive.

[34] Hamer, A. Personal communication. Former private, KSLI and Herefordshire Regiment. Whixall. Shropshire.

[35] It should be noted that the RAF had its own "QF" decoy on the Worthenbury/Shocklach border. It was abandoned on 29 October 1943.

[36] RAF aerial photograph 4286, 106 G/UK 1517, 17th May 1946, RS.

[37] Starkey, C. Personal communication. Former peatman. Bronington. Wrexham.

[38] Hamer, A. Personal communication. Former private, KSLI and Herefordshire Regiment. Whixall. Shropshire.

[39] *Rhubarbs* were small scale fighter-bomber attacks on ground targets of opportunity; *Circuses* were fighter-escorted daylight bombing attacks on short-range targets; *Rodeos* were exclusively fighter sweeps over enemy territory. Spitfire VBs (1,440hp Merlin 45 engine) had two cannon and four Browning machine guns; Spitfire IXs were produced in low, medium and high altitude versions with four cannon or mixed cannon/Browning armament.

● Peat as Product

• Acknowledgements

Grateful thanks are due to all those who contributed to the Fenn's and Whixall Oral History Project and gave so freely of their time, treasured memories, documents and photographs. Particular thanks are due to Mr. Edward Wardle for access to family papers concerning the Lordship of the manor of Whixall and the *English Peat Moss Litter Company Ltd;* to I.G. Richardson for access to records of *L&P Peat;* to J. Swire for access to material amongst the Hanmer Estate papers; to M. Limbert for assistance in identification of peat cutting machinery; and to D. Houlder at Companies House for valued assistance in tracing company records.

• References

[1] Bagshaw, S. (1851) *The History of Shropshire.* Privately Published. 307, 308.

[2] Flintshire Record Office, Hawarden. D/DM/329/42.

[3] N.G.R. SJ 5039 3662.

[4] N.G.R. SJ 5113 3667.

[5] Flintshire Record Office, Hawarden. D/DM/329/43.

[6] Flintshire Record Office, Hawarden. D/DM/329/45.

[7] Flintshire Record Office, Hawarden. QS/DR/61.

[8] Public Record Office, BT 31/477.

[9] Patent No.1671, 15th July 1859. Public Record Office.

[10] *Oswestry Advertiser and Montgomeryshire Mercury,* 17/04/1861. Shropshire Record Office, Shrewsbury. 2013/12.

[11] Davies, W. (1810) *General View of the Agriculture and Domestic Economy of North Wales.* London: The Board of Agriculture and Internal Improvement. 371.

[12] Papers in the possession of Edward Wardle, Fenn's Cottage, Fenn's Wood. Photocopies are lodged in English Nature and Clwyd Archaeology Service site archives.

[13] e.g. see *Whitchurch Herald,* 29/04/1893.

[14] Bradley, V.J. (1992) *Industrial Locomotives of North Wales.* London: Industrial Railway Society.

[15] Allmark, H. Personal communication. Retired peatman, Creamore, near Wem. Shropshire.

[16] Allmark, W. Personal communication. Former peatman and currently Lead Hand Estate Worker, English Nature, Whixall. Shropshire.

[17] *Whitchurch Herald,* 02/05/1914.

[18] *Whitchurch Herald,* 09/05/1914.

[19] Wardle, E. Personal communication. Formerly *H.H. Wardle Ltd,* Fenn's Cottage, Fenn's Wood.

[20] Richardson, I. Personal communication. Director, *Richardson's Moss Litter Company Ltd,* Carlisle.

[21] e.g. see *Whitchurch Herald,* 26/05/1917; 15/09/1917; 29/09/1917; 13/10/1917.

[22] *Whitchurch Herald,* 01/04/1916.

[23] *Whitchurch Herald,* 24/08/1918.

[24] *Whitchurch Herald,* 13/07/1918.

[25] *Whitchurch Herald,* 22/11/1919.

[26] Allmark, A. Personal communication. Retired peatman, Welsh End, Whixall. Shropshire.

[27] *The Contract Journal,* 25/06/1919.

[28] Lindsay, J. Personal communication. Farmer, Cambrian Cottage, Bettisfield; and Allmark, H. Personal communication.

[29] Railway plan *circa* early 1920s, in possession of Hanmer Estate. Photocopies are lodged in English Nature and Clwyd Archaeology Service site archives.

[30] Public Record Office, BT31/32480.

[31] *The Illustrated Official Journal (Patents)*, 08/04/1925.

[32] *The Illustrated Official Journal (Patents)*, 10/06/1925.

[33] Heath, L. Personal communication. Retired peatman, Calverhall. Shropshire; and Allmark, A. Personal communication.

[34] Hallmark, H. Personal Communication. Retired peatman/forester, Stretton. Staffordshire.

[35] Contract and Conditions of Sale of bungalow in Bettisfield in possession of Chris Allman, Tilley. Shropshire. Photocopies are lodged in English Nature and Clwyd Archaeology Service site archives.

[36] Starkey, C. Personal communication. Retired peatman and farmworker, Bronington. Wrexham.

[37] Clorley, M. Personal communication. Peatman, Moss Cottages, Whixall. Shropshire.

[38] *Eighty Years in Peat: A Historical Note on Richardson's Moss Litter Company Ltd* (1963).

[39] Records of the *L&P Peat* consortium in the possession of I.G. Richardson, *Richardson's Moss Litter Company Ltd*, Carlisle. Photocopies are lodged in English Nature and Clwyd Archaeology Service site archives.

[40] Evans, T. H., (1927) *Great Western Railway Magazine*, March. 101-102.

[41] Hamer, A. Personal communication. Whixall, Shropshire; and Starkey, C. Personal communication.

[42] *Whitchurch Herald*, 01/03/1940.

[43] *Whitchurch Herald*, 06/03/1942.

[44] *Shrewsbury Chronicle*, 03/09/1954.

[45] Starkey, C. and Lindsay, J. Personal communication.

[46] Daniels, J.L. Personal Communication. Site Manager, English Nature.

[47] Hankers, J. Personal communication. Housewife, Whixall. Shropshire.

[48] Bailey, A. Personal communication. Retired peatman, Whixall. Shropshire.

[49] Heath, R. Personal communication. Peatman, Whixall, Shropshire.

[50] *Whitchurch Herald*, 13/08/1887.

[51] *Whitchurch Herald*, 13/07/1918.

[52] Clorley, B. Personal communication. Housewife, Whixall. Shropshire.

[53] Limbert, M. Personal communication.

[54] Bellingham, C. Personal communication. Retired peatman. Whixall. Shropshire.

[55] Grice, R. Personal communication. Company Director, Stoke on Trent.

● Fact Panel Two: Whixall Bibles

• References

[1] Allmark, H. Personal communication. Retired peatman, Creamore, near Wem. Shropshire.

● Fact Panel Three: Going Dutch

• References

[1] Allmark, H. Personal communication. Former peatman. Creamore, near Wem. Shropshire.

[2] Clorley, M. Personal communication. Peatman. Moss Cottages, Whixall.

● Fact Panel Four: The Peat Railway

• References

[1] In accordance with Bradley, V.J. (1992) *Industrial Locomotives of North Wales,* London: Industrial Railway Society, p.13, the term "tramroad" is used to describe the horse-drawn track system and "railway", that operated with locomotives.

[2] Flintshire Record Office, Hawarden. D/DM/329/42.

[3] Ordnance Survey 25in plan. 1914 edition, Flintshire XXVI, sheets 7, 10 and 11, surveyed for Flintshire in 1872, revised in 1909.

[4] Weekly accounts for the *English Peat Moss Litter Company.* Mr. Edward Wardle, Fenn's Cottage, Fenn's Wood. Photocopies are lodged in English Nature and Clwyd Archaeology Service site archive.

[5] Bradley, V.J. (1992) *Industrial Locomotives of North Wales,* London: Industrial Railway Society. 416-7.

● Fact Panel Five: Wreath Making

• References

[1] Heath, E. Personal communication. Housewife, Whixall. Shropshire.

[2] Simcock, M. Personal communication. Housewife, Ellesmere. Shropshire.

[3] e.g. Mr. Abbie Austin.

[4] e.g. Albert and Bill Allmark always include a sprig of conifer in their wreaths. Allmark, W. Personal communication. Former peatman, now Lead Hand Estate Worker with English Nature, Whixall. Shropshire.

[5] Clorley, S. Personal communication. Peatman, Whixall. Shropshire.

● The Works

• References

[1] Cadw: Welsh Historic Monuments, Scheduled Ancient Monument No. F182, Ref CAM 1/1/6401.

[2] *Shrewsbury Chronicle,* 3/09/1954. Shropshire local studies library, Shrewsbury.

[3] Interviews conducted under the Fenn's and Whixall Mosses Oral History Project, Clwyd Archaeology Service. Part of the Fenn's and Whixall Mosses Historic Landscape Project. Clwyd Archaeology Service and English Nature site archive.

[4] *Whitchurch Herald,* 16/12/1938, p.6. Whitchurch library. Confirmed by Andrew Dekker. Personal communication. Foreman, Whixall.

[5] Hallmark, H. Personal communication. Peatman/Forester, Stretton. Staffordshire.

[6] National Leaflet 81 0. Export. Clwyd Archaeology Service and English Nature site archive.

[7] Clorley, C. Personal communication. Steel fabricator, son of John Henry Clorley, Engine Operator.

[8] Millington, K. (1983) L.T.E.C. *Newsletter*.

[9] Clorley, C. Personal communication.

[10] Limbert, M. (1986) The Exploitation of Peat at Thorne in, Redmonds, G. (ed) *Old West Riding*, 6, No.1. 9-16.

[11] Hallmark, H. Personal communication.

● Mending the Mire

• References

[1] Wheeler, B.D. and Shaw, S.C. (1995) *Restoration of Damaged Peatland*. Department of the Environment.

[2] Reily, J.O., Page, S.E. and Smithhurst, P.R. (1984) *Wem Moss SSSI: Chemical Analysis of Surface Waters*. Report No.4 to the Nature Conservancy Council. James Davies and Partners, Nottingham.

[3] Holliday, C. (1993) *Investigation into the Effects of Canal Water on Fenn's Moss, Shropshire*. Undergraduate thesis. University of Wolverhampton.

[4] Karpouzli, E. (1994) *An Investigation into the Water Pollution and its Effects on the Vegetation Distribution of Whixall Moss, Shropshire*. Unpublished Honours project. Wolverhampton University.

[5] Seddon, A. (1991) *Fenn's, Whixall and Bettisfield Mosses NNR: Management Plan 1991-1995*. Nature Conservancy Council.

[6] Phillips, J. (1992) *Fenn's, Whixall and Bettisfield Mosses SSSI: Evaluation of Land which may Affect National Nature Reserve Management*. Countryside Council for Wales internal report.

[7] Mills, O. (1994) *The Hydraulic Properties of Peat*. M.Sc. project report, School of Earth Sciences, University of Birmingham.

[8] Titcombe, J. (1995) *Fenn's and Whixall Moss NNR: Presentation of Hydrological Data Collected Between 1993 and 1994*. English Nature internal report.

[9] Hall, L. (1995) *Oaf's Orchard: A Hydrological Investigation*. M.Sc. project report, School of Earth Sciences, University of Birmingham.

[10] Pringle, A. (1994) *The Hydrogeology of Fenn's & Whixall Moss*. M.Sc. project report, School of Earth Sciences, University of Birmingham.

[11] Phillips, J. (1992) *Survey of the Nutrient Status of Surface Water and Associated Vegetation of Fenn's and Whixall Mosses SSSI*. Undergraduate thesis, Chester College.

[12] Scurry, T.D. (1993) *Distribution and Ecology of* Typha latifolia *on Whixall Moss, North Shropshire*. Undergraduate thesis, University of Wolverhampton.

[13] Currie, D.R. (1993) *A Survey of the pH Changes in the Waters of Fenn's and Whixall Moss NNR*. Undergraduate thesis. University of Wolverhampton.

[14] Hooper, S.A. (1993) *A Comparison of Methods to Control* Betula spp. *on Fenn's, Whixall and Bettisfield Nature Reserve, Shropshire*. Undergraduate thesis, University of Wolverhampton.

[15] Joy, J. (1991) *Fenn's and Whixall Mosses: General Survey*. Nature Conservancy Council internal report.

[16] Ross, S.Y. (1991) *Vegetation Monitoring Programme 1991-1992: Permanent Quadrat Recording; Uncut Areas*. English Nature internal report.

[17] Thomlinson, V. (1991) *Vegetation Monitoring Programme 1991-1992: Old Handcut and Old Commercial Workings*. English Nature internal report.

[18] Newton, M. (1993) *Fenn's, Whixall and Bettisfield Mosses NNR: Bryophyte Survey*. Countryside Council for Wales internal report.

[19] Joy, J. (1991) *Vegetation Monitoring of Recent Commercial Cuttings at Fenn's & Whixall Mosses*. English Nature contract report.

[20] Boardman, P. (1993) *Fenn's, Whixall and Bettisfield Mosses, Recent Commercial Cuttings, Permanent Quadrats, 1993*. English Nature contract report.

[21] Hill, A. (1995) *An Investigation into Conditions Determining the Distribution of Utricularia minor at Fenn's and Whixall Mosses, N Shropshire/Clwyd*. M.Sc. dissertation, Chester College.

[22] Groome, D. (1995) *Fenn's, Whixall and Bettisfield Mosses - Report on Breeding Bird Survey 1995*. English Nature internal report.

[23] Clayson, P. (1994) *The Coleoptera of Whixall Moss*. Undergraduate thesis. Nottingham Trent University.

● Peat Speak

• References

[1] Dutch pattern hand tools illustrated form part of the collection of English Nature, Manor House, Whixall. The Whixall Bible cutter is in the possession of Mr. Abbie Austin, and formerly owned and used by Mr. Les Heath. Drawings: Timothy Morgan.

[2] 26th October 1626. Whixall Manorial Records. Book 4: 1613-1659, p.46.

[3] 19th September 1653. Whixall Manorial Records. Book 4: 1613-1659, p.93.

[4] 13th November 1716. Whixall Manorial Records. Book 7: 1702-1777, p.37.

[5] Paper given by Hamilton, W.P., *Transactions of the Caradoc and Severn Valley Field Club*, 3. (1901-4), 72-5.

[6] *Northwich and Winsford Chronicle and Mid Cheshire Advertiser*, 7th September 1889. See *Bog Bodies*.

[7] For derivation see Vol.II (P-Z) Compact Edition, Oxford English Dictionary, Oxford University Press (1971).

[8] For definition of terms see p.13, Bradley, V.J. (1992) *Industrial Locomotives of North Wales*. London: Industrial Railway Society.

● Scientific Names

• References

[1] Rose, F. (1981) *The Wild Flower Key*. London: Frederick Warne; Rose, F. (1989) *Colour Identification Guide to the Grasses, Sedges, Rushes and Ferns of the British Isles and North-western Europe*. London: Viking/Penguin.

[2] Brooks, M. and Knight, C. (1982) *A Complete Guide to British Butterflies*. London: J. Cape.

[3] Skinner, B. (1984) *Colour Identification Guide to Moths of the British Isles*. London: Viking/Penguin.

[4] Hammond, C.O. (1985) *The Dragonflies of Great Britain and Ireland*. Harley Books.

[5] English Nature's Recorder Programme.

[6] Feltwell, J. *et al.* (1987) *Britain's Wildlife, Plants and Flowers*. Readers' Digest Association.

[7] Holden, P. and Sharrock, J.T.R. (1988) *The RSPB Book of British Birds*. London: Macmillan.

[8] Burton, J.A. (1991) *Field Guide to the Mammals of Britain and Europe*. London: Kingfisher Books.

Charred prehistoric Scots pine, Lindow Moss.   Photograph: André Q. Berry

A

B